BIOLOGY, PSYCHOLOGY, AND MEDICINE

Biology, Psychology, and Medicine

By
Mortimer J. Adler
and
V. J. McGill

Preface by
Dr. Franz Alexander
Former Director, Psychiatric and
Psychosomatic Research Institute
Mount Sinai Hospital, Los Angeles

ENCYCLOPÆDIA BRITANNICA, INC.

Chicago • London • Toronto • Geneva • Sydney • Tokyo • Manila

PREFACE

Man is a biological organism which has an immensely greater faculty of self-awareness than any other living being. This is why efforts to describe completely and explain human behavior in terms of mechanistic-materialistic principles have consistently failed. The subjective awareness of one's motivations, goals, hopes, and frustrations, of loving and hating—all of which are man's main concern—do not yield to the same mechanistic explanations which are successful in the physical sciences. An engine, for example, an automobile, registers by indicators when its fuel reserve is low. Yet, the machine does not feel subjectively this lack of fuel as hunger. And even if a super-automobile with built-in clever feedback mechanisms could seek out the next gasoline station and refill itself, it would not be subjectively aware of a striving for fuel as man is when he is hungry.

Because of this basic difference between man and machines, the sciences of man—biology and its practical application in medicine—could never dispense with psychology. Medicine and biology remained inextricably linked with psychology, in spite of the fact that to observation and reasoning it often appeared completely foreign to them.

For centuries man struggled in vain against this unbridgeable gap between mind and body. Two solutions were open to him: panpsychologism or materialism. The body is ruled over by the mind, or else psychological phenomena are merely "epiphenomena." The modern concept of "complementarity" was not yet known. It was only recently introduced into atomic physics by Niels Bohr. Physicists found that certain natural phenomena—such as light, for example—can be explained only by the application of two seemingly contradictory principles, the corpuscular and the wave theories. That biology and psychology, which study the same thing—man—are not contradictory but complementary approaches is a concept which only recently is becoming generally accepted. Until man reached this solution, the mind-body dilemma remained a comedy of errors. How man finally arrived at the present position of complementarity is one of the most exciting problems of the history of Western thought development.

Subjective awareness of how his needs and desires prompt his activities—psychological causality—is older than man's discovery of an order of regular causal sequences in physical nature. It is natural, therefore, that man's first attempts to explain and influence phenomena of nature have been psychological. He explained thunder and lightning as the expression of the wrath of humanlike but more powerful beings. Rain was the gift of the gods and drought their punishment. He tried to influence these phenomena by the same psychological techniques which he used successfully for influencing his fellow man—by persuasion, supplication, bribery, and intimidation. Demonology was the first philosophy of prescientific man.

Perhaps the most significant event in Western thought occurred in the sixth and fifth centuries B.C. when the ancient Greek cosmologists—Thales, Anaximander, Empedocles, and Anaxagoras—and the mechanistic atomists Leucippus and Democritus attempted to explain the universe not by demonological notions but by rationalistic-materialistic or mechanistic principles. Their theories survived more in their example than in their content. They introduced the "spirit of science" to explain nature by observation and reason rather than by the magical influence of humanlike demons. Hippocrates is one outcome of this development. The four elements of Pythagoras and Empedocles became the foundation of his medical theories, which banned from medicine the demons and postulated that the sacred disease epilepsy has natural causes. Although little has remained valid from the details of his theoretical conceptions, some of his basic principles have survived to our present day. His contention that a disturbed balance among the four basic humors is the cause of disease corresponds to the modern theory of homeostasis. Some of Hippocrates' descriptions of the manifestations of diseases are amazingly accurate. His thesis that the physician's role consists in helping the natural healing powers of the organism is still valid, although unfortunately not always followed. His medical ethics, laid down in the Hippocratic oath, have remained those of modern physicians.

Hippocrates was one of the last representatives of the naïve realism of the old Greek cosmologists, who were undisturbed by epistemological and psychological considerations. With the Sophists and their most brilliant representative, Protagoras, the focus of interest turned from nature to man. The Sophists questioned not the structure of the outer world but the limits and validity of man's knowledge. Protagoras' answer prefigured the eighteenth-century views of Berkeley, Locke, Hume, and Kant. Man is the measure of all things. Our observations and conclusions are determined not only by the character of the observed objects but also by the nature of our sense organs and of our perceptive and reasoning faculties. Now man himself enters into the equation, never to be dislodged from it completely.

The rapid decline of Athenian democracy accelerated this trend toward self-scrutiny, which found its most influential representative in Socrates. Ethics, the problem of the good life, replaces cosmological speculations. Plato was the first to propose a comprehensive theory of personality, and he anticipated Freud's concept of a tripartite mental apparatus. His supreme principle is reason. By close reasoning, resembling that used in geometry, the way of good life can be established.

With Aristotle, the greatest universalist of all time, all aspects of Greek thought became synthesized. Aristotle was a naturalist, a psychologist, sociologist, and logician. Careful observation, however, was perhaps his greatest asset. Little has remained valid from his physics, a great deal from his biological work. Although his contributions to psychology remained mostly in generalities, he recognized clearly the purposeful organization of living beings, a fact which did not find its proper evaluation until Darwin's theory of natural selection. His logic was his most lasting accomplishment. It is difficult to evaluate the tremendous influence of his amazingly comprehensive writings. For centuries he was the symbol of the rational naturalistic observational approach; it was through his work that the cultural accomplishments of ancient Greece were transmitted, from the thirteenth century on, to European thought development, to come to full effect in the Renaissance. Viewed from a broad perspective, our present era represents the continuation and the ultimate consummation of the spiritual awakening of Western man during the Renaissance, when he began to rely on his own powers to interpret the physical world and finally to gain mastery over the forces of nature, over space and time. It can be said without overstatement that no single individual has influenced Western thought more universally than Aristotle. Not his special formulations but the spirit of his approach is what survived and grew until our own era: the spirit of science.

Efforts to understand the phenomena of nature in rational terms go back to the early Greek cosmologists. The spirit of natural science began with them, and culminated in Plato, Democritus, Aristotle. Never again would such a universalist as Aristotle arise to master all streams of thought. Galen was primarily a physician, Aquinas a master of deductive reasoning, Hobbes and Locke social psychologists, Harvey a physiologist, Darwin a naturalist, James and Freud psychologists.

This specialization of interest and knowledge proved of great significance. With it "operationalism," a new phenomenon, appeared on the cultural scene: the discovery and improvement of the methods of observation and reasoning, and making them accessible to verification and suitable for prediction. Galileo crowned the experimental method—the life blood of modern science—with his exemplary success. Harvey and Darwin were the great exponents of theory built on observation and testable by observation. Modern science—or, as many thinkers insist, science in its true sense—begins with their contributions.

The operational approach appeared last in the field of psychology. Freud's historical significance consists in devising a new method for the operational study of psychological, particularly unconscious, phenomena. Most of his theoretical concepts had been stated previously. The dynamic unconscious is foreshadowed by Plato, by St. Augustine, Spinoza, Schelling, Schopenhauer, Nietzsche, Carus, and Hartmann. The Oedipus complex was known to Diderot and Stendhal, Dostoevsky, and Strindberg. The significance of the dream process for the understanding of neurotic and psychotic processes was explicitly postulated by Moreau de Tour. It remained for Freud to develop a technique to enrich psychological theory, to test its validity, and to apply it successfully for treating the mentally ill.

FRANZ ALEXANDER

FOREWORD

This Reading Plan deals with problems and discoveries in biology, psychology, and medicine, as illustrated by selections from *Great Books of the Western World*. It can be understood without acquaintance with the other Reading Plans.

How to Use the Reading Plan. The Plan consists of three parts: the list of readings, guides to each of the readings, and suggestions for additional readings.

1. *The Reading List.* There are fifteen readings; the time required for the earlier readings will be less than that for later ones, as the selections increase in length and complexity. But time and effort will vary for individual readers; what is difficult for one may be easy for another.

2. *The Guides.* These are commentaries on the selections and should be of aid to readers who are working alone, without a teacher. The aim of the guide is to quicken the reader's comprehension of the selections by explanations. The tradition in which the author wrote, his aims, his adversaries, his allies, the facts and evidence he had to go on, the type of argument he used—all these are found to be helpful in understanding and assessing the value of a contribution. It is important in some cases to know how authors of the past have weathered modern or contemporary criticism and which of their discoveries have survived.

The major part of each guide directs the reader to crucial passages in reading, those which present the main line of argument or the most telling evidence. Difficult passages and terms are explained, especially when they are essential to the author's argument or conclusions. Questions are raised about the author's arguments and conclusions from time to time, in order to exhibit alternatives to what he is saying. The idea is to set the reader to inquiring: "Why should the author argue in a particular way?" "Why does he adduce the facts he does?" "And do the arguments or evidence establish the conclusions he reaches?"

Each guide also gives some facts about the author's life, especially such as have a bearing on the selection which is to be read.

The last section of every guide is a page entitled *Self-Testing Questions*. These are factual questions about what has been said in the text. They enable you to test the thoroughness of your reading. The right answers can be found by turning to pages 383-384, where the relevant references in the text are listed.

3. *Additional Readings.* Here the reader is directed to general books in biology, medicine, and psychology, which he may wish to read. Some histories of these subjects are given first, then lists of basic books in each subject. It will be noted that many of the books listed under biology and medicine are concerned with psychology as well. This is what Hippocrates leads us to expect. Healthy biological functioning and disease both depend in part on psychological attitudes. It will be found also that some of the psychology volumes listed deal with psychotherapy and thus with medical theory and practice. Finally, a number of books on scientific method are cited, most of them having special application to the three subjects.

The reader who wishes to make a study of the contributions to biology, psychology, and medicine in *Great Books of the Western World,* without the aid of teachers or of academic courses in these subjects, generally needs help. The present Reading Plan is designed to meet this need, but it is not intended, of course, to take the place of teachers, courses, and textbooks. Nor does it aim to present anything resembling a history of any of the subjects. The history of biology is an exceedingly long story, with thousands of characters, and the same is true of the history of psychology and of medicine. There is no pretense, either, to survey all the contributions to these fields to be found within the covers of *Great Books of the Western World*.

What the Plan can do is to assist the reader to make a start with his program of study. "All beginnings are hard," according to an old German saying. Once the first few hurdles are cleared, the acquired momentum will carry the reader along with much less effort. The problem for him is to set aside regular periods for study and to know what he is about all the time. If he is given a few facts and pointers in advance, he will be able to ask the right questions as he reads and to better understand the author's results, and what they result from, when he reaches them. In some cases the *Great Books* authors themselves supply background and orientation and distinguish the method they are using from other possible methods. Such explanations, however, are usually insufficient and need supplementation, which the Reading Plan endeavors to give. In this way the Plan *introduces* the reader to the history of science.

A word should be said about the authors who speak for biology, psychology, and medicine in this guide. Plato, Aquinas, Hobbes, and Locke are regarded primarily as philosophers, yet they all made contributions to psychology and their ideas are still influential. Their influence is not seen so much on the surface nowadays but shows itself rather in underlying currents or ground swells in the sea of psychological theory. By studying these authors we get a preview in broad outlines of later issues and developments and avoid technicalities and complications, which can be reserved for subsequent study. James and Freud, our last two contributors to psychology, bring our survey up to the platform of current discussions.

Aristotle is also known primarily as a philosopher, although he is the founder of several sciences, including biology, which is the subject of the two selections from his works in this Reading Plan. The other contributors to biology and medicine,

Hippocrates, Galen, Harvey, Darwin, and Freud, represent major beginnings, discoveries, and advances in these fields. Although the two selections from William James are concerned with psychology, James was also a physician, well trained in the biological sciences, and often supports his psychological theories with physiological facts and correlations. On the other hand, John Locke, who was a physician, leaves physiology behind him when he comes to write of the mind.

The fifteen selections which this book analyzes exemplify different methods of investigation. The aim is always to arrive at truth, or at least probability, but the line of argument varies. Sometimes the emphasis is on clarification by way of careful definitions, classification, and deductive or analogical proof, or refutation of contrary views. Elsewhere the emphasis is on accurate observation of empirical facts and on inductive methods, such as were formulated by John Stuart Mill in his *System of Logic,* Book III. In all cases a hypothesis or an intellectual system is put forward to explain observed facts of experience.

Whatever method is used, it is a phase of what is known as the scientific method. The reader who is interested can thus turn from this book to a study of scientific method itself, with some famous concrete examples of its use in mind.

CONTENTS

A NOTE ON
REFERENCE STYLE

In referring to *Great Books of the Western World,* the same style is used as in the *Syntopicon.* Pages are cited by number and section. In books that are printed in single column, "a" and "b" refer to the upper and lower halves of the page. In books that are printed in double column, "a" and "b" refer to the upper and lower halves of the left column, "c" and "d" to the upper and lower halves of the right column. For example, "Vol. 53, p. 210b" refers to the lower half of page 210, since Vol. 53, James's *Principles of Psychology,* is printed in single column. But "Vol. 7, p. 202b" refers to the lower left quarter of page 202, since Vol. 7, Plato's *Dialogues,* is printed in double column.

THE READING LIST

HIPPOCRATES

The Oath

Vol. 10, p. xiii

On Ancient Medicine

Vol. 10, pp. 1-9

On the Sacred Disease

Vol. 10, pp. 154-160

The beginnings of science is an instructive study. We see in clear profile the emergence of the scientific attitude and the scientific method against a background of superstition and magic. This is true of medicine, which is an art as well as a science, and which acquires special interest because of its immediate service to mankind and the dire consequences which may attend errors of diagnosis and treatment when they become pious rituals. Superstitious ceremony which perpetuates itself in spite of its failure to ease or cure the disease, and often in spite of its harmful results, is the great enemy of medical practice. On the other hand, the one sure test of the scientific attitude is the willingness to submit any hypothesis to the test and to discard it when the facts disprove or run against it. It is also shown by a disposition to try out new hypotheses even if, in the light of tradition, they are highly improbable. Nothing of this is possible without acute and patient observation and devotion to facts. It is these things we must look for if we are to see the scientific spirit arise from the tyranny of habit and ritual.

Although the record of medical practice goes back long before Hippocrates in Greece, and even thousands of years in Egypt, Hippocrates is called "the father of medicine." This is because he was the first to bequeath a body of medical writings and because, as Professor Sigerist has remarked, "no doctor ever exerted a more far-reaching influence." For centuries, especially after Galen in the second century A.D., Hippocrates was the ideal physician, and his moderation, honesty, and modesty were as much admired as his wisdom and skill.

First Reading

I

Hippocrates was born in 460 B.C. on the island of Cos, which lies on the southern coast of Asia Minor, across the Aegean Sea from Greece proper. Cos was famous for its poets and for its temple to Aphrodite. Almost nothing is known about Hippocrates except that he traveled widely in Greece and the Greek islands and studied in Athens, supposedly under the Sophist Gorgias. He practiced medicine many years and is said to have been consulted by the king of Macedonia and the king of Persia. He lived to the ripe age of eighty-five or over. He is referred to as an Asclepiad, meaning that he was a member of a guild of physicians who claimed descent from Asclepios (Æsculapius), the patron god of medicine, but we know he had no sympathy with the magical rites performed at some of the temples of Asclepios. He learned much from other physicians, but he was also critical and apparently well in advance of his contemporaries.

Hippocrates' greatness as a physician was acknowledged by both Plato and Aristotle. In Plato's *Symposium,* Socrates agrees with Hippocrates' view that the nature of the body "can only be understood as a whole." This is of importance in evaluating Hippocrates' method. Since the body can only be understood as a whole, diseases should be treated by building up the strength and resistance of the entire organism, even when only organs or organ-systems seemed to be affected. While the rival school of physicians in Cnidus, a few miles away from Cos, were going beyond their knowledge in distinguishing specific diseases, Hippocrates gave his chief attention to general pathology. When we remember that medicines for specific diseases were unknown in the fifth century B.C., we can see the soundness of his approach. Where special

3

remedies were unavailable, Hippocrates recommended a general regimen of exercise, diet, rest, baths, etc., by which nature could be assisted in restoring health.

In his chapter "On the Sacred Disease," he vigorously rejected sacrifices to the gods and other pious frauds that passed as remedies, and declared that medicine must seek natural causes of disease. Concerning the so-called "sacred disease," apparently epilepsy, he wrote: "it appears to me to be nowise more divine nor more sacred than other diseases, but has a natural cause from which it originates like other affections" (p. 154a). Since victims of the sacred disease were regarded as unclean and shunned like lepers, Hippocrates' insight was not only wise but humane. The chapter on the sacred disease emancipates medical practice from magic and supernatural causes and has been regarded as the "Charter of Science."

Hippocrates had none of the common resources of the modern physician. Even the thermometer was unknown, nor was there any understanding of the pulse rate and heart rate, and the common household medicines of today would not be discovered for centuries. How then could he detect and treat chest troubles and malaria, which were the most prevalent diseases of his time and place? Lacking other diagnostic means, Hippocrates and his followers employed patient and methodological observation, classifying fevers of different types, describing their expected course, their phases, critical points, duration, and signs of recovery. The prognosis, or description of the probable course of a disease, was very important at the time, as it is today. It enabled the physician to prepare his treatment or his alleviations in advance. Moreover, the physician who could successfully predict the course of a disease would have the confidence of his patients, and this could be a big factor in the cure.

Hippocrates paid great attention to the time of onset of different diseases, as also to the age and life-pattern of his patients. Their thoughts, their silence, manner of speech, their habits of sleep, their diet, the water and wine they drank, the kind of air they breathed, the weather of the region in which they lived could be of acute and continuing importance. He was interested in such things as the amount of exercise men get, the kind of air they breathe, the water and food they absorb, and the climate they live in, not only for the sake of curing disease but also for the maintenance of health. Here he strikes a very modern note. In his chapter "On Airs, Waters, and Places," he anticipates the goal of all medicine, the goal which is to supersede all the wonderful cures effected by modern medicine, namely, the triumph of *preventive* medicine.

I I

The Oath, which prescribes the basic ethical position of the medical profession, is one of the most influential parts of the Hippocratic writings. It is still administered to the graduates of many medical schools, with a few changes to accord with modern conditions. The new-fledged doctor is no longer bound to honor his master as a parent nor to teach his master's sons the art of medicine *gratis,* but he is enjoined to give full respect and support to the members of his profession.

Some of the precepts laid down by the Oath are reverenced, yet controversial in special cases. The physician, for example, binds himself to "give no deadly medicine to any one if asked, nor suggest any such counsel. . . ." He is forbidden to abet murder and suicide under all conditions and must also have no part in mercy killing or euthanasia. The patient may be suffering atrocious and continuous pain from an incurable disease and be certain to die in a matter of weeks or days. The patient himself and those closest to him may plead with the physician to put him out of his misery and not to prolong the needless suffering. Before the discovery of morphine and other pain-killers the pressure on the physician must have been far greater than it is today. Yet to give way to the appeals of the patient and his family would be a violation of the Oath he had freely taken, in which it is specified that those who do not honor it forfeit the right to practice medicine, the enjoyment of life, and the respect of men.

Is this requirement, in your opinion, too severe? Should exceptions be made in cases of incurable disease and unbearable suffering? If so, how should these exceptions be worded?

Would one not have to allow for the possibility of remarkable recoveries of men who have been doomed to die in a short time? Would it be feasible to specify that the physician must do all he can to promote health and prolong life except where the pain is too severe, the disease is *probably* incurable, and the patient or some relative or both implore him to do the reverse—to bring about a merciful death? You will easily see that there are great difficulties and hazards in specifying the conditions under which a doctor would be entitled to completely reverse his role of healer and prolonger of life. From the point of view of medical ethics it is perhaps best even today to stick to the spirit of the Hippocratic Oath and permit no exceptions; if euthanasia is resorted to, let the physician be prepared to defend his conduct in court.

Another big problem is occasioned by the generally salutary rule that the physician should divulge nothing he hears or sees of the lives of men, "which ought not to be spoken of abroad." Since he enters houses "for the benefit of the sick," he must not use the occasion to do them harm. He must not turn over information detrimental to his patients and their families to interested neighbors or the police. He cannot combine his medical duties with gossip or spying. But suppose he learns that his patient has just committed a crime? Should the physician first treat his wounds and then go to the police? If this were the understood practice of doctors, it would be the equivalent to denying medical aid to criminals and even to suspected criminals.

The duty of the Hippocratic physician in such cases is clear. Since he is concerned not only with wounds and disease but also with the future health and welfare of his patient, he may advise the man to go to the authorities and put his case before them in the most favorable light. But he will not himself divulge anything harmful to his patient. The courts seem now to be extending the right of the doctor to withhold confidences. The legal questions are complicated. But would you not say that the right of the physician to maintain secrecy is at least the *ethical* ideal?

III

The growth of modern chemistry has been so stupendous that it is all a specialist can do to keep up with his own little corner of the subject. In the fifth century B.C., on the other hand, chemistry had discriminated only the four substances—earth, air, fire, and water—and was still at the level of common sense. It would seem that Hippocrates was ill prepared to understand the nature of disease or its remedies, yet students of the history of medicine have been surprised at how far he was able to go. It will be instructive to follow his reasoning. It may be that by putting aside, for the time being, the complications of modern chemistry and physiology, we can see some aspects of disease and medicine in a clearer light than would otherwise be possible.

Consider first the four so-called elements and their corresponding qualities:

Elements	*Qualities*
Fire	Hot and dry
Earth	Cold and dry
Water	Cold and moist
Air	Hot and moist

The opposition between these elements in nature had long since been used to explain differences of climate and of the seasons. The philosopher Heraclitus had held that the strife between the elements is "justice" and that it is this which holds the world together. If water should rise unopposed by fire, or vice versa, it was clear that the world would be destroyed. Nor could life endure if earth or air trespassed too far upon the domain of the other elements. The key to understanding nature was equilibrium or proportion. "Nothing too much" was the famous Doric motto and "Nothing too little" was implied. Proportion and balance became the yardstick of the arts and moderation the ideal, if not the reality, of political life. Greek tragedy taught the mortal danger of excess. Greek mathematicians were discovering proportions in the realm of numbers and geometrical figures traced in the sand, proportions which were already showing their practical worth. The mathematician-philosopher Pythagoras had demonstrated that the pitch of the vibrating string of a lyre was proportionate to the length of the string and that harmony was proportionate to the length of several strings.

There were special reasons for construing health and disease in the same terms. The healthy man was made up of the four so-called elements, but so was the sick man, and disease could thus not be a lack of any one element but must be a disproportion among them. Daily observation showed that some diseases involve a manifest imbalance. The malarial fevers, so prevalent at the time, are an example, and so are conditions in which water is deficient or which arise from impurities in water that is taken without boiling. In the famous chapter "On Airs, Waters, and Places," Hippocrates also describes the effect on health and vigor of the quantity of pure air in various lands and the influence of humidity, dryness, heat, cold, and other qualities of the atmosphere in which men live and breathe.

What interests us now, however, is the Hippocratic conception of health and disease and the inference by which it was reached. The first question is whether, given the data available at the time, such as the interplay of the four elements and the distinguishable tissues and fluids of the body, the inference can be regarded as a reasonable one. In raising this question about disease, we naturally do not include under it mere injuries such as broken bones, unless they involve infection.

How then could we disqualify Hippocrates' inference? Should we not have to point out a disease, with which he was acquainted, which was not a disproportion but a lack of some element, tissue, or fluid? But can you think of any such disease? Is not what is injurious to the sick man generally present in healthy men, though in different proportions? Hippocrates, describing the outlook of his predecessors, says:

For they did not suppose that the dry or the moist, the hot or the cold, or any of these are either injurious to man, or that man stands in need of them, but whatever in each was strong, and more than a match for a man's constitution, whatever he could not manage, that they held to be hurtful and sought to remove (p. 5a-b)

The next question we shall broach is whether the Hippocratic conception of health and disease could possibly be true today. Modern medicine, preoccupied with particular diseases, usually makes no effort to define disease in general and has even less to say about the nature of health. It seems to be assumed that such general subjects are too difficult or speculative and that the main point is whether you need a doctor or not. The question we wish to raise, then, is how far disease can be described today as a disproportion of functional elements. The clearest examples of disease in this sense would be disturbance of the water balance, the oxygen balance, the balance of salts, the endocrine balance, and of homeostasis in general. You will find a good account of these regulatory systems in Walter B. Cannon's *The Wisdom of the Body.*

It will, perhaps, be easy to find diseases which are in rough accord with the Hippocratic conception, but how many can we find which are not? Would germ diseases be an example? Here we must remember that the germs which are responsible for sickness may also be present in healthy men. What is crucial is their number proportional to the amount of resistance the body can offer. Heart diseases, which now take the greatest toll of life, also involve disproportion. The focal point of the disease may be an incapacity of the muscle tissue in the walls of the left ventricle of the heart, with the result that insufficient blood is pumped into the body. But the nature of the disease depends on how far the body is able to compensate. If the action of the other chambers of the heart is reduced proportionately, so that, for example, certain levels of pressure are maintained, the person may make an adjustment on a lower level of energy output.

Similarly, the body can compensate to some extent for defective action of the valves of the heart. And if surgeons, now at work on the project, succeed in transplanting normal valves in the places of weakened valves, they will simply be aiding the body's own efforts to correct a deficiency—which is the Hippocratic principle. Even injuries, such as a broken leg or such as entail the loss of a limb, involve much more than the pain and loss of function. They depend on how far the person is able to adjust to the pain and loss of function. If he is strong, resilient, and immersed in important projects, he is more likely to compensate and to overcome the disability. A new adjustment can take the place of the frustration.

Injuries, like disease, in Hippocrates' conception, are not simply deficit, but include the resistance and compensations of the patient. That the compensations that go on within him are a genuine part of the disease is shown, with special clarity, by the fact that the compensations are not always salutary. Sometimes there is overcompensation. A new disproportion is brought about. What was to effect a cure becomes a new disease process.

I V

Obvious things are not obvious until they are discovered, and the true discoverer is the man who sees their full importance. That health would depend on what is taken into the body—the kind of food and air imbibed—seems self-evident. Yet for centuries magical rites and incantations were regarded as more effective than careful considerations of diet and climate.

According to Hippocrates, the body itself is wise enough to prefer foods suitable to it; the part of medicine is to follow nature's example and improve upon it. He maintains "that the diet and food which people in health now use would not have been discovered, provided it had suited with man to eat and drink in like manner as the ox, the horse, and all other animals . . ." (pp. 1d-2a). Originally, he argues, men ate the same coarse grains as the ox and the horse, but gradually they discovered or prepared food more agreeable to their nature. They learned the hard way, many of weaker constitutions failing to survive the rough fare. And just as men gradually learned what foods are appropriate for the healthy, medicine finds what is appropriate for the sick, varying it according to their malady and their individuality and habits.

Would you agree that Hippocrates' hypothesis about the diet of primitive men is in general accord with present-day anthropological knowledge? Is the diet of civilized man one of the factors which enables him to live much longer than savages do? Does this evolutionary hypothesis help Hippocrates to understand the role of medicine? Is he on the right track in warning that extremely bitter or sour or other "strong" substances, if injurious in isolation, are not so when combined? Would acids and alkalies mixed in the food we eat be injurious if taken separately? (See pp. 5a-c, 7b.) Is he right in claiming that exposure to heat and cold are not generally injurious because the body compensates and, in effect, regulates its temperature? (See pp. 5d-6a.)

The reader will recognize that these questions are all important and that they are all to be answered, with some qualifications, in the affirmative. We know that some diets of civilized men are unbalanced and harmful, and we have heard that the diets of some primitive peoples are well balanced and salutary. But, on the whole, so-called civilized people have steady access to foods of much better quality and of far greater diversity than those of primitive people or the preliterates of today. Diets are now also effectively varied to restore or maintain health in particular cases—thus fulfilling in part the Hippocratic program of *health through sustenance appropriate to the species and the individual.*

Hippocrates' counsel that "strong" substances should not be taken in isolation was also a good insight, especially at a time when medical ignorance was recommending all sorts of drastic remedies. We know, to take an easy example, that acids and alkalies which, taken in isolation, would be deleterious, are nutritious and healthful when combined in salts. The Hippocratic idea that the body has a kind of dietary wisdom, as shown by the distaste for "strong" substances—substances excessively sour or bitter or salty—is borne out by many modern investigations. We know that when very young children are given the opportunity of choosing among different types of food, cafeteria style, they select a balanced diet. Adults are not so wise. They have learned to like things that are not good for them and need the physician or the dietitian to correct their bad habits of eating.

Hippocrates was also acute in recognizing "that of all the qualities heat and cold exercise the least operation in the body"

(p. 5d), the reason being that the body compensates for an excess of both qualities. Hippocrates gives some examples of these compensatory mechanisms, and the reader will doubtless think of others. To balance its own diet the body needs a variety of foodstuffs; to maintain normal body temperature—within limits—it requires no external resource.

V

Is the best diet always the best for you?

The diet of civilized men differs from that of primitive people, according to Hippocrates, in being more appropriate to the human constitution. But he does not deny that it is also more palatable nor that palatability has its own importance for appetite and health. He goes so far as to say:

An article of food or drink which is slightly worse, but more palatable, is to be preferred to such as are better but less palatable. (p. 133c)

Modern dietitians would agree that the finest diet, having all the proper ingredients in ideal proportions, would be inadvisable if it were not pleasant to take. It is generally assumed that the pleasantness of food is an aid to digestion.

What is wrong with the hypothesis that excess of one quality is cured by administration of its contrary?

Hippocrates does not deny that this works in some cases, at least superficially. He does not deny that application of cold packs, for example, would help to control a fever. But would external applications get at the real disease process? Hippocrates says that, according to the hypothesis he is criticizing, if it is hot or cold, moist or dry that is injuring the patient, "it is to be removed by its contrary." But Hippocrates asks whether this would be possible or wise in all cases. He insists that "the surest and most obvious remedy is to change the diet which the person used . . ." (p. 4d). What do you think he means by this? Does he mean that a change of diet might correct the chemical imbalance which produced the fever, the dehydration, or other condition observed? Or is it rather that a well-chosen diet would tend to build up the strength of the body and assist it to restore the balance? You will note that he refers in this passage to a man with a weak constitution.

Are these two interpretations consistent? That is, could both be true? Is it not apparent, in any case, that Hippocrates is distinguishing here between alleviation of symptoms and cure of the disease? Accordingly, it would be one thing to reduce a fever by cold applications, or relieve dehydration by administering water, but quite a different thing to rectify the chemical balance that produced these symptoms. The disease itself could not be removed by administering the contrary of the quality that was in excess.

Does increase of health and strength always aid the body to throw off disease?

Spontaneous recovery from disease, without medical aid, was a common phenomenon in ancient Greece, as it is today. Hippocrates was impressed by the power of the body to restore equilibrium among its contrary elements, and his therapy was designed to aid this natural recuperative process by building up the patient's strength and resistance. Modern therapy also gives large-scale support to "the wisdom of the body," especially where no specific medicines are available. But are there any instances in which a regimen to strengthen the natural resistance of the body is of no use whatever? One thinks first of incurable diseases and of cases where recovery depends on surgery. But consider also parasitic afflictions, which medical practice can cure but the body has no power to combat. The more the diet and general health of the patient are improved, the more the parasite—a tapeworm, for example —grows and flourishes.

The following questions are designed to help you test the thoroughness of your reading. Each question is to be answered by giving a page or pages of the reading assignment. Answers will be found on page 383 of this Reading Plan.

1 Did Hippocrates hold that a mixed or balanced diet is best for man?

2 What was Hippocrates' reason for saying that the effect of heat and cold on the body is less than that of other qualities?

3 What therapeutic consequence follows from the fact that "neither the hot nor the cold, nor the dry, nor the moist, has ever been found unmixed with any other quality"?

4 What is Hippocrates' main reason for saying that the so-called "sacred disease" could not have a divine origin?

5 Why does the fact that it is wonderful and incomprehensible *not* establish its divine origin?

6 Why does Hippocrates say that, if the "'sacred disease" can be cured by incantations, as is claimed, it cannot be of divine origin?

7 Does Hippocrates hold that if the "sacred disease" were of divine order, it would not afflict only people of certain kinds of constitution? If so, why?

8 Does Hippocrates claim that all diseases have natural causes?

14

P L A T O

The Meno

Vol. 7, pp. 174-190

Plato is the only philosopher in history whose writings reach the highest level not only of originality, rigor, and influence but also of dramatic power and beauty. He is also extraordinary in the breadth and majesty of his conceptions, in his "faith in reason." None but the greatest master could have made so convincing the breathtaking view that only the ideal is real, that things are what they are only to the extent that they partake of the precision and perfection of the eternal forms or ideals.

How could it be maintained that imperfect things are real only insofar as they are perfect? Let us think for a moment. Are not the imperfect circles you can draw on the blackboard real as approximations to circularity or as exemplifications of other qualities? And is not a fool real by virtue of his partial, but only partial, realization of human rationality and good sense? What he lacks—his shortcomings—cannot be his reality.

The dramatic form in which Plato cast his philosophy captivates the reader not only because of the literary charm but also because he becomes a witness to the question-and-answer process in which philosophical ideas are forged and tested. He tends to take sides and to imagine that he is himself a participant. The main spokesman in the Platonic dialogues is usually Socrates, Plato's master. Socrates emerges in the dialogues as a man of great charm, wit, and integrity, who made it his business to search for the truth from morning till night and who finally chose to die rather than betray it. Believing as he did that the conquest of truth was a cooperative enterprise and that it is only truth for him who assents to it with reason, he spent his time questioning Athenians who had the quickness of mind to follow him about the philosophical terms they so lightheartedly employed. What was justice? What was virtue? Knowledge? His procedure of advancing toward adequate definitions and real knowledge by asking carefully contrived questions, as if he were drawing the hidden truth from his companions, is known as the maieutic method. It has become a model of procedure in philosophy and in education, while Socrates himself is regarded as the ideal philosopher.

Second Reading

I

About the life of Socrates, who wrote nothing himself, we have considerable knowledge; about Plato, who wrote abundantly, we know almost nothing. The only one of his writings which tells anything about himself is *The Seventh Letter* (pp. 800 ff.). Here we get a glimpse of what appears to be very unusual activity for a philosopher. It concerns Plato's three visits to Syracuse, far away on the island of Sicily, where, at great hazard to his life, he sought to persuade the young tyrant Dionysius to institute a reign of law and justice. At first his efforts met with some success, for Dionysius had a taste for philosophy and a great admiration for Plato, but in the end court intrigue and faction defeated his aims. The lesson we learn is that Plato was not an inflexible idealist but could bend and adapt himself to existing conditions. His aim in the corrupt and dangerous court of Syracuse was not the perfect state but practical reforms.

Plato's contributions to psychology are not separable from his ethical theories, for man's real nature was for him an ideal to which actual men only approximate, and psychological defects were also moral defects. Thus it is man's nature to be governed by reason, but the men of Athens, and Syracuse, and of other cities then and since, are only partly rational, mere imitators of the true rationality which Plato envisaged as the eternal pattern and exemplar.

Plato's most famous psychological theory is that of the threefold division of the soul. Even to this day the powers of the soul, or the capacities of man, are commonly recognized as reason, will, and desire. Plato's theory of the subordination of will and desire to reason is likewise accepted, at least as the ideal. Some idea of the scope and importance of this division of the soul in Plato's thought can be gained from the following scheme:

PARTS OF THE SOUL	VIRTUES	VICES	TYPES OF MEN	TYPES OF GOVERNMENT
Reason	Wisdom	Ignorance	Rational Ideal rulers	Aristocracy or rule of the rational type
Will or Spiritedness	Courage	Cowardice	Soldier type	Timocracy
Desire or Appetite	Restraint	Licentiousness	Worker or Artisan type	Oligarchy Democracy Tyranny

All men have this threefold nature. In some, reason is dominant; wisdom, with suitable education, is within their reach. In them the turbulence of desire is curbed and regulated, and will is directed toward rational ends. These highly exceptional "gold" men are thus capable of all the cardinal Greek virtues. They have the excellence of desire, restraint; the excellence of will, courage; the excellence of reason, wisdom; and finally, they have the crowning merit of justice, which is the proper subordination of the other parts of the soul to reason. Such men, since they can govern themselves, are capable of governing the State. They are the natural aristocrats who, in the ideal State described by Plato in *The Republic,* are to have sole authority.

The men in whom will or spiritedness is dominant are courageous but not wise, and incline to truculence and vehemence; they need the guiding hand of the just men who alone know due proportion. In *The Republic,* the spirited men become the soldiers and constabulary. Should they ever become the rulers, as in timocracy, the State will be plunged into unnecessary wars and suffer from their imprudence.

The great majority of men are so constituted that desire, including the desire for goods and luxuries, has the upper hand. They are not capable of much justice, nor of courage either, but can learn to obey their rulers and to curb their desires when their lives are regulated within a just order. When such men secure the command of the State, however, the reign of desire begins, taking three forms—oligarchy, democracy, and tyranny; i.e., the rule of the few who are rich, of the many who are poor, or of a single despot.

Both man and the State prosper only in so far as reason is at the helm—reason and knowledge. Men cannot excuse their foolish or wicked actions by the claim that they were overcome by pleasure or pain. Plato holds that if reason clearly illuminates the wise course of action, both pain and temptation can be conquered. In this triumph over cowardice or the licentiousness of desire, it is reason that plays the commanding role, and the will is given the part of an obedient and stalwart servant. However excruciating the torture, however insistent the passionate desire, knowledge, when confident and clear, is always decisive. Here Plato inaugurates the long controversy between rationalism and voluntarism by a vigorous espousal of rationalism, i.e., the primacy of reason as against the primacy of the will.

When reason commands, the will obeys, and the body is immediately set in motion. When we understand the proof relating to the opposite angles formed by any two intersecting lines on a plane, the appropriate musculature is activated and we say: "Such angles are always equal." In the same way, once reason finds the best course of practical action, the body obeys without hesitation. It is only when reason is obscured and knowledge fragmentary that the will is weakened, and the body, deprived of rational direction, succumbs to pleasure or to pain. Socrates remained in jail awaiting his execution, although he might easily have escaped with the help of his powerful friends. He remarked, however, that if his body had had its way, it would have long since escaped to safety.

Desires are thus understood to belong to the body and to be dependent upon it whereas reason is not of the body. It rules the body but is not ruled by it. Thus the soul, or rather the highest part of the soul, aspires to the lofty splendor of the True, the

Good, and the Beautiful, whereas desire, the lowest part of the soul, grovels in fleshly pleasures and runs ignominiously from pain. This is the famous Platonic dualism of reason and desire. But we shall now see that this dualism is replaced by a more mature and subtle view which emerges in some of the dialogues.

If the soul is enchanted by the highest forms or ideals—the True, the Good, and the Beautiful—and longs to imitate them in thoughts, in actions, and in works of art, must not the soul be impelled by desire of some kind? In the *Phaedrus,* the answer is unmistakable. Here reason is not the enemy of desire but its mentor and inspiration, its inner tendency. In the *Symposium,* Socrates develops explicitly the theory that all men love the beauty manifested in a fair body, but he who is wise and fortunate passes on to the love of the beauty in all fair things, "for how foolish would he be not to recognize that the beauty in every form is one and the same!" The next stage is to realize "that the beauty of the mind is more honourable than the beauty of the outward form," and the summit of his evolution is the adoration of the Beautiful itself, from which all fair things on earth derive their beauty and their fascination.

Plato's doctrine of the lower and higher loves is a striking anticipation of Freud's theory of "sublimation" two thousand years later, although the associated ideas, presuppositions, aim, and tone are all different. (See, for example, Vol. 54, pp. 8-20.) Like Freud, however, Plato knew that a desire for a sexual object can be rechanneled into cultural pursuits and science.

Desire, so conceived, is not chained to the body and the body's pleasures, but, learning to love more and more fair forms, may mount at last to the highest. Desire is now no longer the adversary of reason. Nor is pleasure. In the *Philebus,* Plato argues that just as there are lower and higher desires, so there are true and false pleasures. There are pleasures which aim at true objects and those which envisage illusory ones. These tendencies of Plato's thought, as they diverge from the dualism of reason and desire, bring him closer to the ideas of Aristotle, to be discussed in the next reading.

In reading the *Meno* or any other Platonic dialogue, it is advisable to have some understanding of the "Socratic method." Socrates (470-399 B.C.) did not himself write anything, and our knowledge of his method and philosophy comes largely from the dialogues composed by his great disciple Plato (*c.* 428-*c.* 348 B.C.). In Plato's dialogues we find Socrates continually asking questions such as "What is virtue?" "What is justice?" "What is knowledge?" Interrogating his fellow Athenians, whether on the street, in the market, or in a private house, was indeed the passion of Socrates' life. The first answers he received were almost never the strict definitions he wanted, but only *examples*. For instance, instead of defining virtue, Meno begins to enumerate the special virtues of the citizen, the housewife, servants and slaves.

When Socrates succeeds in evoking a real definition he proceeds, as in the dialogue before you, to test its worth by further questions. Usually it is shown to lead to a contradiction. When convinced of this, the author of the definition at once withdraws it and, after some prodding, offers what he hopes will be a better one. Although the new definition may be an improvement over the first, it also crumbles before Socrates' questioning. Whatever involves a contradiction, i.e., contradicts itself, cannot be true. This is the principle of noncontradiction, the most famous of all philosophical principles, which everyone seems to understand without having been taught it. With its help faulty definitions are eliminated, and progress toward better ones becomes possible.

What is the purpose of Socrates' perpetual questioning? A century and a half later Euclid, by dint of incisive definitions of geometrical concepts, was able to establish the science of geometry. Socrates was also seeking a science, a science of human conduct and values, but this proved more difficult. The quest, however, has not been abandoned, but continues to the present day.

The end in view was the attainment of real knowledge, as opposed to "right opinion" and also to art. Right opinion is always true, but the handicap is that the man who has it cannot prove that it is. The man who possesses knowledge, on the other hand, both has the truth and is able to demonstrate it. A man who accepts on authority the theorem that the sum of the angles of any triangle is equal to two right angles, or who remembers it from school days but has forgotten the proof, has right opinion but not knowledge. Right opinion can be valuable. Socrates admired the practical skills of cobblers, pilots, shepherds, trainers of horses, and musicians. He wished that the politicians of his day knew how to perform *their* function half as well. But what he was pursuing was something better than the right opinion of the arts and crafts; namely, the laws and principles of conduct that would be proof against wrong opinion and the unreliability of leaders.

I I

Philosophers have become famous not only for their answers but also for their questions. Plato's answers have molded thought for two thousand years, and none of us, whether philosopher or not, has entirely escaped their influence. But even thinkers who reject Plato's solutions and are hostile to the trend of his thought have remained under the spell of his questions, some of which are as crucial today as they ever were. The questions focused by Plato's dialogue *Meno* as to whether virtue is knowledge, whether it can be taught, and as to the nature of the learning process in general, are still in ferment. Continuously greater resources and efforts are devoted to public education and to the training and reform of social conduct. All this would be sheer waste if virtue, or excellence, cannot be taught. And if we believe that it can be taught, Plato's questions are inescapable. Is it then a kind of knowledge or science? If not, is it like the fine arts, which cannot be taught, or can be taught only to a gifted few? Plato's provocative posing of the problem how such teaching is possible was even more influential than his answer.

In studying Plato's *Meno*, we shall deal with the questions whether men desire only the good, or sometimes evil, and whether virtue can be learned from teachers and is therefore like other subjects that are successfully taught. These topics lead to a central issue: the problem of how learning takes place and what it is. We shall witness in this dialogue a dramatic preview of the problem which now engages many research institutions and laboratories throughout the country. In the *Meno,* which is one of the early Platonic dialogues, we may be certain that Socrates is expressing not only his own views but also those of his young pupil, Plato.

The progress of the argument in the *Meno* is easy to follow. Meno, fresh from his teacher, the sophist Gorgias, wants Socrates to tell him whether virtue is acquired by teaching, by practice, or as a gift of nature. Socrates naturally asks what he means by virtue, and Meno eventually replies that "it is the power of governing mankind." Socrates quickly scotches this definition by asking if it includes the virtue of a child and of a slave, and if it matters whether the governing is just or unjust. Meno offers another definition, viz: Virtue is the desire for the honorable and the power of attaining it. In refuting this definition, Socrates first gets Meno to admit that if men desire the honorable they desire the good, and then persuades him that *all* men desire the good, that no one desires evil, that is, if he knows it is evil. This eliminates the first part of the definition, since it implies that one man is as virtuous as another. As for the second part of the definition, Socrates easily shows that virtue is not the power of attaining the good, for Meno is made to admit that it must be attained justly. But this means that virtue is being defined by a part of itself, i.e., justice, which involves circularity, for how could we know a part of virtue without knowing virtue itself? Meno has told us that virtue is the power of attaining the good by a kind of virtue.

The most serious definition of virtue considered is that it is simply knowledge, but against this definition Socrates urges a strong objection, and the dialogue ends rather inconclusively with one of Socrates' pious myths. But one should not be disappointed on this account. The nature of virtue is left open for future dialogues and for continuing discussions to which we can add our new knowledge and insights even today.

III

Our main interest in the *Meno* is psychological. Some of the most influential and controversial theses in the history of psychology are to be found in this dialogue. Let us begin with

Socrates' doctrine that all men desire the good, that no one desires evil. Does not this contradict common sense? Wicked men certainly pursue evils, and does this not imply that they desire them? You will note that Socrates has an answer to this. No man desires evils, he says, if he knows them to be evil, for evils bring misery, and no one wants to be miserable. Accordingly, when men pursue evils, they do so because they think them good; men desire only the good. To test the validity of Socrates' argument, try answering Socrates' questions yourself. Where would your answers have been different from Meno's? (See pp. 177-178.) The crucial question Socrates asks is:

And does he think that the evils will do good to him who possesses them, or does he know that they will do him harm? (p. 178a)

Meno eventually agrees that *whoever* pursues evils thinks that they will do him good, and that therefore what he really desires is good. Now let us test this by an example. A man makes a career of robbery, which he believes will do good to him, i.e., enable him to live well. In this sense he believes that robbery is good, but is there not another sense in which he thinks it bad? He no doubt recognizes that it is bad for his victims and might even concede that it does more harm to his victims than it does good to him, though he might add that he is not much concerned with the misery of his victims but only with the welfare of himself and his family.

It seems clear that a man might choose a life of crime which he recognizes as evil in its total effect. In a sense, then, Socrates is probably wrong; yet he would still be right in the most important sense, namely, that the robber chooses to live by crime not for the evil it entails, i.e., the misery of his victims, but for the good it brings to *him*, the good living he expects to enjoy. In this important sense, then, we might agree with Socrates that men always desire the good, never evil.

But first we should have to consider the claim that men sometimes desire to punish themselves, to subject themselves to pain, a view that receives a modern development in Freud's theory of masochism. (To investigate this subject, see "masochism" in the Syntopicon's Inventory of Terms, Vol. 3, p. 1326.)

If men inflict pain on themselves to assuage the pangs of conscience, then masochism would be consistent with Socrates' principle that men desire only the good, but Freud's theory of the death instinct (see "death instinct," *ibid.*, p. 1312), according to which men have a natural tendency to destroy themselves, is definitely inconsistent with it. In a later reading we shall see how good a case Freud makes against the Platonic view.

The paramount importance of Socrates' doctrine is easy to see. If men desire only the good, then men do wrong only because they do not *know* what is good, that is, do not have full and confident knowledge of what they *ought* to do at a given time. Can we conclude that men themselves cannot be blamed, but only the defects of their education? If there is no such thing as willing evil, when we know it is evil, is there any justification for punishment? The questions raised by Socrates' doctrine still reverberate today and are crucial in ethics, law, education, politics, and other fields.

I V

The consideration of the nature of learning in the *Meno* is introduced by the following paradox:

> . . . a man cannot enquire either about that which he knows, or about that which he does not know; for if he knows, he has no need to enquire; and if not, he cannot; for he does not know the very subject about which he is to enquire. (p. 179d)

In other words, you cannot inquire into a matter unless you already know what it is; but if you *do* know what it is, there is no point in inquiring.

Before discussing Socrates' solution of this paradox—the famous "theory of recollection"—let us see if we ourselves can find any way out of the paradox. Might it not be that prior to inquiring into a subject, say *fireflies,* we know enough about these insects to recognize them but not as much as we should like to know? Hence inquiry would proceed from relatively vague to clearer or fuller knowledge. Similarly, it might be asked how we can define *chair* if we do not already know its nature and hence its definition. One answer would be that we start out with a general, not very accurate idea of *chair,* but then by differentiating chairs from stools, benches, and couches, etc., we finally arrive at a definition which clarifies and articulates our original notion of *chair.*

This is an approach to Socrates' solution, since it suggests that we are possessed of a *latent* knowledge which can be brought out and elucidated by inquiry. The same is shown by another example, namely, how can we recall a name or a face? If we do not know it, we could never recognize it; if we do know it, there is no need to recall it. One answer is that by thinking of appropriate associations we can bring various names or faces to mind. When the right one appears, we at once recognize it, i.e., react to it as we have reacted to it before, and we say, "I knew that all the time." We did: it was latent knowledge. Other examples of latent knowledge will probably occur to the reader.

Socrates' solution of the paradox involves a much more drastic conception of latent knowledge and its role in the learning process. The slave boy whom Socrates interrogates has never been taught geometry, yet his answers to Socrates' questions show that he nevertheless possesses latent knowledge which can be brought to the surface. It requires only Socrates' skillful questioning and some thinking on the slave boy's part. Specifically he betrays a "submerged knowledge" of how to determine the length of the sides of a square whose area is twice that of a given square.

But how could he "know" such things if he had never been taught geometry? Socrates suggests that the only explanation is that the slave boy has learned geometry in an earlier existence and that knowledge is "reminiscence." He can thus recognize geometrical truths, when he sees them clearly enough, because he really knew them already.

At this point a number of objections are likely to occur to the student. (1) It is known that we learn many things which we have never been taught. Has not the slave boy, too, learned enough about the relation of spaces and figures in the course of his present life to answer Socrates' questions? (2) And are not these questions of Socrates' very instructive? When the slave boy makes a mistake, for example, does not Socrates show him how to correct his error? (3) Finally, therefore, is not the slave boy learning geometry just as other boys learn it, except that Socrates is a very skillful teacher and, perhaps also, his pupil a very bright one? It should be remembered, in this connection, that we are now in the midst of a revolution in the teaching of geometry and other mathematical subjects, which aims at greatly accelerating the process.

There would thus be no need for Socrates' drastic inference that the slave boy must have learned geometry in a previous existence. In other dialogues, especially the *Phaedo*, Plato has Socrates present a few arguments for the immortality of the soul and its reincarnation. Socrates, and Plato too, were very much interested in proving the immortality of the soul, but this is not the main point in the *Meno*. What is most instructive for us is Socrates' demonstration of the importance in the learning process of latent learning. If what boys have learned in years of normal explorations and manipulations can be utilized effectively, perhaps they, like the slave boy, can be taught subjects like geometry with surprising rapidity and ease.

V

Can virtue be taught?

If Plato and his teacher Socrates had not believed that virtue can be taught, is it likely that Socrates would have spent his life attempting to instruct the youth of Athens, and is it probable that Plato would have written *The Republic*, a program for a state which is to be "perfect" precisely because of its elaborate system of moral education and controls? And would Plato have three times risked his life in an attempt to reform the government of Syracuse, to discipline the court of the tyrant Dionysius by virtue and science? Yet we find Socrates arguing in the *Meno* and other Platonic dialogues that virtue apparently cannot be taught. What is the explanation of this paradox?

The reader will remember that what Socrates and Plato wanted was *proof* that virtue can be taught. But how could it be taught unless it was a kind of knowledge, which was precisely what people were loath to admit? The best thing then was to force them, by provocative theses such as "virtue *cannot* be taught," to think the subject through for themselves. The Socratic method, after all, aims not to *give* the individual the truth but to enable him to find it for himself. The provocative thesis that virtue can be taught also created an occasion to question the wisdom of democratic leaders. Socrates made a career of being the gadfly to the Athenians and their democracy, and Plato's aristocratic sympathies were also well known. You will note in the *Meno* how Anytus, one of the most respected leaders of the Athenian democracy, bridles at Socrates' criticism. Later on he became the chief instigator of the charges leveled at Socrates, charges that led to his trial and execution.

We should keep such things in mind in evaluating Socrates' argument. Would the fact that Pericles and other Athenian leaders failed to inculcate virtue in their sons prove that virtue can never be taught? The Athenian leaders might have been too busy, or their sons hostile. In a deeper sense, however, we must admit that Socrates was right. What he sought was a knowledge of virtue which would be proof against all obstacles and could be inculcated as surely and universally as is geometry. Such knowledge was lacking in ancient Athens and is still lacking today; it could not have been taught then, nor now.

Is reincarnation a valid explanation of latent knowledge?

We have seen that latent knowledge is knowledge which we have not been taught but which may be elicited by questions. The slave boy's answers to Socrates' questions betrayed latent knowledge which Socrates explains by supposing that he had received instruction in a previous life on earth. The idea of reincarnation has been widely criticized. What would it mean to say of the slave boy that his soul was identical with that of some other individual who existed in the past? How could he or anyone else come to know that his soul was the same as that of some person in the past? Only memory of his past life would have relevance, but this is precisely what is always lacking.

Moreover, why resort to such a drastic and nebulous hypothesis when there is a simpler one at hand which can be investigated by psychological methods? We all learn things by ourselves that we have not been taught, and sometimes surprise our teachers by our ready answers. Our learning of geometry may well begin with our first discriminations of figures.

It has been argued also that the theory of reincarnation would help to explain "love at first sight," and the strong feeling we sometimes have that we have been in certain towns or seen certain buildings of which we have, in fact, had no previous experience in this lifetime. Before accepting this theory, the psychologist must first ask whether we have not experienced similar things in the past, which we cannot recall. Would not this also serve to explain the phenomenon? Is not the simpler explanation always to be preferred? Is it to be preferred when another is more adequate?

The following questions are designed to help you test the thoroughness of your reading. Each question is to be answered by giving a page or pages of the reading assignment. Answers will be found on page 383 of this Reading Plan.

1 Does Socrates think it self-evident that men never desire what they know will make them miserable?

2 Does Socrates correct the slave boy by reasoning with him?

3 Does he think that he is teaching the slave boy geometry?

4 Does Socrates assume that the slave boy's "recollection" can be explained only by reincarnation?

5 Do Socrates and Meno agree that knowledge alone can be taught?

6 What is Anytus' objection to the sophists?

7 What does Socrates say that puts Anytus in a rage?

8 Who does Anytus say can teach Meno virtue?

9 Why is a man with knowledge a better guide, according to Socrates, than a man with only right opinion?

10 How does the citing of a contradiction in Theognis aid Socrates' argument?

ARISTOTLE

On the Soul

Book II

Vol. 8, pp. 642-656

Aristotle may well have been the greatest intellect of all time. He made important contributions to almost every existing field of knowledge, including physics, astronomy, meteorics, biology, and psychology. He created the science of logic almost singlehanded, bringing it to a high level of development. The influence of his work in metaphysics, ethics, and politics has been unparalleled except perhaps for Plato's. His writings on rhetoric and fine arts have eclipsed all others.

The impact of Plato and Aristotle on the philosophy of the western world has been so great that it is sometimes said that every philosopher is naturally either a Platonist or an Aristotelian. This is an exaggeration, for there are other powerful currents of philosophical thought. One is the atomism and materialism of De-

mocritus, a contemporary of Aristotle, which is represented in the *Great Books* by the celebrated poem of
Lucretius. Yet it is true that Plato and Aristotle, like
twin peaks, dominated centuries of western thought
—the Alexandrian period, Medieval times, and the
Renaissance, for example—and that their differences in
outlook and doctrine drew thinkers irresistibly into
opposite camps.

Even where they agreed, sharp differences emerged.
The rationalism of the mathematician Plato was extreme, that of the naturalist Aristotle more moderate.
Reason in the Platonic philosophy was an absolute
sovereign; the truth was to be found in ideal mathematical and ethical forms, and the scientific value of
sense perception was denied or discounted. Reason in
Aristotle's system was a more democratic sovereign;
the truth lay in a conciliation of the ideal and the concrete, and sense perception and induction were royal
roads to it.

Third Reading

I

We know far more of Aristotle's life than of Plato's, but not nearly enough to satisfy our curiosity. He was always too busy with scientific and philosophical investigations to write memoirs, and did not dream how famous he was to become. Moreover, general knowledge was for him the supreme goal, not particular or personal facts.

It is significant that he was born in Stagira in 384 B.C., for this town was on the Greek island Euboea which was soon to fall under Macedonian rule. Like Hippocrates he descended from a line of physicians and early acquired an interest in biological studies. At the age of seventeen he went to Athens to continue his education, and devoted himself to philosophy in Plato's Academy, where he remained for twenty years, until his master's death. After a three-year period in the court of Hermias, ruler of a tiny Greek state in Mysia on the other side of the Aegean Sea, and two years studying natural history on Lesbos, he lived for seven years in the court of King Philip of Macedonia, where he became the tutor of Alexander, the future Alexander the Great. These years deepened his knowledge of human motives in situations where stress and stakes were high.

In 336, after the death of Philip, Aristotle returned to Athens and established his own school of philosophy, the Lycaeum, distinguished by a grove of shade trees under which the master and his followers walked and conversed. The sudden death of Alexander in 323 terminated this very productive period. Powerful factions in Athens rose in revolt against Macedonian authority, and the former tutor of Alexander thought it prudent to retire to Chalcis, where he died the following year. His retirement was hastened by the memory of the execution of Socrates, for he did not wish to see Athens guilty of another such crime.

To understand Aristotle's psychological views it is helpful to recall some general features of his metaphysics. In the first place, he rejected the Platonic theory that reality consists of the ideal forms or ideas. What exists is not the ideal circle defined by the geometrician, the ideal of justice, nor the ideal man, but rather the imperfect triangles we can mark off on the ground, the somewhat faulty justice we find in men and human institutions, and concrete men with all their frailties. Existence or reality belongs to substances or things exclusively, and substances are a unity of form and matter, neither of which exists except when compounded with the other.

About any substance two questions can be asked: "What forms or qualities is it supposed to have?" and "Does it exist, i.e., are the qualities realized in matter?" The forms or qualities could not exist unless realized in matter, nor could pure matter, which is the receptacle of form, exist without qualities. Thus even today we speak of the "formative'" influence of ideas and of the "materializing" of states of affairs we have anticipated.

Every type of life, according to Aristotle, moves toward the goal set by its species. Nature is a process in which matter is ever "realizing" new forms, or, what comes to the same thing, forms, ideas, species are continually being "actualized" in new individuals. After some familiarity with Aristotle's way of thinking, it is easy to conceive of an acorn as gradually taking on the form of the oak tree, and of the egg and caterpillar being determined in their development by the end which they are to attain, the butterfly. Indeed, when asked about the sprouting growth and hirsute developments of a boy, we say: "Well, of course, he is becoming a man."

We say the same about the preliminary stages of a painting, a sculpture, an architectural creation, but with one difference. It is the idea of the finished product in the artist's mind which explains why the work of art takes shape and develops under the brush or chisel, not the finished work itself. In the same way, we account for most of our behavior by purposes we have in mind. According to Aristotle, nature also has clear purposes, but these are defined by the species which ceaselessly renew themselves in fresh exemplifications. Here it is the end itself which is the cause.

Determination by the end or purpose, Aristotle called the "final cause." But when this cause is at work, three other causes also operate. The final cause cannot function without the cooperation of the "efficient or moving cause," which is what we now generally mean by cause in science. The sculptor cannot embody his image in stone without the movement of his chisel, nor can the plant and animal species renew themselves without physical movements and chemical action. The efficient cause is always necessary, and so are the "formal cause" and the "material cause." The formal cause of a thing consists of the qualities or characteristics which explain what the thing is. Thus we sometimes explain a work of art or a class of animals by describing its distinguishing features. The material cause, finally, is the material which is given form—some kind of stone, metal, or wood, in the case of the sculpture. Sometimes Aristotle reduces his famous four causes to two: the final, formal, and efficient causes all represent the agency of form, and thus are formal; whereas the material cause is the passive recipient of form.

You will find that both form and matter are used in an absolute and a relative sense. Pure form has no admixture of matter and is not an existent but only a possibility, the possibility of having such and such a nature. Prime matter, similarly, is only potentiality, or what the possible needs to become actual. The relative use of the terms might be illustrated as follows: The lumber is form relative to the house into which it is to be made. The grub, similarly, is form relative to the egg, but matter relative to the fruit fly into which it develops. Aristotle would also say that the grub is potentially a fruit fly, and that, as it develops, it actualizes forms or possibilities.

I I

Substance, as we have seen, is a unity of form and matter, and living substances are of a special kind. "By life we mean self-nutrition and growth (with its correlative decay)," Aristotle says. The power of reproduction is also common to all living substances. Nutrition, growth, and reproduction are the powers which distinguish plants, but they are also necessary to animals, of course, and even to man. Animals, Aristotle explains, possess the added capacity of sensation, and most of them self-movement as well. Man, finally, has the crowning ability to reason; he can employ reason in practical matters and in the creation of artistic productions, but also in disinterested science and speculation. It is in this power of disinterested demonstration and contemplation that Aristotle sees man's closest approach to divine perfection. If there is any part of human nature which is immortal, it is this activity of reason emancipated from partiality and the service of human needs.

The scale of organic nature goes from the lowest plants, which are scarcely distinguishable from inorganic forms, through the gamut of animals, beginning with the sponge, which has no power of self-movement and scarcely any sensation, and ending with the highest mammals and finally with man. It would be better to say that the scale of nature for Aristotle begins with man and ends with the lowest forms of life, for a series of forms below man on the scale is represented as a progressive deprivation of the powers belonging to man.

The primacy of man in the universe is illustrated by Aristotle's famous division of the human soul.

The Human Soul

Irrational		Rational	
Vegetable	*Animal*	*Practical*	*Theoretic*
(nutrition, growth, reproduction)	(sensation, movement)	(reason applied to the conduct of life and the production of things)	(reason applied to philosophy and science)

To have a soul is to be able to function in certain ways. Human beings are capable of nutrition, growth, reproduction, and also sensation and self-movement, but their crowning distinction is rational activity, both practical and theoretic. Plants are to be understood as living forms deprived of sensation and movement, as well as reason; and animals, as deprived of reason. Men thus have all the functional capacities of both plants and animals, and much more besides.

The lower capacities are always necessary to the higher: sensation and movement are impossible without nutrition, and rational activities require all three. Similarly, reason must first be applied to life and to the arts if man is to have the leisure and zest for contemplation and scientific pursuits. The functions thus form a hierarchy: the higher one depends on the one just below, but the lower ones, as in plants and animals, can exist independently of the higher.

A certain excellence is implied in being a plant, an animal, or a man. The plant which fails to grow and reproduce properly is not much of a plant, nor is an animal that is almost insensitive a good example of an animal. Would the same thing be true on the human level? Could we say that a man who fails to use reason in the conduct of his life is not quite human— that he is not living on the human level? Suppose a man's main interest is in eating and reproducing, or in moving about and having sensations. Would it be fair to say that he is living like a vegetable or an animal? Would you say that the infant and the young child live mostly on the vegetable and animal level, and only gradually attain to the human estate as reason develops? Are there men who have no opportunity or desire to live on the highest human level, who take no interest whatever in questions of a scientific or philosophical nature, or is it always just a matter of degree? In the former case, could we speak of them as less than human?

III

You will have noted that Aristotle's conception of the soul is very different from Plato's, although in both the domination of reason is the mark of human excellence. Aristotle insisted on the continuity of human life with other living forms and held that the soul, in the highest forms of life as in the lowest, is inseparable from its body.

Aristotle agreed with Plato that the soul is the source or origin of the body's movement (see p. 645d) and also the end, but he added something quite different—that the soul is "the essence of the whole living body" (p. 645d). Let us consider these properties, beginning with the soul as the end of the body's movement. If we are asked why we are walking down the street, we mention some aim or purpose. We are going to the restaurant or library; this is, in effect, why our body is moving. The soul is thus the final cause of the body's movement. But if it is also the source or origin of the same movement, is it not the efficient cause as well? And could not the soul also be the formal cause of the movement? After all, the form or character of the body's action had first been envisaged by the soul, and the body merely enacts it.

Can it be then that the soul is the final, efficient, and formal cause of our bodily movements? And would the body then be the material cause of the same movements? It is well to note that Aristotle is evidently talking about self-movement or spontaneous movement. It is obvious that if a man falls off a cliff, or moves in any other accidental fashion, the soul is neither the final nor the efficient cause. It is some physical movement, such as a mechanical sliding of rocks underfoot. Here we encounter a serious problem. We can understand how the body moves when it receives a mechanical push or when its support gives way, but how can the mere idea or purpose of going to the theatre set our legs in motion? The law of inertia—Newton's first Law of Motion—tells us that some physical force is necessary to start or alter the motion of a physical body.

We all tend to agree with Aristotle that our body moves when and because we want it to move, that it responds to our desires and projects. Yet how is this possible? One clue is furnished by Aristotle's doctrine that changes of all kinds are at bottom changes in the position of particles in space. Our legs could be set in rhythmical motion by our idea of going to the theatre, but only *via* particles moving within the body.

The solution of our problem lies in the third sense in which the soul produces the body's movement, namely, by its being "the essence of the whole living body." As the essence of the body, the soul is the inner meaning of the body's movement, not something extraneous to it. If the eye had a soul, Aristotle says, it would be vision, and the body is thus related to its functions as the eye is to vision. The soul thus conceived could put our legs in motion and set us walking toward the theatre, but it would do so by virtue of adjacent physical motions of which it is the essence or inner meaning. Does the soul's initiation of bodily movement, thus understood, violate the law of inertia? This law is as follows: "Every body continues in its state of rest, or of uniform motion in a right line, unless it is compelled to change that state by forces impressed upon it" (Newton's *Mathematical Principles of Natural Philosophy*, Vol. 34, p. 14a). This question we have raised is certainly a difficult one, but we have at least taken the first steps toward answering it. In a later chapter we shall return to this problem.

If the soul is the inner meaning of the body's movements, what is the body's role in this inseparable unity? The living body, Aristotle says, is potentiality, and the soul is what actualizes this potentiality. We see a man lying asleep on his couch, and we explain that he is a sprinter, a good talker, that he knows the multiplication tables, etc. Yet he is doing none of these things at present. We mean that given an incentive he sprints, given an excuse he talks, and that when the need arises he will do his sums. Now the question is whether the living body is anything but a set of potentialities. A living hand is an anatomical pattern of bones and tissues, of course, but so is the hand of a man who has just died. To understand what the *living* hand is, must we not supplement anatomical with physiological knowledge? And must we not understand the hand, as Hippocrates insisted, in relation to the action of the whole body? And also in relation to the society in which the man in question lives and functions? The living hand, as Aristotle implies, is a bundle of potentialities ready to be actualized: it is the wielder of sword, spear, pen; it is a welcomer, rejecter, waver of goodbye, etc. It is composed of bones, tendons, tissues, to be sure, but these are also to be understood in terms of their potentialities, their functioning.

IV

In dealing with the senses, Aristotle makes the modern distinction between those which require contact—touch and taste—and distance receptors, i.e., sight, hearing, and smell. Touch is in the service of the nutritive function and is possessed by all animals; many have no other sense. Aristotle was well aware that the tactual sense is in reality a group of senses, including hot and cold, dry and moist, hard and soft.

The function of light rays and sound waves in mediating vision and hearing, respectively, was not well understood in Aristotle's time, but it is surprising how far he was able to go without this knowledge. He points out that some external stimulus must be needed for sensation, for otherwise would not the senses perceive themselves? Even in touch it is not the skin that is felt; the skin is really a medium conducting the impulse within the body. This medium of skin can be extended if we touch things with a walking stick. In vision, unlike touch, the object perceived must *always* be at a distance. We must draw a painting closer to the eye for clearest vision, but if we bring it into contact with the eye, there is no vision at all. Intervening space is essential. How then can vision bridge the distance between the painting and the eye?

Since the eye must be affected by the object if it is to see it, there must "be *something* in between," Aristotle points out. Yet what is in between is obviously not itself visible. Aristotle thus concludes that the color of the painting is not transmitted to the eye; the color rather sets in motion the intervening air, which is transparent, and this in turn engenders motions in the eye. Similarly, an audible object sets up movements in the mass of air which are continuous from the object to the ear, but the air itself is quite soundless. Aristotle recognized that such a mass of air could be reflected, resulting in echoes, just as light can be reflected, and hence diffused, even to objects lying in shadow.

Although it is easy to find errors in Aristotle's account of perception, it is remarkably advanced, for the time, and the reasoning is often exemplary. He saw the weakness of the

Democritean theory that the perceived objects continually give off "effluences" or images of themselves, for since these would be composed of matter, would they not be seen in the intervening space? His own theory was that what was transmitted by the transparent air was only the *form* of the perceived object—something akin to the impression of the thing in wax.

Actual seeing depends on current stimulation of the eye, yet we sometimes say that a man can see things when he is not looking. Aristotle lists three uses of "can see." We say that a man can see the constellation of the Great Bear, even though he is fast asleep or looking into his wineglass; we mean that he is capable of seeing it because he has normal vision. If the Great Bear is plainly visible from where he is, we hold that he can see it in a further sense, namely, there is no obstruction to his seeing it. Finally, we say that he can see this constellation in the actual sense; that is, that he has normal vision, there is no obstruction to his seeing it, and he is looking at it. (See p. 647c-d.)

Could we not add one or two more meanings of "can see"? Suppose the man can see the pattern of stars but does not know its name, or knows it only as "the Big Dipper." Would not the fullest actualization of "can see" include a knowledge of the name of what is to be seen? The reader will readily see that all the cases of "can see" except actual seeing are, in Aristotle's language, different senses of potentiality.

Aristotle knew that what you can actually see depends not only on the present stimulation of the eye but also on the state of the eye and on emotional factors, and that this is true similarly for the other senses. He pointed out that when we touch an object that is midway between hot and cold, we have no experience of temperature whatever. It is in terms of this neutral point that we determine what is hot and what is cold in any perceptual experience. Hot and cold are thus not absolute qualities but relative to each other and to the mean. The warm or hot is a progressive series on one side of the mean or neutral point, and the cool or cold is a progressive series on the other side. "What we perceive must have a degree of the sensible quality lying beyond the neutral point," Aristotle says.

"This implies that the sense itself is a 'mean' between any two opposite qualities which determine the field of that sense" (p. 655d).

What does it mean to say that the sense itself is a mean? It implies something very interesting—that the state of the sense organ itself determines the mean or neutral point. It is easy to see that this is so when you remember how the neutral point shifts toward the cold after adjusting yourself to a cold shower or to a long walk in the cold, snowy out-of-doors. A piece of ice on the skin, which ordinarily would feel very cold, is now only cool or even neutral. An even more obvious example is the lemonade which tastes sour after sweet candy, but sweet after an accidental gulp of vinegar.

The state of the sense organ, as Aristotle implies, determines the mean or neutral point. The precise shift of the mean has been determined mathematically in many experiments in recent times. What is judged light or dark depends on what the eye takes as the base line or neutral shade; and what is felt as heavy or light depends on the heaviness of the weights you have been lifting, for this determines the mean weight, which we experience as neither heavy nor light. The shift of the mean is even more obvious in the case of the pitch and the intensity of tones. The phenomenon first described in general terms by Aristotle is now usually called the "adaptation level" and finds its exemplifications throughout sensory experience.

V

Can we see heavy objects and hear big ones?

There are three "objects of sense," according to Aristotle: (a) those perceptible by only one sense, e.g., the pitch of a tone; (b) those perceptible by two or more senses, e.g., the shape or the size of an object; and finally, (c) "common sensibles," which are common to all the senses, i.e., movement, rest, number, figure, and magnitude. (See pp. 648d-649a.)

Often we say that we see heavy things—a massive, ponderous building or a huge, heavy church bell. We see the massive-ness and hugeness but not the heaviness, for there are no visual sensations of heaviness. If we hear the loud tolling of a bell in the darkness of the night, we say that we have heard a great bell toll, but of course we do not actually hear the size of the bell, or even the bell. These things we have learned to associate with what we do hear, and Aristotle calls them "incidental objects of sense."

Elsewhere he tells us that we associate things by contiguity in time and space, similarity, and cause and effect. Thus we hear the tolling of what seems to be a large bell even when it is invisible to us; the reason is that a large bell and sonorous tolling have often been associated in space and time by cause and effect. We have often perceived them together; now the one calls the other to mind. Similarly, we associate the visual aspect of the church bell with iron, which we have often experienced as heavy; the appearance of iron and the heft of it have been found together countless times.

Three questions now arise. Do we first see the large black bell and then infer, on the basis of past experience, that it is also heavy? Of course not. The association is so automatic that the inference has been eliminated, and we *seem* to see the heaviness as directly as we actually see the size. In the same way, to use one of Aristotle's examples, we immediately recognize our friend coming down the street, although what strikes the eye is only a pattern of color. There is no time for an inference. We seem to see our friend the very instant we see the patch of color.

The second question is: In what way is this perceiving of "incidental objects of sense" useful to the human race? How would we be handicapped if we did not have this habit of perceiving in things far more than is given in sensation? What if we could not perceive water at a distance, and had to touch it every time to convince ourselves it was liquid! The reader can easily think of many more examples.

Finally, we have the question whether the perceiving of "incidental objects of sense" is a source of error. This we shall touch upon in the section just below.

Is sensory experience infallible, i.e., is it impossible to err about sensory experience?

It is easy enough to make mistakes about incidental objects of sense. We see a welcome watery expanse in the distance, but it turns out to be a cruel mirage; there is no water there, but only the visual appearance. But is it possible to err about what is perceptible to only one sense? Color is an example. At first glance it might seem that a man could mistake purple for blue. He might certainly call a purple color blue, but would this be an error of judgment or an error in what is experienced? We may think that purple is a kind of blue. We may classify it wrongly. But how could we *see* the purple as anything but what it is, namely, purple?

To Aristotle it is self-evident that what is plainly given in sensation is what it is and cannot be anything else. Most philosophers who have taken up the question in the past two thousand years have agreed with him. When only one sense is in play we are infallible, but when an incidental object of sense is involved, Aristotle implies, error is not only possible but embarrassingly frequent. What we *see* as water may be a mirage and not *feel* like water at all. The mournful cry of the whippoorwill at dusk sounds close by, but visually the source is distant. The coin that we revolve in our fingers changes its visual shape every moment, but it never ceases to *feel* round. Here we say that the tactual sense gives the real shape, whereas the eyes give us apparent shapes. In what has become known as "Aristotle's illusion," on the other hand, the eyes disclose one object, which is correct, whereas we *feel* two objects, which is an illusion. (See p. 704d.) This, however, is a rare exception. Although the range of vision is far greater than that of touch, it is also far more subject to error. Visual illusions are far more common than tactual illusions.

Our world is riddled with mistakes and illusions of this kind, but since they are of regular occurrence we can compensate for and guard against them. But are mistakes impossible where only one sense datum, such as color, is involved? To test this we need modern experiments which attempt to show that inferences are involved in seeing colors, inferences that might be wrong. Do we, for example, tend to see a colored expanse as green when we recognize it as grass, even though it is actually not green, but brown?

How can we perceive things that do not stimulate our sense organs?

We look about us and see trees, flowers, streams, the sky, animals, habitations, men. All of these are based on sensation; none of them is a sensation. All of them involve the "common sensibles"—movement, rest, number, figure, magnitude—for whether we see or hear or feel these objects, the common sensibles are always perceived. We have seen that it is by association according to contiguity in space and time, similarity, or cause and effect that we perceive so much more than is given in sensation. It was Aristotle's merit to have seen the full measure of difference that separates sensation from perception. The one marks the most primitive animals; the other reaches its zenith of development in the rational animal.

In the interplay of the senses we get a rounded view of objects, and one sense corrects and completes another. Often what is perceived by one sense is perceived by another analogously. Aristotle says:

There seems to be a sort of parallelism between what is acute or grave to hearing and what is sharp or blunt to touch . . . (p. 651d)

In such passages Aristotle introduces the whole subject of "synesthesia," the carrying over of a sense quality from one sense field to another. Examples are "high" and "low," "bright" and "dull." Both pairs are carried over from vision to hearing, and dull applies to taste as well. The problem then is whether dull colors, dull tones, and dull tastes have anything in common. The answers to questions of this sort will have a lot to do with the understanding of poetry, which employs synesthesia continually.

The following questions are designed to help you test the thoroughness of your reading. Each question is to be answered by giving a page or pages of the reading assignment. Answers will be found on page 383 of this Reading Plan.

1 How does Aristotle explain the fact that we cannot taste anything when the tongue is dry?

2 What are the flavors, or taste qualities, distinguished by Aristotle?

3 Does the intervening medium affect us when we see and hear? When we touch something?

4 Are there certain things, according to Aristotle, that we can see in complete darkness?

5 Is darkness, according to Aristotle, merely the absence of light, and nothing positive?

6 "A man can exercise his knowledge when he wishes, but his sensation does not depend on himself." Why does Aristotle say this?

7 Of all sounds, the voice alone "has a soul in it." How is it, then, that we can speak of the voice of a flute or of a nightingale?

8 Can we properly speak of one who learns as being "acted upon" by something?

9 What is a "special object of sense"?

10 Is it possible to err about a special object of sense?

ARISTOTLE

On the Parts of Animals

Book I

Vol. 9, pp. 161-169

Aristotle was the father of several new sciences, as we have seen, and his genius advanced almost all the others known in his time. For many scientists it is his biological writings which constitute his greatest contribution to human knowledge. On reading Aristotle's *On the Parts of Animals,* Charles Darwin wrote to Dr. Ogle, the translator: "Linnaeus and Cuvier have been my two gods, though in different ways, but they were mere schoolboys to old Aristotle." In the light of the biological knowledge of Darwin's time, as of ours, Aristotle was of course wrong about many important matters, but this was to be expected; what was amazing was how many he managed to be right about.

Some of his particular findings were not rediscovered for five hundred, a thousand, and even two thousand years. Biologists have been impressed with the number of his individual discoveries relating to the traits, habits, adaptations, organs, and habitat of animals. According to the distinguished biologist Joseph Needham, he made prophetic discoveries in the field of embryology. He was the first clearly to distinguish between preformation and epigenesis; and, in deciding in favor of the latter, foreshadowed the outcome of the famous nineteenth-century controversy over this issue. His conclusions as to the order in which the characteristics of the embryo appear anticipated the nineteenth-century theory of recapitulation. Even more important was discovery that the head end of the embryo grows more rapidly than the tail end, for this pointed ahead to the modern theory of axial gradients.

Equally remarkable was the sweep of his over-all classification of the 540 species then known. It is mainly with the problems involved in this classification, which prefigured the evolutionary theory, that we shall be concerned in this reading.

Fourth Reading

I

We can be certain that young Aristotle followed the medical practice of his father, Nicomachus, with the keenest attention, but he was always more interested in the patient than in the cure. From this early period dates his lifelong interest in the mechanics and principles of the life processes throughout the scale of nature, from man to the most primitive plants. The physician observes physiological functions from a vantage point, and his art opens the doors to biological phenomena in general. It was during the years he spent on the coast of Asia Minor and in Lesbos that Aristotle found the big opportunity to pursue his biological studies, especially of marine forms. It is interesting that most of the places mentioned in his biological works are in Asia Minor rather than in Greece proper. Here cuttlefish, starfish, sea urchins, sharks, squids, and many other forms swarmed in abundance, including whales, porpoises, and dolphins, whose mammalian nature he recognized centuries before anyone else. There were also the torpedo and angler fish, the paper nautilus, the chameleon, which he studied minutely. No animal was too lowly for his careful investigation, and indeed, for him, "every realm of nature is marvellous."

Aristotle observed the embryos of many species at successive stages of development, habitat, methods of procreation, and the anatomy of organs of all kinds, and did a great many dissections. He saw that nutriment was carried to different parts of the body by the blood, and detected the function of secretory organs. He discovered the four chambers of the stomach of cattle and other ruminants, and he knew that the human heart has four chambers. Here he was misled, however, by the lack of blood in the left auricle of slaughtered animals, and supposed that it normally contained air. He was wrong also about the function of the brain.

It is interesting that he made more mistakes when he took his facts from others than when he made his own observations. There seems no doubt that if the dissection of human bodies had been permitted, Aristotle would have anticipated even more modern discoveries than he did. Had even the beginnings of modern chemistry been available to him, there is no telling how far he would have gone.

II

Aristotle was the first to undertake a systematic classification of animals, and the problems he faced were enormous. The profusion of nature was anarchic, with no clear order or boundaries of the groups. There were no books to consult, of course, and the ideas Aristotle inherited from earlier philosophers were sketchy and, in his opinion, mostly wrong.

What "principles of division" should he adopt? One such principle of division, attributed to the philosopher Democritus, was shape and color. The advantage of this is that shape and color are easily observed, and that many birds and animals are identified in practice by their distinctive form and hue. What then is wrong with this principle of division? Aristotle points out that the shape and color of animals do not tell us anything about the way they function—grow, reproduce, find food—and that if we go by these qualities alone, a wooden carving could qualify as a horse. (See p. 163c-d.) It is easy to see also that with this principle of division we should never arrive at the class of mammals, for mammals, which include whales and bats, differ too much in shape and color. Nor would we ever reach the useful class of crustacea, for this includes such diverse forms as lobsters, shrimps, the waterflea, etc.

The division of animals according to shape and color has a certain utility on the common-sense level, but it is not good enough for science. It enables us to make quick identifications of orioles, sheep, antelopes, etc., but it has no explanatory value. The mere fact that an animal has a certain form and hue tells us nothing about its anatomical structure or physiological functions, nor how it relates to and compares with other groups of animals. The mere fact that an animal is a mammal, on the other hand, tells us a great deal.

The same objection would apply to the division of animals into terrestrial and marine forms, or into those which walk, fly, or swim. These classifications lead nowhere. They also violate rules of classification. For example, some animals, such as the frog and the seal, live both on land and in water, and therefore would belong to contrary classes. The rule violated is that things should not belong to more than one of the classes into which the phenomena are divided, or, otherwise expressed, the classes should not overlap. For when animals are classified as either terrestrial or marine forms, it is understood that they are not both.

If animals are divided according to whether they walk, fly, or swim, there is also overlapping. Moreover, many species have no power of locomotion whatever, and would therefore be excluded from the animal world. The rule of classification transgressed here is that the classes into which a subject matter is divided must contain the whole subject matter—in the case we are considering, all animals.

I I I

There is only one way in which we can be absolutely certain that we have included the whole subject matter in our division: this is when we use a dichotomous division, viz: A and not-A. Since the fundamental logical principle of excluded middle states that a thing is either A or not-A, we conclude that a dichotomous division must include everything. Thus Aristotle's first division of animals into sanguinous and nonsanguinous (or blooded and bloodless) cannot fail to embrace all animals. This dichotomy is roughly equivalent to the modern division of vertebrate and invertebrate, which also comprises all animals. Thus we have

Animals

sanguinous (= *vertebrate*)   *nonsanguinous* (= *invertebrate*)

The difficulty at once arises that, though the class of sanguinous animals can be divided into different kinds of sanguinous animals, nonsanguinous cannot be so divided. The reason is that "nonsanguinous" is a negative or privative term; and "privative terms . . . admit of no subdivision," as Aristotle says. Nonsanguinous cannot be divided into *kinds* of nonsanguinous animals because they have in common only the *lack* of blood. This can be illustrated by a hypothetical division of mammals into animals with feet and those lacking feet. The first class could be subdivided, but the attempt to divide the second, as we divide the first, leads to absurdities, as follows:

Animals

Footed	*Footless*
Those with two feet,	Those which do not have two feet,
Those with four feet, and	Those which do not have four feet, and
Those with more than four.	Those which do not have more than four.

The division on the left is not sophisticated, but it makes sense, because two-footedness is a differentiation of footedness; the division on the right results in nonsense, since not-having-two-feet does not specify a definite class.

If we try a further dichotomy under the division feathered and featherless, the result on the right is even more absurd:

Animals

Feathered	*Featherlesss*
Those with barbed feathers and those with nonbarbed feathers.	Those lacking barbed feathers and those lacking nonbarbed feathers.

Such dichotomies are open to another objection pointed out by Aristotle. If "we start with the two contradictories, Feathered and Unfeathered; we shall find that the ant, the glow-worm, and some other animals fall under both divisions" (p. 166b), since, as he claims, the ant and the glowworm can be "in some cases both winged and wingless" (*History of Animals*, p. 48d). This is highly interesting. Remember that dichotomy divides a subject matter into A and not-A. How then can anything be both A and not-A, both winged and wingless, feathered and featherless? One answer would be that an animal, such as a butterfly, might be winged at one time and wingless at another. Another answer would be that certain subdivisions of a group have wings while the rest do not. Thus since bats are mammals, mammals are both winged and wingless.

This gets rid of the logical difficulty of being both A and not-A. But it does not avoid the puzzles occasioned by intermediate forms, forms which seem to lie in between A and not-A. Aristotle says, for example, that "sanguinea [sanguinous animals] are either viviparous or oviparous" (*On the Generation of Animals*, p. 272d), that is, give birth to a living organism or produce an egg. Then his genius for close observation led him to discover intermediate forms, the ovoviviparous fish and reptiles. These produce eggs covered by a shell, as do oviparous animals, but the eggs are hatched within the body of the female, which later delivers them alive. (See p. 206a and *On the Generation of Animals*, pp. 272d-273b.) These ovoviviparous forms are partly oviparous and partly viviparous; the female lays eggs with shells, but within the body, and then brings forth live replicas of herself. In making such discoveries, Aristotle was moving toward the modern view that, since an egg is laid in either case, the distinction between vivipara and ovipara is only of minor importance.

Aristotle also recognized intermediate forms between animals which lay eggs and those which do not. The reason is that there is no sharp line between eggs and non-eggs. Thus insects bring forth larvae, but some of these, Aristotle says, are indistinguishable from eggs (see *On the Generation of Animals*, pp. 273c-d, 299c-d).

You will find that Aristotle gives numerous examples of intermediate forms between A and not-A, and this is his main objection to dichotomous division. He calls attention to intermediate forms between plants and animals. "A sponge," he says, "in these respects completely resembles a plant, that throughout its life it is attached to a rock, and when separated from this it dies." Other animals such as the sea-lugs are free and unattached, "yet they have no feeling and their life is simply that of a plant separated from the ground." Since animals, according to Aristotle, are distinguished by mobility and sensation, in which plants are lacking, we have here yet another instance of intermediate forms. In a number of passages, Aristotle recognized that there are no sharp lines of division between plants and animals nor among the main groupings of animals.

In criticizing dichotomous classifications of animals, which had been recommended by Plato, he was anticipating the theory of organic evolution which did not arrive on the scene for more than two thousand years. According to the contemporary biologist Charles Singer, Aristotle did not attain the evolutionary point of view, "but it is evident that he was moving in that direction, and perhaps if he had lived another ten years he might have reached it."[1] It will be remembered that what brought the world to accept organic evolution, more than anything else, was the evidence that Darwin presented of the continuity of nature. He demonstrated that the main groupings of animals do not exist in water-tight compartments but are linked to other groups in a fairly continuous sequence of development. It is little wonder that Darwin praised Aristotle so highly. By his discoveries of intermediate forms in nature and his sense of their importance, Aristotle was laying the foundations for the theory of evolution.

IV

Aristotle's theory of the soul, as we have seen, definitely orders the whole animal kingdom in a scale of development, a ladder of increasing perfection. Some of Aristotle's predecessors declared that the soul—the principle which imparts life and movement—was present everywhere in nature. For Aristotle, on the contrary, the soul functions fully only in man, less so in animals, still less in plants, and not at all in inorganic nature. Man is at the top of the ladder, and "higher" than the animals because he possesses all their capacities and more besides. He reaches excellence, or virtue, insofar as he lives up to the human level, and fully deploys his reason, both practical and theoretic. To be at the top of the ladder, to be fully human, he must be guided by reason in civil life and have a taste for science or philosophy.

[1] Charles Singer, *A History of Biology*, revised edition (New York: Henry Schuman, Inc., 1960, p. 39.

It will be remembered that the classification of things or substances in Aristotle's *On the Soul* was as follows:

THINGS OR SUBSTANCES

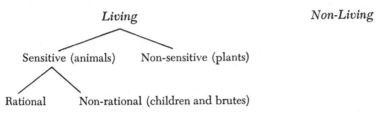

Living   Non-Living

Sensitive (animals)   Non-sensitive (plants)

Rational   Non-rational (children and brutes)

This classification is dichotomous throughout: we have Living and Nonliving, Sensitive and Nonsensitive, and Rational and Nonrational. In *On the Soul* Aristotle thus employs precisely the kind of classification that he criticizes and rejects in his biological works.

He rejects dichotomous classification for a number of reasons. It divides the class always by one crucial difference or differentia, but as Aristotle insists, in *On the Parts of Animals,* "no single differentia . . . can possibly express the essence of a species" (p. 167c). Quadruped is not a good differentia, nor is cleft-footed; we must combine them to divide the class usefully. But cleft-footed-quadruped is not a single differentia but involves at least two. Or take the present-day suborder of ruminants. Chewing the cud would not suffice to demarcate the group; there are also complications of the stomach, no upper incisor teeth, and often bone-cored horns that have to be taken into account.

Aristotle also insists, in his biological works, that the traits which set off the group must be positive, for the mere lack of a trait cannot be divided into kinds. We have just seen what absurdities result in attempting to divide negative classes dichotomously. Dichotomous classifications seem to work only when the negative class is not further divided, or divided according to a variety of positive differentiae. Thus, we can still divide all animals into vertebrates and invertebrates (though vertebrata is only a subphylum), but the negative class, invertebrata, would be a vast series of phyla and subphyla, sharing no positive invertebrate features. They are distinguished from one another by the most diverse criteria. The protozoa are either one-celled animals or are composed of colonies of like cells, whereas the metazoa are composed of unlike cells. The differentiae which distinguish more advanced phyla—the sponges, the coelenterata, etc.—are altogether different.

The question then is why Aristotle should have given great prominence to the above classification of things or substances, which employs dichotomy at every step. Is it not open to all the objections he has advanced? In this classification, you will note that no effort is made to subdivide the negative side of the dichotomy. No subclasses appear under Nonsensitive and Nonrational. Here also Aristotle takes growth, nutrition, elimination, regeneration, reproduction, and other traits of living forms to be reducible to one single differentia, namely, Living. This serves his purposes in *On the Soul,* for there he is concerned with a broad division of the functions of the soul. This classification, moreover, seems ideally suited to point up the position of man at the top of the scale of living forms. Man is superior in that he possesses not only the powers of both plants and animals, often heightened, but also his own distinctive nature besides.

Can we conclude, therefore, that dichotomous classifications, though unsuitable in biology, may serve other purposes very well? We must remember that dichotomous division has one unique advantage; it formally includes all the members of the class divided. On the other hand, of course, the negative class, as when you say "my friends and *others,*" is rather nondescript and in the nature of a wastebasket. Yet it is sometimes very important to divide mankind into "your friends" and all others, whoever they may be.

We should do well, however, to follow Aristotle's example and to be on the lookout for exceptions to neat dichotomous divisions. The line between your friends and all others may not be as fine as you suppose, and some people may fall between the two. Aristotle himself has noted that the precise line between the sensitive and the nonsensitive is difficult to draw, and that some animals seem to anticipate the rationality of men, while some men live, whether they are capable of more or not, on the plane of brutes. Could the same be said of dichotomous classifications in general?

We cannot object to Aristotle's employing two types of classifications. Classifications do not exclude each other, as if one were true and the other false. Yet there is one criticism of Aristotle's use of two methods of classification that can be made, and to this we now turn.

V

How are Aristotle's two methods of classification related?

In the classification presented in *On the Soul*, living beings are divided into but three kinds of species, namely, man, animal, and plant. They have a common genus, living thing, and each is distinguished from the others by a specific difference, so as to form the following hierarchy:

Living Thing	Man ....vegetative, sensitive, *rational*
	Animal ....vegetative, *sensitive*, not rational
	Plant ....*vegetative*, not sensitive, not rational

The specific difference, which is italicized in each case, is a single essential difference determining a unique species. Since a species is a final determination of being, in Aristotle's view, species admit of no further essential divisions. There are thus no species of man, animal, or plant. They can be divided into classes, determined by *accidental* characters, such as method of reproduction, nature of organs, etc., but these classes are not *species*. This follows from what Aristotle says in his logical works about the five predicables—genus, species, property, specific difference, and accident.

The classification we find in *On the Parts of Animals* and *On the Generation of Animals* is also a "ladder of nature" with man at the top. In other respects it is altogether different. Although man is still distinguished by the specific difference *rational*, animals and plants are divided into many groups, as follows:[2]

---

[2] Aristotle did not write down his classification of animals in full. The above is a reconstruction from Aristotle's biological works given by

MAN

MAMMALS

WHALES

REPTILES AND FISH

OCTOPUSES AND SQUIDS

JOINTED SHELLFISH

INSECTS

MOLLUSCS

JELLYFISH   ASCIDIANS

SPONGES

ZOOPHYTES

HIGHER PLANTS

LOWER PLANTS

INANIMATE MATTER

The classes of animals listed are not differentiated by "specific differences," as Aristotle understood this term, but by the nature and function of organs of the animals, such as the sense organs, organs of digestion, blood circulation, respiration, locomotion, etc.; by the method of reproduction, feeding, habits, habitat, etc. No one of these differentiae can be used throughout, and usually more than one is required to demarcate a single group.

There might seem to be a contradiction between the two methods of classification, since according to the second there are numerous kinds of animals and also some division among plants. But there is no real contradiction. There are only three proper species in Aristotle's strict sense, but there can be many kinds of animals and plants, distinguished by their accidents, i.e., their nonessential characteristics.

Nor is there any objection to employing both classifications, as was pointed out above. Each is appropriate and necessary for its purpose. The only complaint we can have is that Aristotle does not present these classifications as critically different and opposed, but runs them together as if they were the same.

Charles Singer, *A Short History of Medicine* (New York: Oxford University Press, 1928), p. 28.

The closest he comes to pointing up the distinction is in his occasional reference to man as "a featherless biped," whereby he suggests that, even though featherless biped characterized men and only men, it would do so by an accidental trait, not essentially.[3]

Why did Aristotle consider the final cause primary, rather than the motor cause?

The primary cause, according to Aristotle, is the purpose or end of a process, whereas the motor (or moving) cause is the mechanical forces which are in action throughout the process, and the material cause is the material on which the motor cause acts. The egg of a sea urchin consists of organic tissue which must be acted upon by environmental forces if it is to survive and develop. The end or purpose of the process in this case is the modest one of becoming a sea urchin, and it is this which Aristotle insists is the primary cause. Why? Because in nature, as in the arts, reason comes first. Thus the doctor and the builder never set about their work (motor cause) until they decide what end they wish to achieve (final cause). In the same way, nature does nothing without an end or purpose. The sea urchin does not exist in order that the sea urchin egg may be nourished and grow; on the contrary, the motor cause involved in nourishment and growth exists in order that the mature animal should exist.

It is true that when they are asked what they are doing, the doctor will say "attempting to restore health" and the builder "building a house." Both would answer in terms of final cause. But can we ask this same question of the sea urchin egg, or of nature in general? Does nature have purposes or ends? Or do only conscious beings have ends or purposes? You will have seen that Aristotle has an answer. He says that physiologists talk about ends or purposes in nature. What is meant is that the organs animals possess are necessary either for their survival or well-being. If not, how would you explain their existence?

[3] See Mortimer J. Adler, "Solution of the Problem of Species," *The Thomist*, Vol. III, No. 2, April 1941, pp. 279-379, for a discussion of Aristotle's two methods of classification.

Did Aristotle, by making the final cause primary, exclude evolution?

Some of his predecessors, Aristotle says, were primarily interested in the process in which species were formed, or evolved, whereas he thinks that primary attention should be given to "the characters of a given creature when formed" (p. 162c). These earlier philosophers raised the question of how a species of animals had evolved, but Aristotle replies that the essential structures of an animal cannot have come about by accident, for they are essential to the species. If an animal has a backbone, so must its parent, and the parent of its parent, and so on. And he adds that in nature, as in art, the conception of what is produced must exist prior to the production. Just as conception of a piece of sculpture must pre-exist in the sculptor's mind, so also must the species be prior to its realization in particular animals.

Does Aristotle's emphasis on final cause rule out the development of new species? We have seen that in certain respects he was moving in the direction of evolutionary theory. In the present respect, did he not move away from it?

Why is the method of dichotomy in zoology contrary to "the instincts of mankind"?

Dichotomy divides groups of animals according to only one differentia, as, for example, breathing or not breathing, flying or nor flying. But it is impossible by this method to reach any of the "natural groups" of animals recognized by mankind, such as birds and fish, for these comprise in their essence many differentiae. Flying, for example, would not define birds, nor swimming fish, for other animals do both. During all the centuries since Aristotle, and for a few before, men have classified animals not by dichotomies but by means of a number of easily observed characteristics. This natural classification is immensely useful, appears in far-flung parts of the world, and in many languages.

The following questions are designed to help you test the thoroughness of your reading. Each question is to be answered by giving a page or pages of the reading assignment. Answers will be found on page 383 of this Reading Plan.

1 Is man a group, according to Aristotle, which is not differentiated into subordinate groups?

2 Is any part of an animal, according to Aristotle, purely material or purely immaterial?

3 Did Aristotle regard "the instincts of mankind" as a good general guide in classifying animals?

4 Why is it unwise to classify animals according to "analogies in their corresponding parts"?

5 Why do not birds and fish form a class together?

6 Why, if "the process of evolution is for the sake of the thing finally evolved," was Empedocles in error?

7 Should the biologist, according to Aristotle, concern himself with the soul, or with matter?

8 Does the whole soul constitute the animal nature, or only a part of the soul?

9 What distinction does Aristotle make between "necessity" and "final" cause?

61

GALEN

On the Natural Faculties

Books I-II

Vol. 10, pp. 167-199

T here are two approaches to the study of the health
and disease of human beings—the clinical and the experimental. Each has its special advantages and both
are essential. Without clinical observation of the sick
man, medical practice could not even make a beginning; without experiment, which is observation from a
special vantage point or under controlled conditions,
it would remain superficial and uncertain. Clinical
medicine makes close observations of the course of a
disease as indicated by symptoms appearing on the
surface of the body; even subtle and inconspicuous
changes in outward appearance may have diagnostic
value; i.e., they may tell us something about the disease and how the organism is coping with it. The
clinician is also concerned with what is now called the
case history of the patient, which includes his record

of disease, his habits, associates, manner of living, regimen of food and drink, and so forth.

Clinical medicine, however, cannot study the disease process directly in most cases because it does not usually lie on the surface of the body, and the instruments aiding observation do not often probe far below the surface. The physicians of ancient and medieval times were more handicapped in this respect than are modern physicians. Dissection of the human body was prohibited, and post-mortem examinations, which might have confirmed or discounted the presence of an assumed disease, were ruled out as impious. Medication could be given and any change of external symptoms carefully noted. But what change did the medication bring about beneath the surface, in the disease process itself? This could not be directly observed and had to be inferred. And it must often be inferred today. The difference is that a great mass of knowledge has accumulated which renders our inferences far more certain. Moreover, exploratory surgery can give us an inside view.

However, by imagining ourselves back in the historical period of Hippocrates or in that of Galen six hundred years later, we can perhaps form a clearer picture of the central predicament of the physician, which is that he can never be sure that if the patient gets well it is because of the medicine he prescribed. The patient might have recovered without it, and even sooner than he did. How is this predicament to be resolved?

Galen, and to some extent Hippocrates before him, endeavored to learn the nature of human organs, functions, and malfunctions, by dissecting animals of various species. Inferences from animal to human physiology are always hazardous, but much less so when the animal closely resembles the human. Galen, for example, was on pretty safe ground in inferring the character of human bones, muscles, tendons, etc., from those of the Barbary ape. But how can one discover animals which are afflicted with human diseases or with diseases similar to those of man? This presented a great difficulty, especially in ancient times, since animals cannot tell you how they feel, nor can they describe their symptoms or the conditions which preceded them. In modern times diseases can often be *produced* in animals and their course and cure observed directly by exposing the affected organs at different stages of the disease or in post-mortem investigation. Galen, in the second century A.D., had no such resource, and one can have the greatest sympathy for any efforts made at that time to locate animals with human or humanlike diseases.

But there was another use to which animals could be put in the study of human disease. Galen dissected animals of many species and even resorted to vivisection in many cases, in order to study normal or healthy functioning. He also performed experiments on animals, some of which were of great importance for medicine. The physiology of the normal functioning of tissues, organs, and organ systems can tell us a great deal about malfunctioning, especially when disease is conceived, as it was by Hippocrates and Galen, as a disproportion or imbalance of normal functioning.

Fifth Reading

I

The physician-philosopher Galen was born at Pergamum in Asia Minor about A.D. 130 and practiced medicine in Pergamum, Rome, and other cities until about the year 200. His father was a rich and celebrated architect who saw to it that his son had a good education in the sciences and philosophy, especially that of Plato, Aristotle, and the Stoics. When it was disclosed to the father in a dream that his son was to become a great physician, Galen began the study of medicine in his native city, and his vocation was thus given divine sanction. His love of study and his industry were remarkable. With tireless energy he pursued his studies in Pergamum, Smyrna, Corinth, Alexandria, and Rome, and collected and systematized most of the medical knowledge of his time. He wrote 500 treatises, most of which were concerned with medicine, and of those which bear his name today some 80 or so are thought to be genuine. Although his 124 philosophical works have been lost, his medical writings make clear his indebtedness to Plato, Aristotle, and the Stoics.

When Galen was thirty, a revolution broke out in Pergamum and he removed to Rome, where he lectured and practiced medicine with great success, arousing the envy and resentment of fellow physicians. To make matters worse, Galen plainly showed his contempt for other practitioners and condemned all schools of medicine and all masters except Hippocrates alone. For Hippocrates he always expressed great reverence, and professed to follow his example in everything. But Galen's contentiousness and his luxurious imagination, which so often committed him to theories far removed from the facts, contrasted sharply with the calm reticence and caution of his master. In Rome his contentiousness blew up such a storm that he thought it prudent to retire from the city. After five years of wandering, however, he was persuaded to return to Rome by the earnest appeal of the emperor Marcus Aurelius, and there became court physician to his son, the future emperor Commodus.

II

Galen was not only a physician but also a philosopher, and many of his works were concerned with logic and metaphysics. He always desired to be in agreement with Aristotle as well as Hippocrates, though this was not always possible in fact. From the Stoics also he learned a great deal, and Stoical philosophy was in turn influenced by developments in medicine. Galen's great opponent, on the other hand, was the atomistic, mechanistic philosophy of Leucippus and Democritus. Epicurus had developed this system, and Lucretius' great poem *On the Nature of Things* had put a masterly exposition of it before the Roman world in the preceding century. Epicureanism accordingly enjoyed great prestige among medical practitioners at the time, and Galen's continuous polemics against it are understandable.

Galen was violently opposed to both atomism and mechanism. Human beings are not composed of atoms, qualitatively alike, whose chance motions and collisions explain action and passion, functions and malfunctions. Nature is governed throughout by purpose and does nothing in vain; every tissue and organ has its predetermined use. Moreover, the functioning of the biological organism is not to be accounted for by the action of its parts, for it is the whole which determines the parts, not the parts which determine the whole.

Let us consider the relation of whole and parts in medicine for a moment. Following Hippocrates, Galen insisted that the living thing is predominantly a unity, and that only in terms of this unity can health or illness be understood. He went so far as to insist that disease itself is only a focus of a general *affection* which vitiates the bodily economy. A man's illness, in other words, always extends beyond the focal point of his disease. If he suffers from cancer or tuberculosis of the lungs, for example, his general vitality is also affected, and disease in the narrower sense is seen as a part or perhaps an outcome of a wider disturbance. Insofar as this is true, the treatment of the particular organ manifesting the disease, even if specific remedies were available, would not cure the patient. The bacilli could lodge elsewhere. Strictly speaking, it is the patient who is to be cured, not the diseased organ.

How far would this be true today? Is disease now regarded as a focus of a wider disturbance, or is it considered an isolated infection or failure of function? The answer might be that it all depends on which diseases you are talking about; some are localized, others more general. On the other hand, there are certain recent developments in medicine that definitely favor the whole-man approach of Hippocrates and Galen. First, there is growing recognition that all diseases have a psychological origin or a psychological component and involve some depletion or disruption of the whole organism, and that cooperation or a change of attitude on the part of the patient is an essential aspect of the cure. Duodenal ulcer is not merely a localized ailment but a general disorder, and so also are cancer of the lung and heart failure. Even an injury, such as a broken leg, is a wound to the ego which must be healed along with the leg. In short, a good half of the diseases treated in hospitals at present are psychiatric (i.e., they affect the whole personality), and the rest have an important psychological component.

A further sign that disease is always a part of a wider disturbance is the modern trend toward the medical clinic. Medical practice has become so specialized that general practitioners are hard to find, and the specialist himself is often not able to detect and evaluate symptoms which lie beyond his specialty. The remedy proposed for the prevalent overemphasis on the localized disease is not, of course, a return to the general practitioner, but a tremendous expansion of medical clinics, providing the full gamut of specialists and a general practitioner besides.

There is thus some modern support for Galen's view that disease is a part of a general disorder. But it would be rash to conclude that the physiological whole always determines its parts, or that final causes, or explanations in terms of purpose, are to be found everywhere in the organism. Even Galen, in spite of his Stoicism and his Aristotelian devotion to final causes, does not stick to either.

III

It will be noted that in his *Natural Faculties,* Galen vigorously rejects mechanical causes, as set forth by Erasistratus of Alexandria (300-225 B.C.), Asclepiades (100 B.C.), and other eminent physicians. He ridicules the view of Erasistratus that digestion is accomplished by the mechanical motion of the walls of the stomach (see p. 202) and that the secretion of fluids is facilitated by the size and shape of the vessels involved (see p. 184). He complains that Erasistratus tries to explain the circulation of blood and other fluids to different parts of the body by contractions of the vessels, gravitation, the production of vacua which tend to be filled, and other mechanical principles. Such principles, according to Galen, are incapable of adequately explaining why each organ of the body gets just what it needs from the blood and why fluid that is to be eliminated terminates in the bladder and not elsewhere. The various tissues and organs of the body need nutriment, presumably of very different kinds. What can assure that the heart, the veins, the nerves, the brain, the eye, will each get the specific kind of nutriment which is necessary to it, and that waste products will find this proper route? Mechanical principles of action, being blind, cannot give appropriate direction to the bodily economy.

For there is not a single animal which could live or endure for the shortest time if, possessing within itself so many different parts, it did not employ faculties which were attractive of what is appropriate, eliminative of what is foreign, and alternative of what is destined for nutrition. (p. 185b)

But if such an attractive faculty, present in each organ of the body, is capable of drawing to itself what is needed or appropriate, Galen says, there is no need for groundless mechanical explanations.

Summing up his general theory at the opening of Book III, Galen writes:

> . . . the actual bringing up of nutriment from the veins into each of the parts takes place through the activation of the attractive faculty, whilst to have been finally brought up and presented to the part is the actual end for which we desired such an activity; it is attracted in order that it may be presented. After this, considerable time is needed for the nutrition of the animal . . . (p. 199b)

In order that the nutriment should stay in one place long enough to be assimilated, the animal's "nature" requires another faculty—the retentive faculty—and this must not come from outside but belong to the organ involved. Besides these two faculties, there exists in every part of the animal a faculty which Galen calls "alterative," that is, "assimilative and nutritive" (p. 199a). Galen does not describe this faculty, but this should not surprise us since the organic chemistry involved in assimilation began to be developed only in the present century.

The faculties invoked by Galen can be regarded as ingenious devices of nature for the preservation and health of the species. For

> . . . Nature which, at the beginning, well and truly shaped and disposed all the parts of the animal, and, after carrying out this function (for she left nothing undone), brought it forward to the light of day, endowed with certain faculties necessary for its very existence, and, thereafter, gradually increased it until it reached its due size. (p. 185b)

Whereas the great sculptors Phidias and Praxiteles shaped their materials only on the surface, the more profound artistry of nature contrives each inner part.

> Every part of a bone she makes bone, every part of the flesh she makes flesh, and so with fat and all the rest; there is no part which she has not touched, elaborated, and embellished. (p. 185c)

This is an eloquent but very extreme expression of the view which has come to be called "vitalism" and sometimes "teleology." The vitalist holds that mechanical forces do not suffice to explain biological phenomena, such as generation, growth, regeneration, assimilation, adaptation, and so on; that a purpose or directive tendency in nature must be recognized. The vitalist, of course, need not deny the validity of mechanical explanations. He simply insists that they are not sufficient to account for biological phenomena, that purposive forces or directedness are also needed. Even today, as in the time of Galen, vitalists and mechanists cross swords.

Galen was certainly right in arguing that the mechanists of the second century and earlier had not given a satisfactory account of biological phenomena; they were certainly in need of criticism. But were not the mechanists on the right track in at least looking for mechanical explanations? Only by seeking them could they be found; only by failing to find them could it be fairly argued that mechanical explanations would not suffice. Standing where we do today, in the middle of a scientific century which is developing organic chemistry at an unprecedented pace, Galen's faculties are apt to impress us as mere verbal explanations. If we ask: "What is this process of assimilation in which nutriment is transformed into tissues and organs?" the answer seems to be: "It is brought about by an assimilative faculty." When we further ask what the assimilative faculty is, we are referred to Aristotle's account of substantial change (i.e., the change of one substance into another), but we learn nothing about the assimilative process, or how it works. Is not this explanation, then, purely verbal? Is it not like saying that opium puts people to sleep because it has a dormitive property?

Before jumping to this conclusion, however, we must recall that Galen, following his master Aristotle, is really giving the final cause of assimilation; or, following the Stoics, he is explaining the process as part of the plan of a perfectly wise and benevolent deity. Is not an explanation in terms of plan, purpose, or end-in-view often sufficient in itself? When we say that we are going downtown in order to buy shoes, have we not given a sufficient explanation of our walking down the street? But is there not a big difference between the two cases? We have independent knowledge of our own purposes but not of God's purposes. We know *his* only through their supposed effects. Would not Galen's argument then run as follows: Assimilation, which is necessary for the survival of the human race, takes place because God in his goodness and perfection so willed it, and God's wise and benevolent purpose is proved by the evidence of his design, such as the assimilative process, which we find everywhere in nature. The argument, so construed, would be circular.

At this point we should bear in mind what we previously said about Aristotle's four causes. Final cause is not the complete explanation at best, but must be supplemented by the efficient cause (and the formal and material causes as well), and the efficient cause, as we have seen, is the moving or mechanical cause. If it is God's plan that certain biological functions beneficial to the species should be carried out in the world, there must be some regular mechanism to do the work. The search for mechanical causes must continue, whether the world is God's design or not. For the mechanist, mechanical explanations will be sufficient; for the teleologist, who believes in world purpose, or for the vitalist, who believes in a vital principle of some kind, mechanical causes will not be sufficient in themselves.

It is easy to see that Galen does not entirely neglect mechanical causes but sometimes gives them an important place. He naturally admits that gravitation and the action produced by a vacuum, as in a bellows (see p. 213d), have a role in biological processes. While discerning that swallowing is not merely the result of gravitation, he does not deny that gravitation plays a part in it, nor that the bulk and weight of food affect the digestive process. On countless occasions, he tells us, he has found, in the still living animal, the intestines "contracting . . . upon their contents" (p. 202b). Moreover, Hippocrates was right in saying that "excessive movement on the part of the embryo itself brings on labour" (p. 208d). "Excessive bulk, or weight, or irritation" may also be causal factors (p. 208d). Mechanical reflexes were also taken into account, and Galen was the first to note the pupillary reflex. Even the attractive faculty works mechanically, like a lodestone or bellows. Thus Galen says that "we shall ascribe to the semen [what we should call the fertilized ovum] a faculty for attracting blood similar to the possessed by the lodestone for iron" (p. 186a-b).

These are a few examples of Galen's recognition of mechanical causes in the bodily economy. Had organic chemistry existed in his day, and physiology been out of its infancy, we can be sure that he would have supplemented his final causes by mechanical causes systematically. In later sections of this guide, we shall see that attention to the functions that organs perform can furnish valuable clues to the mechanical forces involved.

IV

Galen was the greatest systematizer of physiological and medical knowledge that the world had yet seen. Though he leaned heavily on the wisdom of Hippocrates and Aristotle, as also on the still developing theories of the Stoics, he was also a keen observer and conducted original experiments. Even when he took over theories from others, he usually added something distinctive of his own.

It will be profitable to consider a few examples of his originality and systematizing genius. Galen's experiment on the function of the motor nerves was one of the most important in ancient times. Galen discovered that section (or severing) of the spinal cord between the first and second vertebrae causes instantaneous death. When the section was made between the third and fourth vertebrae breathing stopped; and if the cord was severed below the sixth vertebra, the intercostals, or chest muscles, were paralyzed and only diaphragm breathing was possible. If the cord was cut still lower down, the legs of the animal were completely paralyzed, as were also the intestines and bladder.

This discovery would be of great significance not only in physiology but also in medicine. For example, it would easily suggest the reason why there are so many more cases of general paralysis of the lower limbs than of the upper, and why, when both arms are paralyzed, the legs are usually so as well. The ground was now prepared for the study of diseases which attack the spinal cord. What are the disease processes which can cut through the spinal cord, at one level or another, just as a sword does on the battlefield? Another step forward was possible now, and that was to distinguish two basic types of paralysis: first, the paralysis caused by severing of the motor nerves; and second, the paralysis caused by destruction of the sensory or afferent nerves, as in locomotor ataxia. In the first case, the muscle is unable to contract; in the second case, the muscle can contract but sensation is cut off, with the result that the patient has no control of his muscles.

Galen went part way toward a correct understanding of the function of the sensory nerves, but he was misled by certain ideas current in his day. He was right in distinguishing between the "impression," or sensation, and the perception proper, but wrong in holding that, after the external object has produced a change in the sense organ (or nerve ending), the "pneuma" or "vital spirit" flows out to the sense organ to constitute the perception. We know today that it is no vital spirit which is conducted by the nerves, but rather the nervous impulse, which is a complicated electro-chemical process still not well understood. We know also that the nervous impulse is transmitted from the excitation in the sense organ to the brain and not, as Galen thought, from the brain to the sense organ. On Galen's theory it would seem that any organ in the body to which the pneuma or vital spirit flowed would be sensitive (i.e., capable of sensation), and that seeing would be the same as hearing or tasting. Galen avoided this last difficulty by supposing that the pneuma takes on a visual quality when it goes to the eye, an auditory quality when it goes to the ear, and so on; that it assumes the character of what it perceives.

Galen's reasoning is understandable. If one is to perceive a tree, for example, must not a likeness of the tree be somehow transmitted to the perceiver—to the sense organ and nerves? The nineteenth-century theory of "specific nerve energies" made this assumption. Nowadays we understand that in perceiving a tree, neither the excitation of the sense organ nor the nervous impulses transmitted to the brain need resemble the visual tree. Yet there was an important truth in Galen's theory which is sometimes forgotten, even in modern times. Galen recognized that there is a big distinction between sensation and perception, and that it is the brain and nerves which contribute all the difference between collections of bare colors, sounds, tastes, odors, etc., and our rich perceptions of a meaningful, highly structured world.

Galen's discovery of the pupillary reflex was also a step that was needed for further advance. It might seem easy to note that when a man goes out into the sunlight his pupil narrows down to a pinpoint, and that when he returns to the dim light of an interior the pupil gradually expands. Someone, however, has to observe the phenomenon first and to know that it is important, for merely to observe it would be nothing. Once attention has been called to this reflex, however, the question that Galen was always asking—"Why does it occur, or what purpose does it serve in nature's plan?"—would become wise and pertinent. Could this reflex protect the eye from the glare of the sun, as the closure of the eyelids protects it from noxious material in the air or the supraorbital ridges guard it against sudden blows? Eventually the protective function of the reflex would be confirmed, and the mechanism involved, the doughnut-shaped smooth muscle—the iris—would be studied. It would be found that rage, and drugs such as atropine, can also enlarge the pupil, and many new questions and investigations would be opened up. But all such trains of development would depend on the essential first steps.

Although Galen perpetuated some current errors about the circulation of the blood, his insistence on the role of blood in bringing nutriment to the tissues of the body was clarifying and guided future research broadly in the right direction. He also corrected a persistent misconception of the action of the heart which had plagued his predecessors for centuries. Misled by the fact that in freshly killed animals the left ventricle of the heart is drained of blood, they supposed that it is normally so, and is filled instead with air. By closer inspection, and perhaps by the use of vivisection, Galen found that the left auricle also contains blood, and thus removed a fatal obstacle to the understanding of the circulatory system.

Besides making numbers of crucial discoveries, Galen systematized and extended the work of Hippocrates and other predecessors. Although many authors, even before Hippocrates, had elaborated the doctrine of the four humors, Galen was

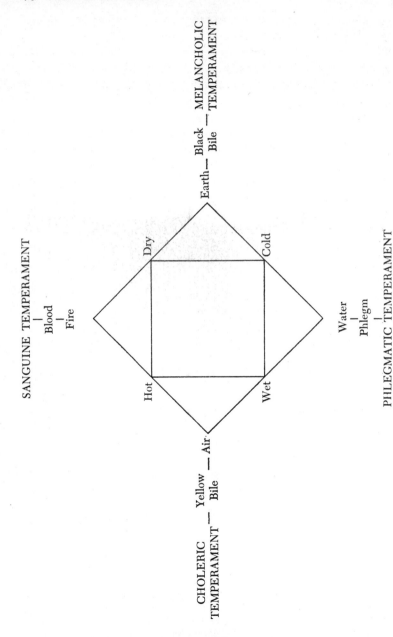

able to systematize the doctrine further and to add something new. The four humors, as will be remembered, are based on the four elements—fire, earth, water, and air—which were the basic chemical ingredients of all things, according to ancient and medieval thinkers. In the chart below,[1] these elements are shown in their relation to their qualities, hot, dry, cold, and wet, which were regarded by Galen and his predecessors as fundamental causes, and to the humors—blood, black bile, phlegm, and yellow bile. The four temperaments, each of which is determined by the preponderance of one of the humors in an individual, are also indicated.

The chemistry of the four elements and their qualities really retained its hold on scientific and popular thought until the work of Robert Boyle in the seventeenth century gradually led the way to modern chemistry. The four humors also maintained their sway for many centuries, and were only gradually supplanted with the advance of organic chemistry. The idea of the humors still remains, as we shall see; that is, the endocrine secretions now constitute what is called the "humoral" system. The temperaments have proved the longest-lived of all. A great literature of the temperaments beginning with Aristotle and Theophrastus, was produced through the centuries, in which physiological considerations played little part; and even today we often speak of sanguine, choleric, melancholic, and phlegmatic men, and the pictures that come to mind are illuminating.

Galen extended the list of four temperaments to nine, and his reasons for doing so are understandable. In the first place, the temperaments were regarded as disproportions of the humors, as conditions of pathological imbalance. Galen accordingly added a normal, perfectly balanced temperament. He next recognized four temperaments determined by the predominance of one of the four qualities—hot, cold, wet, and dry. Clinically, the relative excess of each of these qualities is observable, as in persistent fever, low body temperatures, dehydration, and dropsy. He acknowledged in addition the cele-

---

[1] Adapted from Charles Singer, *A Short History of Biology* (Oxford: At the Clarendon Press, 1931), p. 8.

brated four temperaments, the hot and dry, the hot and wet, the cold and dry, and the cold and wet, which are indicated in the chart above.

Although the physiology of the ancient humoral theory is something that belongs exclusively to the past, the idea behind it lives on. The idea is that the same blood that transports nutriment to the tissues of the body also conveys active elements to these tissues which, as Galen claimed, affect water retention and body temperature and dispose one man to laugh when a second would weep, a third rage, and a fourth go to sleep. Nowadays we know that the dominance of one of these active elements, now known as hormones, can promote or retard growth and development, affect the metabolic rate, the oxygen balance, salt balances, as well as the water balance and other homeostatic regulative systems of the body; and profoundly affect the temperament of the individual. Some thirty years ago, physicians spoke of thyroid-centered and pituitary-centered individuals, and of other psychophysical types determined by the dominance of one of the endocrine glands in the system of the endocrines. But progress in this field has been very rapid of late, and it is now realized that other factors are involved and that things are much more complicated than had been supposed. The idea of Galen and other Greek humoral theorists still lives on, but it is continually undergoing elaboration and implementation.

V

Can your temperament be changed, or is it inescapable?

Temperament refers to the range of things to which you react, and to the degree of your intensity, persistence, changeability, gaiety, resilience, dejection, irritability, truculence, apathy, and the like. So understood, a man is much more than his temperament. He also *is* or *has* a personality, which includes more or less freely chosen aims and pursuits, including the project of becoming a better person—a different person. To test the possibility of this, we have to begin by trying to think of men who have cured their apathy by developing a new life interest or cured their hot tempers by cultivating calmness and forbearance. Galen does not seem to give a clear answer to this problem. He was influenced by the Stoics, who held that everything in nature is necessary, and could not be otherwise than it is, and insisted that we must therefore acquiesce in nature's order. On the other hand, their cardinal teaching was that men, or at least an elite class among men, can acquire the serenity of acquiescence which they lacked before. Hippocrates and Galen certainly held that changes of attitude and outlook of the patient may be an important part of the cure. The question how far the leopard can change his spots will come up farther on, especially in the reading of Freud.

How does growth differ from genesis?

A basket, a house, or a ship when it is being constructed does not really grow, Galen says, for it does not develop in all directions at the same time. In the case of a house, the foundation is first built, then the basement, then the first floor, and so on. We can thus speak of the "genesis" of a house but not of its growth. If the house were to grow, as does an organism, the foundation, the basement, the first floor, and so on, would all have to evolve at the same time. For the boy's legs, torso, head, ears, etc., all grow simultaneously, though the rate of growth is not the same. Growth, properly understood, occurs only in living things.

Is this generalization entirely true? Can you think of any exceptions?

How does growth differ from mere increase and from development?

Galen points out that when children inflate the bladders of pigs there is an increase in size but no growth, because the tissue merely becomes thinner and more extended, and there is no addition to it. For growth, which takes place only in living things, nutrition is needed. It is also necessary that the same nutrition be transformed into very diverse tissues and organs, such as the liver, heart, veins, etc. This, according to Galen, is the work of the alterative or assimilative faculty. There is also a "shaping faculty" which is seen at work, especially in the embryo, when form and constitution are transformed, and between birth and maturity (see p. 170b).

The four faculties—the growth, nutritive, alterative, and shaping faculties—actually function at all times, according to Galen, but before birth the shaping and alterative faculties take the lead, while in youth the faculty of growth is in command.

In modern times we do not speak of faculties but rather seek to discover specific causal factors which determine growth and development. Galen's distinction between growth and development, remarkably clear for his time, helped to set the stage for modern investigations. One simple modern experiment which showed the role of the thymus in growth and of the thyroid gland in development was as follows: when ground thymus was fed to tadpoles, they evolved into large tadpoles; when ground thyroid was fed to them, they became tiny frogs.

The difference between growth and development is sometimes worth pondering. We are often unduly impressed by the mere size of a man and are pleased to hear that a boy is growing by leaps and bounds without inquiring whether he is also developing.

Can the embryo behave purposefully though lacking in intelligence?

Galen contends that although the embryo, which he calls "semen" (see pp. 185d-186b), draws to itself all the blood that it needs, we must "take care not unwittingly to credit the semen [embryo] with reason and intelligence." We should not make the embryo into a living animal or endow it with nature's purposes. "And if we retain these two principles—that of proportionate attraction and that of the non-participation of intelligence—we shall ascribe to the semen [embryo] a faculty for attracting blood similar to that possessed by the lodestone for iron" (p. 186a-b).

Here Galen says that the embryo acts purposefully in attracting the blood it needs but that it has no purpose nor any intelligence; rather it behaves in a blind, mechanical fashion.

The same would be true of all the tissues and organs of the body. And if this is so, would it not be possible to explain all "purposeful activity" without assuming that nature actually has a purpose or intelligence? In this case, why should Galen continuously assail the mechanical world-view of Epicurus, taken over by Asclepiades and other physicians? What is your own view of this matter? Do you think it is possible for a thing to act in what would be called a "purposeful" manner, without having a purpose?

The following questions are designed to help you test the thoroughness of your reading. Each question is to be answered by giving a page or pages of the reading assignment. Answers will be found on page 383 of this Reading Plan.

1 Does Galen hold that bones, cartilages, nerves, membranes, ligaments, veins, etc., arise at the first stage of the animal's genesis?

2 What inconsistency does Galen attribute to Aristotle?

3 When food turns into blood, which, according to Galen, is active in the process, the food or the blood?

4 Does Galen charge the atomists and their followers with despising dreams, birds, omens, and the whole of astrology?

5 What objections does Galen make to the hooklike extremities of Epicurus' atoms?

6 What physiological faculty does Galen illustrate by his story of the dishonest peasants who bring corn to the market?

7 Does the attractive power of the stomach, according to Galen, make recourse to the theory that a vacuum is involved unnecessary?

AQUINAS

Summa Theologica

Part I-II, QQ. XLIX-LIV

Vol. 20, pp. 1-25

T he great compendiums of medieval knowledge reached a climax in the thirteenth century with the *Summas* of Albertus Magnus and St. Thomas Aquinas, his pupil. Scholars have sometimes complained that these thinkers succeeded all too well. Their thorough analysis and resolution of the controversies of the time were so effective that disputation ceased and fruitful discussion was stifled. This is only a half-truth. The fourteenth century ran up new colors and sought new paths, but the old controversies continued. The fame of Aquinas, which soon eclipsed that of his master, Albertus Magnus, has held its own for centuries, though with ups and downs, and is probably more influential today than ever before.

The over-all achievement of Aquinas in psychology was the overcoming of the Platonic-Augustinian dualism of soul and body. It was a remarkably subtle reconciliation of "the two worlds" of spirit and body, based on Aristotle's theory of development. So long as the human soul was considered a spiritual substance apart, it was alien to the body and a derelict in the world. If the soul was made the mere form of the body, it became a mere harmony of bodily functions which, like the harmony of the lyre, would die when the instrument was broken. But when the soul was conceived as a substantial form—as the form of the body but also capable of having an independent status—it could have its lodgment in the world and also a putative place in heaven. It was not only the form of the body but also its mentor and guide. Its highest faculty—the intellect —was thought to operate in a manner that is independent of the body. This conception was so difficult that both Duns Scotus and Occam returned to Platonic dualism; the present tendency is back to the dynamic synthesis of Aquinas. The discussion which follows relates to one aspect of the total picture of man—the theory of habits.

Sixth Reading

I

The life of Thomas Aquinas has been told many times, and what is known about it can be found in many places. He was the son of the Count of Aquino, was born in the Kingdom of Naples, and received his early education in the abbey of Monte Cassino. In 1239 he entered the University of Naples, and in 1244, contrary to the wishes of his family, he entered the Dominican order. On his way to Paris to study theology, he was intercepted by his family and put under guard. Arriving in Paris the year following, he became a student of Albertus Magnus, and three years later followed his master to Cologne, where he continued his studies. It is clear that he learned much from Albert but also that he made innumerable departures and developments. In 1252 began his life of teaching and writing, of preaching and counseling, of illuminating and safeguarding the truth and interests of the Church. This was to continue until 1273, the year before his death at the age of forty-nine.

How "the Angelic Doctor" was able to produce such an immense number of closely reasoned volumes in a short twenty years, occupied as he was by lectures, preaching, and many other duties, is not easily understood. We do know that he frequently applied for free time to pursue his writing. For all his devotion to theology and his untiring efforts to substantiate and unify Church doctrine, he did more than any other medieval thinker to separate philosophy from theology and to establish it as an independent discipline. Although he was not a stranger to mystical experience, nothing personal or merely edifying appears in his philosophical writings, and he seeks always to meet contention with argument. In the *Treatise on*

Habits, to which we now turn, there is little appeal to authority, unless it be to that of the philosopher Aristotle, and even this is not essential.

II

Before we investigate *habits,* we should have some understanding of the *powers* of man as they are conceived by Aquinas, for habits are simply specializations of powers. Prior even to powers is the *soul,* which has these powers. Aquinas' conception of the soul is based on that of Aristotle, which we discussed in the Third Reading.

It will be sufficient to recall here that the human soul, according to Aristotle, is the source and final cause of all our activities, that it is a "substantial form" in the sense "of the form of a natural body having life potentially within it" (Vol. 8, p. 642b). It is thus the inner meaning of the body's movements, that for the sake of which they occur; for taken by themselves the movements would be incomprehensible. When we ask why such and such a movement has occurred, the answer is that the soul had certain proclivities or powers. The soul, however, is not to be identified with the exercise of its powers, since it is still a soul when they are not exercised, as in sleep. We have seen that the soul's relation to the body is subtle and complex in Aristotle's account. The body, as human and alive, as breathing, as digesting, as running or sailing a ship, as a powder keg of potential activities, is not something apart from the soul, nor vice versa. The body animated by soul is like the wax to which a form has been given by the stamp; the wax and its form are one. It is like an ax in relation to its axness; without its axness—its usefulness as an ax—the ax would not be an ax.

It is the soul as substantial form that endows the living body with its powers. It is the powers which we are now to consider. Aquinas begins by assuring us that the *essence* of the soul is not its power. (See Vol. 19, pp. 399-400.) This was perhaps clear from Aristotle's account of the soul, for Aristotle says that just as knowledge can exist without being exercised, so the soul can *be* without exercising its powers.

Is there not another reason for this conclusion? If its powers constituted its very nature, would not the soul be obliged to act in accordance with its nature? Could it then delay or withhold the exercise of its powers? If not, would free will be possible? Though they do not constitute the essence of the soul, the powers do flow from it, and are caused by it, in the sense of final and active cause. (See Vol. 19, pp. 404-405.) The powers are generated by the soul and are subject to it.

The powers flowing from the soul have two orders, the order of perfection and the order of generation. Named in the order of perfection, they are the rational, the sensitive, the vegetative; named in the order of generation, they are the vegetative, the sensitive, the rational. The more perfect comes before the less perfect in the order of perfection, whereas the order in generation is reversed. The rational powers depend on sensations furnished by the sensitive powers and these upon the vegetative powers.

How far now do these powers depend on the body? It might seem that since the soul is the substantial form of the body, present in its entirety in every part of the body, it would have to act *through* the body. But this is not always the case, for you will remember that the soul has a being independent of its powers. The vegetative powers, Aquinas tells us, operate by means of the alimentary tract and other such organs, and the operation can be described in bodily terms. The sensitive powers depend on sense organs and on their constitution, but they are not performed "through a corporeal quality" (*ibid.*, p. 408a). The properties of the eye, for example, would not explain the perceived pattern of sounds and colors, though they are necessary to an explanation.

The rational powers are in a class by themselves. The operation of the rational soul "so far exceeds the corporeal nature that it is not even performed by any corporeal organ" (*ibid.*, p. 407d). If the rational powers were dependent upon the brain, Aquinas says, we should be able to understand corporeal things, but not the incorporeal. Mathematics, logic, and theology would be beyond our reach forever. But since this is obviously false, Aquinas argues that the rational powers cannot be dependent upon the functioning of the brain.

A "power" is simply an ability of organisms to perform certain kinds of acts and get certain results, both of which are observable. Why, then, do modern psychologists almost always reject powers or faculties? A misunderstanding has arisen owing to a misuse of these terms. When the faculties of perception and memory were used, by the phrenologists, for example, to account for particular perceptions and memories, the explanation was circular and worthless. The argument was to the effect that a man perceives and remembers because he possesses these two faculties, which is as much as to say that he has the abilities because he has them. This criticism, however, does not seem to apply to Aquinas. There is a question, however, as to the degree to which perception, memory, reason, and other powers can be separated one from another. Modern psychology is now grappling with this problem experimentally.

At this point it will be useful to look at a table showing the orders, genera, and species of powers in relation to habits and acts and to the objects of the latter. The classification will be largely self-explanatory, and since we are concerned only with putting the subject of habits in its proper context, we shall make only a few comments. First, it should be remembered that acts and objects are first in the order of investigation, for these are directly observable, whereas the powers themselves are not. Habits, of course, have the same objects as their corresponding acts, and can be regarded as organizations of acts which have a certain persistence.

The division of the cognitive powers of sense is instructive. (See chart on p. 89.) The first five are called the *exterior senses*, whereas the last four are the *interior senses*. Popular usage has reserved the term "senses" for the exterior senses, and until recently there were supposed to be five and only five senses. With the discovery of the sense organs for pressure, heat, cold, and pain (the organ here being a simple nerve ending), there was no longer any reason for speaking of *one* tactual sense. What is interesting is that Aquinas, and Aristotle before him, had recognized that touch may be a group of senses rather than one. Their reason for speaking of only one sense was that there is apparently no diversity of sense organs. (See Vol. 8,

THE POWERS OF MAN

Orders	Genera			Species or Kinds	Acts	Objects, i.e., Bodies
Vegetative	vegetative			nutritive power	nutrition	the organism
				augmentative power	growth	
				reproductive power	reproduction	
					Habits and Acts	
Sensitive	cognitive	exterior sense		tactual sense	touching, etc.	as tactual, etc.
				olfactory sense	smelling	as odoriferous
				gustatory sense	tasting	as tasteful
				auditory sense	hearing	as audible
				visual sense	seeing	as visible
		interior sense		common sense	perceiving	as synthesized
				mnemonic power	remembering	as past
				imaginative power	imagining	as absent
				estimative power	estimating	as useful or harmful
	appetitive			concupiscible appetite	love; hatred; desire; disgust; joy; sorrow	as good and bad
				irascible appetite	hope; despair; courage; fear; rage	as good and bad
	motor			power of locomotion and movement	movements of body	as muscular
Rational	cognitive			agent intellect	abstracting	their essences
				possible intellect	understanding	their essences
	appetitive			will	volition	as desirable

p. 654b, and Vol. 19, p. 411c.) Neither philosopher would presumably have had any objection, once the sense organs were discovered in the skin, to recognizing four or five tactual senses rather than one only.

The "common sense" is not generally called a sense today, for there is no sense organ nor corresponding sensation (i.e., nothing like a sensation in the sense that blue, cold, and pain are sensations). Yet the "common sense" refers to facts of perception which are of overriding significance. The common sense has already been discussed in the Third Reading. We saw that it is that interior (or internal) sense by virtue of which we experience different kinds of sensory qualities as belonging to the same object. The same rose, for example, is both red and sweet; the same bell, at once hard, black, cold, bitter, and mellow in sound. At the same time the rose and the bell are experiences as belonging to the perceiving subject, and discriminated from others. The common sense, Aquinas says, enables animals and men to "make some judgment about the sensible qualities received, and distinguish them one from another. . . ."[1] Since sight cannot discern the sweetness of the rose, nor the olfactory sense its color, there must be an interior sense to explain the perception of the sweet, red rose.

The second interior sense is memory, by which past impressions are retained, and the third is imagination, which permits the animal to "apprehend a thing not only at the actual time of sensation, but also when it is absent" (Vol. 19, p. 412c). It should be pointed out that these two powers are not attributed to all animals but only to "the perfect animal," i.e., the animal which fully realizes the animal nature. (See *ibid.*, p. 412b-c.) Imagination is not to be ascribed to all animal forms, but it is realized by some highly developed animals, as recent studies of chimpanzees seem to have shown. In man, another type of imagination is found in which images derived from sensation are combined in forms which do not occur in the world, e.g., golden mountain and centaur. Aquinas refuses to count this higher form of creative imagination as an additional interior sense, as does the Arabian Aristotelian Avicenna. His reason is that this power does not occur in animals.

The estimative power—the fourth interior sense—is present in animals, for "the animal needs to seek or to avoid certain things not only because they are pleasing or otherwise to the

---

[1] John Patrick Rowan (trans.) *The Soul, A Translation of St. Thomas Aquinas' De Anima* (St. Louis: B. Herder Book Co., 1949), p. 167.

senses, but also on account of other advantages and uses, or disadvantages . . ." (*ibid.*, p. 412d). Thus, a sheep runs away from a wolf, not because of its color or shape, but "as a natural enemy." Aquinas' examples suggest that he is thinking of instinctive reactions rather than the learned responses, yet he does not at all exclude learning on the part of animals. Whether the sheep runs from the wolf instinctively or has learned the response, the process involves more than sensation and memory. It requires a putting of two and two together—the estimative power. The result is "animal prudence," so called because it so much resembles prudence in men, though real knowledge and reasoning are lacking. But the estimative power, like the other sensitive powers, does not act alone; it has the support of organic processes.

The difference between the cognitive and the appetitive powers is fundamental. Both the concupiscible appetite and the irascible appetite, although passive in relation to the objects that cause them, have the capacity to set the body in motion. The role of the cognitive powers is to direct appetite to the objects which will satisfy it or away from objects that are harmful. The end of cognition is information furnished by the senses (and knowledge on the human level), while the completion of desire or appetite is satisfaction or avoidance of pain.

The two appetites must be distinguished, Aquinas says, for several reasons. First, the soul, in accordance with the irascible appetite, often opposes the inclinations of the concupiscible appetite in order to combat obstacles to desire. Thus a man breaks off a feast, although he is still very hungry, to fight off enemies who would destroy his home and provisions. But the irascible appetite, "the champion and defender of the concupiscible" (*ibid.*, p. 430b), sometimes opposes concupiscible desires, especially when they are harmful. It therefore happens that the two appetites often seem to be in conflict, for love banishes anger, and anger weakens love. The love, however, is primary, and anger, in curbing it temporarily, may achieve its eventual satisfaction.

The importance of this division of appetitive powers seems to be supported by various lines of modern evidence. The autonomic nervous system, which is concerned with the emotions, has two divisions—the sympathetic and the parasympathetic systems. The former is active in fear and rage (Aquinas' irascible appetite) and the latter in love and the milder, more agreeable emotions (Aquinas' concupiscible appetite). The opposition between the action of various endocrine glands also seems to support something like Aquinas' division of the appetites, as does the opposed action of cholesterol and adrenalin. In studying the table of the powers of man, it might occur to you that hatred belongs with fear and rage rather than with love. We shall see at the end of this book, however, that, according to Freud, love is never found without some hate— that love is naturally ambivalent.

We have been trying to present a background against which Aquinas' theory of habits can be understood. A very brief description of the nonrational powers has been offered, although we have not yet commented on the rational powers which are distinctive of man; these we shall reserve for later discussion.

III

If you are new to Aquinas' method of exposition you may at first experience a little difficulty. You will soon find, however, that the "Question" is always the subject into which the inquiry is to be made, while every "Article" asks a question which had been in dispute at the time. It was logical and convenient, and also chivalrous, to listen to opponents first, to hear all their objections, before stating one's own view. Aquinas accordingly begins by asking the question, then states the opponents' thesis, and then their objections to his own thesis.

The statement of his own thesis always begins with "*I answer that,*" and it is often clarifying to turn first to this italicized phrase to find out what it is that Aquinas himself is arguing *for*. Thereafter, you can turn to the series of objections and the answers to them. Sometimes the Angelic Doctor's position and argument are more readily grasped from the replies to objections than under "*I answer that.*" Aquinas' style in the *Summa Theologica* represents the zenith and perfection of a long process of dialectical and expository development in the Middle Ages.

Article 1 of Question XLIX, following Aristotle, distinguishes between different senses of the verb "to have" *(habere)*, from which habit *(habitus)* is derived. There may be no medium between the haver and what is had: there is nothing at all between the quality and the object that has it; the green is glued to the grass. When you have a friend, however, there is always an intervening medium. In the case of clothes (e.g., your riding habit) there is contact. This is "having" in a third sense. (See pp. 1d-2a.)

The sense of "to have" that is important for the subject of habits, however, is the sense in which "a thing is ordered in regard to itself or to something else" (p. 2a). For whatever is so ordered or disposed, is so ordered or disposed "well or ill," and here we have the first essential of habit as understood by Aristotle and Aquinas. A habit always serves the one who has it, or some other end, either well or badly, and is thus always purposive. Aristotle thus defines habit as "a disposition according to which that which is disposed is either well or ill disposed, and either in itself or with reference to something else; e.g. health is a 'habit'; for it is such a disposition" (Vol. 8, p. 544a).

The only example of habit given in Article 1 is *health*, and this may seem surprising. We do not usually think of health as a habit, for it involves physical and chemical conditions over which we have no direct control. We sometimes say that a man has the habit of taking care of himself or guarding his health; but we tend to forget to what a large extent health is a matter of morale and purpose and how much illness is psychogenic. If health can be wrecked by bad habits, and improved by learning new habits, cannot we say that health itself is a habit? According to Aristotle's definition, in any case, health is a habit: It is a disposition which well serves the ends of the individual and of nature as well.

Articles 1 and 2 of Question XLIX are chiefly concerned with the status of habit as a quality and with its relation to the other Aristotelian categories. This is not a psychological but a metaphysical problem and falls outside the scope of this guide.

Article 3 deals with the relation of habit to act and to power. We have already seen that we can discover a power and its nature only by examining the acts through which they are manifested. Is there an estimative power? We find out by examining particular acts of animal prudence; e.g., a dog comes when his master calls but not when a stranger does. Yet the animal could not act with prudence if the animal soul did not have the estimative power. The relation between the power and the act, as Aristotle says, is like that between the possession of knowledge and its exercise. Except for its exercise, we should not be aware of the knowledge, and yet the knowledge must be possessed before it is exercised. A power is not merely the potentiality of a performance but also an actuality which precedes the performance.

Habit, as a specialization of a power, is midway between power and act. Your knowledge of the multiplication table is a habit, and, like other habits, it is usually potential in the sense that it is on command but not in actual use. Yet it cannot be merely potential. The ability to give products and quotients is based on something actual that the individual has acquired. The habit of giving correct sums and products when they are called for is immensely useful to the individual, but it is also in accordance with nature, with our natural powers, and is a realization of them. It is well disposed in itself and in relation to nature.

In explaining why habits are necessary (Article 4), Aquinas distinguishes three conditions required for our actions to be disposed by habits, as they are said to be in Aristotle's definition. First, "that which is disposed should be distinct from that to which it is disposed; and so, that it should be related to it as potency is to act" (p. 5b). Thus the habit of study is the potentiality of an activity distinct from it, namely, actual studying. Where potentiality and actuality are not separated, as in God, there can be no habits.

The second requirement for *being disposed* is illuminating. When a habit disposes to act A, it must not only be the potentiality of A but also leave open an alternative to A. We do not say that bodies have the habit of falling to the earth; the reason is that there is nothing else that they could possibly do. But it is proper to speak of charity and mendacity in human beings as habits, because men have alternatives. They have at the same time the potentiality of doing contrary things. Thus while planets have potency to only one fixed movement, men have potency to contrary movements.

Would this imply that if determinism were true, and the same cause always had the same effect, habits in Aquinas' sense would be impossible? Or could not the determinist argue that there are plenty of alternatives in the world, but only when the causal conditions of an action are incompletely stated, which is almost always the case? Secondly, does not this requirement of potency to more than one thing hold much better for operational habits, such as studiousness, than for structural habits, such as health and beauty?

The third condition of *being disposed* and of the possibility of habits is that the quality involved be complex. The very meaning of "dispose" and "disposition" implies the rearrangement or adjustment of several things. Thus health and beauty can be habits, Aquinas says, but not the length of one's nose nor the color of one's eyes.

In Article 1 of Question L Aquinas considers whether habit is *in* the body. He begins by emphasizing the distinction between habit as potency to form and habit as potency to operation. Some habits consist in the form or structure of the person, e.g., health, beauty, and strength; others consist in operations, e.g., temperance and studiousness. The former habits can be in the body, "which is related to the soul as a subject is to its form" (p. 6c). That is, just as the soul is the form of the body, so the habit is the form which leads us to pronounce it healthy or beautiful.

But what about the habits which are *operations?* We have to rule out such processes as the beating of the heart, which follow from the nature of man and are essential to survival, for these, as we have seen, cannot be habits. They cannot be habits because they afford no alternatives. Operative habits do not proceed from the *nature* of the subject; they must therefore proceed from the soul. In this case, however, they are principally in the soul and secondarily in the body, provided the body is able "to help in the operations of the soul" (p. 6c). Can you think of an example in point? Could we say that two men have the habit of walking every day for health, but one is lazy and his body reluctant, whereas the other is energetic and his body responds enthusiastically? Does one boy have to force his fingers to do daily scales on the piano, whereas another's fingers seem to move of themselves and without effort?

The main point in Article 2 is that operational habits, which derive from the soul, cannot derive from the *essence* of the soul, for then the operation (e.g., breathing) would offer no alternatives and could not give rise to a habit. If studiousness followed from the essence of the soul, as having the sum of its angles equal to 180° follows from the definition of triangle, we should all be automatically studious. Operational habits must therefore derive from the powers, the demonstrative habit from the rational power, and taking daily walks from the power of locomotion. These are specializations of powers in *some* men; but they are not entailed by these powers.

Article 3 argues that there are no habits in the nutritive powers—the nutritive, augmentative, and reproductive powers —because they do not have "an inborn aptitude to obey the command of reason" (p. 8c). These powers operate as natural instincts and are ordered to one thing only. The plant, for example, has no alternative to growing or reproducing. But what of the sensitive powers? Can there be no habits of the gustatory, auditory, visual senses, nor of memory, imagination, and the estimative power? Aquinas answers that the sensitive powers can have habits insofar as they are at the command of reason but not when they act on an instinctive level. Thus we would not say that a man has a habit of tasting sweetness whenever he eats honey. What else could he taste? On the other hand, a man might very well have a habit of listening to music he admires, or of taking walks in the garden, or of calling to mind scenes of his youth. For these activities are matters of choice and involve the interior senses—the common sense, memory, imagination, or estimation. (See chart of the Powers of Man, p. 121.)

Where only the exterior senses—sight, hearing, etc.—are brought into play there are no habits (see p. 9a). We automatically see or hear what is there to be seen or heard. But when memory, comparison, imagination, inference or reason play a part, and we are free to act or refrain from acting, habits may arise. Does this seem right to you? Are there habits which involve *only* seeing, *only* hearing, or *only* tasting?

IV

There is no question that there are intellectual habits, such as thinking, reflecting, and solving problems, but Article 4 raises the question whether they are *in* the intellect. Intellectual habits seem to involve both the soul and the body, as when a man solves an arithmetic problem. But how can this be so since, according to Aquinas, the intellect operates independently of the body? Aquinas' answer is that intellectual habits exist by virtue of the "possible intellect."

Let us see what role the possible intellect has in rational understanding. The materials of understanding are furnished by the exterior senses—hearing, seeing, etc.—and are unified by the common sense. Then imagination, memory, and the estimative powers organize the materials into the phantasm which is common to soul and body. From this phantasm "the agent intellect" abstracts the universals or predicates which are commensurate with the capacity of intellect, whereupon the possible intellect assimilates the universals, and understanding is completed. Possible intellect is thus not form alone but also the potency of understanding whatever is furnished by the agent intellect. It is "midway between pure potency and perfect act" (p. 10a-b). The process terminating in understanding is as follows:

The exterior senses and the common sense furnish	Imagination, memory, and the estimative sense furnish	Agent intellect abstracts	Possible intellect understands
→	→	→	
THE PERCEPT	THE PHANTASM	UNIVERSALS	UNIVERSALS

(It will be understood that these various steps in understanding are not discrete but tend to fuse into one process.) Aquinas thus concludes that possible intellect provides for the elements of choice and diversity to be found in the intellectual habits, and the body need not be involved. "The potency to more than one thing" is provided by the possible intellect.

Another objection to intellectual habits is very interesting. The Arabian Aristotelian Averroës had held that there is only one intellect for all men and that this is the part of soul which survives after death. Thus anything like personal survival was excluded. Moreover, the intellect could have no habits since, if it did, it would necessarily possess contrary habits, e.g., studiousness and laziness. It is interesting to note that Aquinas does not condemn Averroës' view because it is heretical but attempts to refute it by rational argument, by reference to the role of the possible intellect and other features of the intellectual process.

"Every power," Aquinas says, ". . . needs a habit whereby it is well disposed to its act" (p. 10c); that is, every power of the sensitive and rational soul needs a habit. It is easy to see that, if we had no habits, we should have to make a fresh decision on every occasion of our lives, reviewing all the considerations favoring one line of action rather than another thousands of times over again, even when the occasions are routine and offer nothing new. Aquinas naturally regards habit as a perfection of action, having in view especially the importance of virtuous habits.

If every power susceptible to rational control needs a habit, the will does; but there are certain celebrated difficulties. How can the will, which is not a cognitive power, discriminate the *kinds* of volitions which are to be habitual? Aquinas' reply is that "in the will and in the other appetitive powers there [must] be certain qualities to incline them, and these are called habits" (p. 10d). The will is drawn to the good, just as desire is, but since the good appears in many partial forms, the will has alternatives and can form vicious as well as virtuous habits. There is indeed nothing to prevent the will from acquiring habits. It is not, like the agent intellect, a purely active power, but rather, as Aristotle says, both "mover and moved" (p. 10d).

Potency to more than one thing is necessary to habit, as we have seen, and potency belongs to matter. How, then, can the angels, who are immaterial substances, form habits? Aquinas replies that angels must have *some* potency, since God alone is pure actuality. It follows that the angels must possess an immaterial potentiality.

We can hardly quarrel with Aquinas' general conclusion that habits depend on both nature and experience. He also allows nicely for the diversity of habits in human beings. Although men have a common nature which inclines them all to the same classes of goods, there are also individual differences in the appetites. Some men are naturally meek, others bold, etc., and their situations are also different. Accordingly, we should expect the habits of men to present a great diversity, yet also a common pattern, and close similarities.

Articles 2 and 3 of Question LI inquire whether habits can be caused by acts, and whether one act is sufficient. How could we know except by observation or experiment? Aquinas, however, proceeds by deduction and analogy. He is concerned to remove theoretical objections, not to prove existence. He concludes that there is no apparent reason why acts cannot induce habits. The powers exercised in appetitive and cognitive acts are passive, so that when the acts are repeated "a certain quality is formed in the power which is passive and moved, which quality is called a habit" (p. 14a). This does not mean, of course, that acts can form the powers by themselves, nor that the influence of reason or the consent of will is excluded. As to the possibility of one act being sufficient to form a habit, Aquinas remarks that it takes more than one swallow to make a summer and more than one act of reason to overcome appetite. Yet is not the child's propensity to touch a hot stove sometimes conquered by one painful experience? This, however, is an exception. Hundreds of experimental studies have shown that habit formation in general requires repetition of the act.

Question LII concerns "the increase of habits," which would

also appear to be an empirical topic. Aquinas, as usual, is concerned with theoretical problems. For example, how can a quality like blue increase? If it is blue, it could not become *more* blue. Secondly, blue has no parts; but change involves a rearrangement of parts. How, then, can habit, which is a quality, increase and become *more* than it is? The Stoics held that the virtues do not admit of degrees. You either conform your will to the laws of the universe or you do not. Aquinas cites several authors who deny diminution and increase of habits, and shows that their arguments are based on confusions. He points out, in effect, that though *justice* as an idea or ideal may be one and immutable, the *habit of justice* can wax and wane, and in two respects: (1) in the number of just acts a man carries out, and (2) in the number of areas (the family, the business world, etc.) to which it is extended. (See p. 17d.)

For the same reason, there is no theoretical difficulty in strengthening a habit through repetition. Moreover, as Aquinas points out, there is no doubt that repetition of the act makes it easier and speedier. Thus the *specific habit of science in a man increases itself by addition.* (See p. 18d.) Science does not increase thereby, but only man's *participation* in science. Beginning in the late nineteenth century quantified studies have shown, in many cases, just how many repetitions are necessary to establish a habit. Such studies also support Aquinas' further conclusion that *not every* repetition strengthens a habit. It is not every act but the accumulation of repeated acts that builds the habit. Moreover, since it is subject to the will, the individual may act in accord with his habit or contrary to it and is thus free to intensify and extend his virtuous habits and to weaken and narrow his vicious ones. (See p. 19c.)

Our first reaction to Question LIII may be that, of course, habits can be corrupted—broken or diminished. Nothing is more common. But we must admit that some of the worst and some of the best are very tenacious. Habits become "a second nature." If a miser should start throwing his money away, or a famous scientist begin to talk nonsense about his specialty, we should wonder whether he was the same man—whether he had not lost his mind. Very often, too, as with alcoholics, daredevils, and gamblers, the man does not kill the habit, but vice versa.

One of the best-known ways of losing a habit is to stop practicing it, but why should this be so difficult in so many cases? Consider a desirable habit, such as politeness. Aquinas contends that habits are destroyed or diminished by ceasing to perform the act "in so far, that is, as we cease from exercising an act which overcame the causes that destroyed or weakened that habit" (p. 22b). Now what would be the causes which tend to destroy or to weaken our habit of being polite? They are our irritability, our egoism, our lack of patience and perspective, our craving for immediate pleasure. Is it not clear, then, that the continual practice of polite acts prevents these contrary tendencies from gaining the upper hand? The polite act, by its very occurrence, prevents the occurrence of impolite acts. Thus when we relax our politeness for a considerable period the result is the formation of boorish habits which hinder our return to politeness.

Is it not the same with other virtues? Courage, as understood by Aristotle and Aquinas, is not warlike bravado but a rational mean between needless daring and ignoble submission. An act of courage prevents both foolhardiness and cowardice, but when we cease to exercise the habit of courage these tendencies are given full play and may develop into habits contrary to courage. The same thing happens in the case of intellectual habits, Aquinas says. "Hence when man ceases to make use of his intellectual habits, strange fancies, sometimes in opposition to them, arise in his imagination" (p. 22c). Unless intellectual habits continue to thrust such fancies aside, his judgment is impaired and the habits are weakened.

A problem arises, however, when a habit is formed in the intellect, for the intellect functions independently of the body. How can such a habit be corrupted, i.e., destroyed? The disposition to assent to first principles, such as *things equal to the same thing are equal to each other,* Aquinas says, "cannot be corrupted by any forgetfulness or deception whatever" (p. 20c). The reason is that such habits have no contraries. There is nothing in our nature which can oppose them. There are inclinations which oppose our habits of courage, politeness, and scientific disinterestedness, but there are none which could conflict with the habitual understanding of first principles. For first principles are provided by the *agent intellect* and understood by *possible intellect,* which are both independent of the sensations and appetites of the body and are opposed by nothing in our nature.

When the habit is founded on the apprehension of first principles alone, it is incorruptible, but the moment *reasoning* from first principles enters in, habits can be weakened or destroyed. Even the habits of reasoning in rigorous syllogisms may be corrupted, for we may mistake a sophistical syllogism for a valid and true one. The moment that habits depend on sensations and appetites, deception becomes possible, and this holds for scientific and moral habits alike.

A number of questions may have occurred to the reader. We shall see in a section to follow that John Locke holds that there are no first principles which receive general assent. Assuming that this is true, would Aquinas have any answer? He could not reply that the reason savages do not assent to these principles is that their experience is insufficient. For if understanding first principles depends on the amount of experience people have, how do we know that with more experience we ourselves might not understand them differently? Would Aquinas, then, be obliged to deny that there *are* savages who do not readily assent to first principles?

V

In what different ways are habits distinguished from one another?

Habits, according to Aquinas, are specifically distinct in three respects: "First in respect of the active principles of such dispositions; secondly, in respect of nature; thirdly, in respect of specifically different objects . . ." (p. 24b). In the case of the habit of proving propositions, the active principle would be the principle of the syllogism, or other deductive or inductive rules; the habit of giving money to others might be activated by the principle of justice or charity, depending on which end the habit has in view.

Secondly, habits may differ with the individual nature of the man who has them. According to tradition it was natural for Democritus to laugh and for Heraclitus to weep. Habits feasible to one man need not be so to another. One man learns mathematical habits quickly, another has the specific capacity for music or for making statues. (See pp. 12-13.)

Thirdly, habits are differentiated by their objects. But here several objections crop up (Q. LIV, Art. 2). (See pp. 23-24.) If their objects distinguish one habit from another, then medicine cannot be one scientific habit but must be two, for it is concerned with both the healthy and the unhealthy. And other sciences also deal with contraries. Aquinas' answer is ingenious. The sciences are concerned with objects in their "formal aspect," i.e., as possessing a quality. Thus the quality *having health to be maintained or restored* would order both the healthy and the unhealthy into *one* class. Another objection is that two sciences, i.e., two scientific habits, may nevertheless have the same object. For example, we say nowadays that psychology, anthropology, and sociology are all concerned with human behavior and share some of the same conclusions. Aquinas' reply would be that these sciences use different premises, premises which describe their common subject matter differently. In other words, these sciences do not deal with the same object in the same respect. Hence two or more scientific habits could have the same object, so long as they considered it in different respects.

Can one habit be made up of many habits?

Aquinas answers that since a habit is a quality, it "is a simple form. But nothing simple is made up of many" (p. 25c). It is quite true, he says, that an operational habit (habit proper, we might say) extends to a multiplicity of things. But it does so only when they refer "to some specific aspect of the object, or to one nature, or to one principle" (p. 25c). We say that a man has a habit of going to the office every morning, although he gets there sometimes by streetcar, sometimes by automobile. or on foot. These different activities all get him to the office. and this function is what they have in common. Usually a habit has similar things as its object, as well as a unitary principle. The arithmetic habit is always concerned with numbers, and the unitary principle is the obtaining of sums and products, etc. It is not so clear, however, how "nature" could furnish a principle of unity. How could the mere fact that a habit was commensurate with human ability, or with the special ability of a particular man, give it the unity of *one* habit?

The use of "habit" in comparative psychology tends to agree with Aquinas' dictum that a habit is always something more than a sum of habits. It might be thought that the habit which the rat has learned—getting through the maze to its food with few errors—is simply a series of subhabits, viz., running so far, turning left, running so far, turning right, etc. But the moment we say *series* we admit that the total habit is something more than a set of subhabits. It is the set of subhabits ordered to an end. Aquinas' criterion of habit—well or ill disposed to an end —clearly applies even here.

Does a habit well learned tend to become automatic?

In so far as this is so, we are spared a great deal of trouble and can turn our minds to problems that need our attention. Walking, swimming, cycling, and even driving a car or talking become largely automatic, so that our attention can be transferred to other things. The habits of walking and swimming become so automatic that they are difficult to perform when we attend to them or try to follow a rule. William James lays down the general principle that *"habit diminishes the conscious attention with which our acts are performed"* (Vol. 53, p. 74b). But would this be true of operational habits emphasized by Aristotle and Aquinas, such as science and the virtues? The answer seems to be that many habits within the scientific process and the moral life tend to be reduced to a routine requiring little consciousness. On the other hand, the larger habits in the intellectual and moral spheres often involve heightened attention as they become better established. The general habits of seeking scientific truth and of distinguishing right from wrong require continual vigilance and ingenuity.

The following questions are designed to help you test the thoroughness of your reading. Each question is to be answered by giving a page or pages of the reading assignment. Answers will be found on page 383 of this Reading Plan.

1 Is habit one of Aristotle's predicaments or categories?

2 In what three ways does disposition imply an order of something that has parts?

3 What is the difference between "natural" and "adventitious" habits?

4 In what ancient book was it said that "by habits we are directed well or ill in reference to the passions"?

5 Does Aristotle call incurable disease a habit?

6 Why are health and beauty said to be imperfect habits?

7 In what two ways can one thing be natural to another?

8 Are all of our habits acquired, according to Aquinas, by natural means?

9 In what two ways can a form (and also a habit) differ in degree or amount?

10 In what part of the soul are the "moral" virtues and vices?

11 How is it that "the intellect cannot understand several things at the same time actually"?

12 In what two ways can a habit be "suitable to nature"?

HOBBES

Leviathan

Part I, Ch. 1-10

Vol. 23, pp. 49-76

Thomas Hobbes's greatest contribution to philosophy was his new foundation for the authority of the state. It was an innovation in theory which greatly shocked his contemporaries and arouses indignation even today. Plato, Aristotle, and medieval thinkers had taught that the purpose of the state was to advance the good life of the community, to promote the well-being, happiness, or virtue of citizens. Although the privileges and immunities of the state did not extend to all its subjects, or in equal degree, and many injustices were committed in its name, yet the aim of the state was considered essentially moral, and this was the justification for its authority. Hobbes challenged this tradition. He also broke with the Stuart theory of the divine right of kings, upheld by his contemporary Sir Robert Filmer, and indeed, on the question of the justification of authority he stood alone and isolated in his day.

In his defense of the absolute authority of the king he was ultra-conservative, going almost as far as Filmer, but in his theory of the source of the king's authority he was ultra-radical. It is not divinity nor moral purpose that endows the monarch with sovereignty but rather a "social contract" in which men sacrifice their individual liberties and powers to him for the sake of the peace and security that a commonwealth can provide. God plays no part that could possibly be known, and indeed, in Hobbes's world, God was really incomprehensible. Nor could the state arise from a moral purpose, for morals come into existence only with the establishment of the state and are completely conventional.

What makes the state a practical necessity is that, according to Hobbes, men are motivated only by fear and the lust for power. Left to himself in a "state of nature," every man would seek power at the expense of the others, and fear itself would impel him to greater violence to prevent a lesser. "A war of all against all" would ensue and life would become "solitary, poor, nasty, brutish, and short." It is to escape this grim alternative that men are willing to hand over their liberties and powers, and those of all their descendants, to the king, agreeing to obey him henceforth in all things, so long as he continues to exercise his office and to maintain public order. The so-called social contract, according to which men turn over their powers to a sovereign, was probably not conceived by Hobbes as an actual historical event but rather as the only possible justification of the authority of the sovereign.

The powers of the king must be absolute, for otherwise the ruthless war of all against all could break out again within the state. When not bound by law and cowed by the fear of punishment, one man cannot but seek to overpower another, and since men are nearly of equal strength the outcome might well be the destruction of the state. It is with this conception of man as thoroughly egoistic, and with the natural foundation of all his knowledge in sensation, that we shall be concerned in what follows.

Seventh Reading

I

The news that the Spanish Armada was approaching England in 1588 so frightened the wife of the Vicar of Westport that she delivered her son, Thomas Hobbes, prematurely. "She bore twins," Hobbes said in his autobiography—"myself and fear." The oddity of his birth may have affected his disposition, as he claims, but it did not prevent him from pursuing an energetic and sometimes dangerous career up to the age of ninety-one. Although his father, an ignorant and truculent vicar, gave him no help, his education was provided for by a rich and childless uncle, who sent him to a private school in Malmesbury. By the age of fourteen he had acquired a remarkable knowledge of Greek and Latin, and he continued his studies in Oxford for the next five years, where he pursued logic and physics, but thought little of his Aristotelian teachers. In 1608 Hobbes became acquainted with Kepler's *New Aetiological Astronomy*, which had just been published, and formed friendships with leading thinkers of the time, especially with Francis Bacon who, like himself, had turned against a degenerate Aristotelianism.

With Bacon, Hobbes shared a distrust of the wisdom of the past and a conviction that knowledge is power and that the misuse of words is a great obstacle to its attainment. They both wrote in a clear and pithy style and both sought new foundations and a reform of the system of knowledge. But whereas Bacon derided deduction and praised the experimental method, Hobbes, who at the age of forty had suddenly discovered Euclid's *Elements,* was dazzled by the prospect of constructing a deductive system of knowledge, which was to be extended even to ethics and politics. Although fascinated

110

by mathematics, Hobbes never became a mathematician, and his polemical insistence, late in life, on the possibility of squaring the circle drew ridicule from contemporary mathematicians.

From 1634 to 1637 Hobbes was on the continent, where he joined the brilliant circle of men patronized by Abbé Mersenne, including Descartes and Gassendi, and in 1636 he visited the celebrated Galileo, the founder of the new physics. It was at this time that he formed the project of elaborating an extensive threefold deductive system of matter, man, and the state, based on the laws of motion. His most famous book, the *Leviathan,* which appeared in 1651, dealt with these three broad subjects, but the bulk of it with the last. In this book you will find a chart (see p. 72) showing Hobbes's own organization of the sciences and their subject matters. In a number of other volumes, Hobbes concerned himself with the state, civil law, human nature, optics, liberty, and necessity. Early in life he had made a translation of Thucydides' *History of the Peloponnesian War* and had learned a great deal from its frank realism and pragmatic outlook. For Thucydides, as for Hobbes, what was important in history was neither ethical norms nor moral sentiments but the power and strategy of states, and the state which they most admired was the one that had the greatest power to promote peace and security.

Hobbes's long life was rich in personal and intellectual interest, and historical developments loom very large. It deserves to be read in some full account. The reader will want to decide for himself whether Hobbes was essentially a timid and prudent man or a daring thinker who had good cause for fear. It will be found that in France, whither he followed the Stuart court when Cromwell was victorious, as well as at home in England, his opposition to ecclesiastical power in affairs of state, and the suspicion of atheism that clung to him, aroused powerful enemies and made his life uneasy and dangerous, even in its triumphs.

I I

Hobbes does well to begin the *Leviathan* with some account of "sense" or, as we should say, sensation, for in a way this is the beginning of everything. "There is no conception in a man's mind," he says, "which hath not at first, totally or by parts" (p. 49a), arisen in sensation—either visual, auditory, or some other sensation. Thus, a man who had never seen blue could not have an idea of blue, nor could a man who had never felt hardness imagine what hardness was. Our simple ideas of sense qualities obviously have to be first experienced in sensation. As a matter of fact, many of our complex ideas are derived from sensation. The ideas of green grass and blue sky, or of a fragrant red carnation, for example, are also given in sensation. But how about our idea of a centaur—half man and half horse—or our idea of a round square? The visual shape of a man must first appear in sensation, if we are to have an idea of a man, and so also the visual appearance of a horse, if we are to have an idea of a horse, but the two visual shapes are never conjoined in sensation to make a centaur. Is this the kind of thing Hobbes is thinking of when he says, "There is no conception in a man's mind which hath not at first, *totally or by parts*," appeared in sensation? The idea of round-square is not given in sensation, but its two parts must first appear there. We shall return to the question of the origin of our ideas in the next reading on John Locke.

Hobbes outlines his theory of sensation so quickly, and his style is so terse, that we must consider what he says with great care. The cause of sensation (sense), he states, is the external body which "presseth," or stimulates, the various sense organs, the eye, the ear, the tongue, etc., and the pressure or stimulation is then carried from the sense organ to the brain, and also to the heart. There it meets a counterpressure and the movement is now reversed, going to the sense organs. In sensation we ourselves are active. We ourselves are doing the seeing, hearing, etc. The "endeavour, because outward," Hobbes says, "seemeth to be some matter without" (p. 49b). In very compact language Hobbes is explaining why we see sense qualities, which consist of motions in the eye, out in space beyond the body—why we see the green in the tree and hear the roar out in the surf. But why should this be a problem? Is not the green out there in the tree and the roaring sound in the distant surf? The answer of Hobbes is No. Colors, sounds, tastes, and odors are not in the objects where we seem to perceive them. It is a mere "seeming or fancy" that they are outside us. They seem to be external because of a movement of matter it "outward" in the direction of the objects we perceive. As movement of matter must be, because in Hobbes's world, as we have seen, there is in the end nothing but matter in motion.

Let us take a look at the problems with which Hobbes was faced. It will be helpful first to indicate that even today, three hundred years after Hobbes, the way in which we experience qualities out in the object is not altogether clear. When we see the green of a tree, in the usual modern account, certain wave lengths of light stimulate photochemical structures on the retina of the eye, and nervous impulses are transmitted along the optic nerve to the brain. When the impulses reach a certain end-point in the brain, however, something altogether novel and surprising happens. We see green out in the distant tree. In the usual modern account, as in Hobbes's theory, colors, sounds, tastes, and odors—the so-called secondary qualities— are not in the objects, where they seem to be, but only in our minds. The objects themselves do not differ from one another in color but only in the molecular structure of their surfaces, which determines what wave lengths of light will be reflected to the eye of the beholder. And the same is maintained, similarly, with respect to the other secondary qualities.

Hobbes's view that secondary qualities are subjective was an important insight, although it was not new. We find it in Democritus and Lucretius, and it had been advanced by Galileo shortly before. Hobbes's keen mind penetrated to the fact, no less true today than it was three hundred years ago, that the assumption that the secondary qualities exist in objects where we seem to perceive them does not help to account for the perception of these qualities. The mere greenness of the tree could not set up motions in the sense organs, nerves, and brain; only matter in motion could accomplish this. The object therefore need only possess the so-called primary qualities, i.e., motion, mass, figure, number, etc.

Hobbes's arguments for the subjectivity of the secondary

qualities are indicated with the utmost brevity. "And as press-ing, rubbing, or striking the eye makes us fancy a light," he says, "and pressing the ear produceth a din; so do the bodies also we see, or hear, produce the same by their strong, though unobserved action" (p. 49c). In other words, if a blow on the eye causes us to see colors, it is evident that we could see a green tree without its being green. All that is necessary is that the tree, as matter in motion, impart some motion to the eye or, expressed in modern terms, all that is needed is that the tree have a molecular surface that reflects only one wave length of light—the one that corresponds to the green we see—to the retina of our eye, where distinctive photochemical changes then occur.

Another of Hobbes's arguments for the subjectivity of colors can be expressed as follows. If you look into a mirror four feet away, you see a pattern of color that you recognize as "your-self," but located four feet behind the mirror, eight feet away from your actual body. Hobbes now argues that if colors can be separated from bodies supposed to have them, then the bodies do not *really* have them. But is this a good argument? The colored appearance might still belong to the body, though the mirror, or other obstacles in the intervening medium, dis-places it in space. The same thing could be said of Hobbes's example of echoes, yet he is right on one important point. Both mirror images and echoes do show that *where* secondary qualities are perceived may depend on the intervening medium.

In his book *Human Nature* Hobbes also points out that the qualities we perceive in an object depend also on the condition of the sense organs, nerves, and brain. This line of argument has much more weight. For if colors and other secondary qualities change continually with subjective conditions, we have a good reason for calling them subjective. In fact, varia-tion of qualities with subjective conditions is recognized as one of the best proofs of subjectivity. Hobbes was certainly on the right track in emphasizing the dependence of sensory qualities on conditions in the sense organs, nerves, and muscles, and we shall see that Locke gives a number of examples of such conditions which, rather than their objects, determine what qualities we see. In contemporary research on perception, these conditions have been studied exhaustively.

Some of Hobbes's examples, however, cut both ways and were dangerous to his position. He argues, for example, that seeing double, as after too much alcohol, shows that what we see need not be *in* the object. For the images of the object—a chair, for example—are two, whereas the object is only one. Accordingly, what we see cannot be identified with the object. There is nothing wrong with this example except that number is not a secondary quality but a primary quality, and is thus supposed to exist in the object, along with motion, mass, and figure. Do primary qualities, then, also vary with the conditions of perception? If so, must Hobbes not conclude, in all consistency, that they are also subjective? But would this not make a shambles of Hobbes's whole universe? In this universe, the secondary qualities—colors, sounds, tastes, and odors—come into existence only as a result of the stimulation of our sense organs by matter in motion. But if motion and the other primary qualities are also subjective, do not sense organs, nerves, brain, and matter itself disappear? What could stimulate our sense organs, and how could the sense organs be there to be stimulated? Everything cannot be subjective.

Could Hobbes answer this objection, and still retain the distinction between primary and secondary qualities that he prizes so highly? Might he not affirm, as his arguments tend to prove, that both primary and secondary qualities are "subjective"? That is, what we get in sensation is always different, to some extent, from what exists in the external object. He could then go on to say that the object possesses primary qualities nonetheless, similar and corresponding to what we get in sensation, whereas it has no secondary qualities at all. Hobbes could justify this position as follows. We must assume that primary qualities exist in the object if we are to explain sensation, whereas there is no need whatever to assume that the object has secondary qualities. Hobbes is close to this position but does not actually state it.

On another point, too, Hobbes seems to be wrong but is

actually right. He claims, as will be remembered, that the "pressure" or stimulation of the sense organs is carried by the nerves to the heart as well as to the brain. Can this be true? Let us begin with the well-known fact that seeing a lion or hearing it roar causes the heart to beat faster. In many more commonplace perceptions the heart rate is affected, and so are the rate and depth of breathing, the amount of saliva and gastric juices secreted, the size of the pupil of the eye, etc. Seeing and hearing, smelling, tasting, and touching are emotional as well as cognitive experiences; the heart and other visceral organs as well as the brain are involved. Our sensations are not mere bits of color, sound, etc., but also signals, warnings, threats, invitations, gratifications, reassurances. They are suffused with feelings and emotions. As Hobbes maintained, impulses are transmitted from the sense organs by way of the autonomic nervous system.

III

As Hobbes opens his discussion of imagination (Ch. 2) we are reminded again that his program is to explain mental life in terms of matter in motion, that he is, in short, a materialist. He points out why people find it hard to accept one side of the law of inertia, i.e., Newton's first law of motion. This law states that every body continues at rest or in uniform motion unless acted upon by an external force. The continuance of a state of rest is readily accepted, but the idea that a body would continue in uniform velocity to eternity is rejected, Hobbes explains, on the ground that the body would sooner or later get tired and have to rest. This tendency to understand nature in terms of the human condition is, according to Hobbes, a serious impediment to clear thinking.

The reader will have noted that Hobbes's explanation of imagination and learning is based upon this law. The motions aroused in the organism by a perception, let us say, of the Tower of London, do not come to a stop when we turn to look at something else, but continue, in some measure, as before. We are thus able to imagine or remember the Tower of London the next moment, the next day, or a year hence. Since fewer particles are in motion in the case of the image, the image is less clear and distinct than the original perception, but it is otherwise similar. From the decay of motions aroused in us by sensory stimulation it follows that the older memories are, the weaker they will be, which is, in general, what we find.

Is this idea of Hobbes's plausible? A little reflection will convince us that something like this must be the case. The perception of the Tower of London must imprint some neural pattern or produce a "trace" or "cell assembly," as it would be put today, which gets reactivated in imagination and memory. How otherwise could we have in imagination or memory an image so similar to the perceptual image? But is the neural pattern a motion of material particles or is it like a fixed mold? The picture we get today of the neural pattern certainly involves a vast network of moving particles. Hobbes was basically right, though the chemical and electrical features of the phenomenon were still to be discovered.

But how does Hobbes explain why it is that, at a given time, we do not imagine or remember everything, but only one item such as the Tower of London? If imagination and memory are simply *decaying sense* (i.e., if the thinning out of the number of particles in motion is a general and continuous process), why do we not remember everything at every moment? Hobbes's answer is, in effect, that the decay of the motions is at different rates. We imagine or remember the items which involve the liveliest motion—those perhaps which have been reinforced or not so much inhibited. Thus if we have seen the Tower of London often, or our interest in it is exceptional, we are apt to bring it to mind rather than other things. In the same way, Hobbes points out, we see no stars when the sun is in the sky, though the stars are there. It is the relative strength of the sensory impressions that determines which of them comes to mind, but of course it is also the connection of interest and the association of ideas. This we shall return to shortly.

The question which cannot be delayed any longer is whether Hobbes's theory provides any satisfactory distinction between imagination and memory. He sums up the matter with tantalizing brevity: "This *decaying sense,* when we would express the thing itself . . . , we call *imagination.* . . . But when we would express the *decay,* and signify that the sense is fading, old and past, it is called *memory.*" This means that when we have an image (say) of the Tower of London, it is a case of imagination if we attend to the Tower itself but a memory if we attend to the fading, the oldness or pastness of it. But how can we detect such things in the image? The image might be dim or obscure, but this is not at all the same as oldness, pastness, decay, or fading. He also claims that what distinguishes memory is that the image is seen as something we have had before and that it "supposeth the time past." Here we must again ask how we can see in our present image of the Tower of London what could be described as "our having had the image in the past." Hobbes is here wrestling with a real difficulty. William James, at the beginning of the twentieth century, made the distinction when he said that memories, unlike mere images, have a feel of "warmth and familiarity." Other answers have been given, perhaps none of them entirely satisfactory.

Closely connected with this problem is Hobbes's treatment of representation. It is one thing to have an image in the mind, i.e., a pattern of colors or of grays, and quite another thing to experience it as a representation (from a certain angle) of the Tower of London. A dog looking in a mirror may see a certain visual pattern, but he does not see himself, or a representation of any dog, and he walks away with complete indifference. Show him a large photograph of a dog that he always fights or courts, and he is bored to death. He knows that it is not a dog that he sees, and he is incapable of recognizing the likeness as a *representation of* a dog. Babies under a year of age are similarly incapable of seeing a picture as a picture *of* something. The problem we are raising is whether Hobbes's materialistic system, in which there is only matter moving in accordance with the laws of motion, is able to explain what representation is and how it comes about. The system can give a causal account of the presence of the memory image in the mind; it is *"decaying sense."* But can it explain how the image is experienced *as a representation of* something? This problem is a big one and not easily resolved. We shall see that it also worried later thinkers.

When Hobbes speaks of a "train of imaginations," he includes under "imaginations" what we should call "thoughts." He takes thoughts in fact to be images, and would like to interpret images as the fading or decay of motions produced in us by sensory stimulation. This task is so difficult, however, that he does not pursue it very far.

Now trains of imaginations or thoughts, we read, are of two kinds: unguided and guided. Examples of unguided trains of thought are daydreams and dreams. In them there is "no passionate thought to govern and direct those [images] that follow . . . as the end and scope of some desire, or other passion; in which case the thoughts are said to wander, and seem impertinent one to another, as in a dream" (p. 52d). Our thoughts do seem to wander undirected in daydreams and dreams. But is this actually the case? We shall see that Freud maintains that our thoughts or images in these cases are governed by strong unconscious desires and are far from haphazard. Hobbes himself was close to making this discovery, for he tells us that often a train of thought which seems to be willy-nilly is found, on examination, to have an inner coherence. The reader has probably observed how it is possible to go back and discover a linkage of associations by which, having started from one subject, he wound up on one which is very remote from it.

Trains of thoughts when guided are connected by the association of ideas, or they are regulated by a persistent desire or purpose. The laws of association—association by similarity and contrast, by spatio-temporal contiguity or by cause and effect— were known as far back as Aristotle, and Hobbes's scant discussion of the subject adds nothing to what was known before. But his conception of mental regulation by need or purpose, and by seeking and invention, is original and important. "Sometimes," he says, "a man seeks what he hath lost; and from that place, and time, wherein he misses it, his mind runs back, from place to place, and time to time, to find where and when he had it; that is to say, to find some certain and limited time and place in which to begin a method of seeking." In the same way, "a spaniel ranges the field till he find a scent . . ." (p. 53b-c).

Here we have a kind of mental process which is apparently quite different from association and which might be called "problem solving." Much of the time when we are really thinking, and not merely daydreaming, the mind seems to work this way. We are seeking and inventing means to solve some problem or to get into a position where we can begin to solve it. We are trying to discover a feasible beginning of a route out of the woods, or into a more profitable job, or around an imposing woman we have offended, or toward the solution of a mathematical problem. Once we have found the route, the rest may be fairly easy. Even a mathematician, Bertrand Russell once remarked, seldom thinks; he mostly follows rules. But he has to think first to find which rules apply.

Hobbes recognizes also that the first step in a solution often has to allow for several possible second steps, for we cannot predict in advance exactly what the situation will be at that time. As in a game, we have to keep in mind not only our own alternative plays but also the alternative moves of our adversary. That reasoning is predominantly problem solving has proved a fruitful idea, and Hobbes was the first to see it.

It is most interesting that Hobbes attributes this problem-solving capacity to animals as well as to men. Reasoning, however, since it involves the use of words, is confined to men. Hobbes here agrees with Aristotle, who also, in his biological works, recognizes that animals are capable of learning. At many points Hobbes is closer to Aristotle than he thinks he is or wants to be. Naturally the problems that animals can solve, according to Hobbes, are far simpler than those that can be mastered by human beings. Men also possess abilities, according to Hobbes, not shared in any way by animals, which are called "*foresight,* and *prudence,* or *providence,* and sometimes *wisdom*" (p. 53c). It will be noted that these abilities presuppose language and moral persuasions which are possessed by man alone.

I V

"For words are wise men's counters; they do but reckon by them: but they are the money of fools, that value them by the authority of an Aristotle, a Cicero, or a Thomas, or any other doctor whatsoever, if but a man" (p. 56d). This witty saying of Hobbes shows the way the wind is blowing. He wants to expose the misuse of speech in the past and to chart a new and sensible course. He first insists that language is purely conventional and thus entirely different from the expressive cries of animals, which come from nature and by necessity. Names are adopted for objects not because they have any natural connection with them but merely for convenience. The name "dog" is purely arbitrary, and a dog by any other name would be as canine. But the convention of common names and other parts of speech is of paramount value. Without it there would be no commonwealth and men would be no better off than ravening wolves. The social contract itself is a connection which depends upon and consecrates the common consent to language.

It may be that Hobbes carries his conventionalism too far. If you think so, you might enjoy seeing what Socrates says in Plato's *Cratylus* (Vol. 7, p. 85). Would you be inclined to the view that, though the elements of a language may be purely conventional and rest on social agreement, the combination of words is governed by logical and by philosophical laws? If all languages in a certain group of languages develop in certain regular ways, could language be wholly conventional? And does not logic guide the combining of words in any language?

Hobbes's classification of the misuses of words, namely, the employment of equivocal, metaphorical, deceitful, and abusive language, reminds us of Bacon's "Four Idols" of language, so dear to mankind. (See Vol. 30. pp. 107 ff.) Both men campaigned vigorously against verbal self-deceit, humbug, and trickery, especially in philosophical usage. One target of Hobbes's attack is the revered doctrine of universals. In Greek and medieval times universals, such as *justice, virtue, triangle*

—which we often call "concepts" or "general ideas" today—
were usually given the status of entities of some kind, i.e.,
abstract entities. For Hobbes, there is "nothing in the world
universal but names" (p. 55c), and it is the *use* of a word like
"man" which gives it its universality. It is the fact that it
applies to every member of the class man. Whereas a name
like Julius Caesar names only one individual, the universal
man is a word that applies to each and every man. This denial
of universals is called "nominalism" and was developed long
before Hobbes, by the Greeks and in the Middle Ages. In
Hobbes's system of thought it was of the utmost importance;
it enabled him to replace metaphysics by psychology—the psychology of speech, which was what he wanted.

These universal words, however, are essential to science
and to the order and dignity of human life. Without them a
man's knowledge would reach only as far as the particular
objects he has examined, and he could never predict the future.
But once the word "triangle" and other such words have been
defined, it is apparent that "triangle" denotes all the objects
that are denoted by "having angles the sum of which is equal
to two right angles." The latter therefore can always be inferred from the former. Thus inferences, which are the heart
of science and prudent foresight, are relations between words,
and their validity depends on how we decide to define these
words. "For true and false," Hobbes says, "are attributes of
speech, not of things" (p. 56b). Is there anything wrong with
this view? Would not the geometrical theorem "the sum of the
angles of any triangle is equal to two right angles" be true
even if men had not fixed upon certain definitions of the terms
involved? Would not the true propositions of science be true
even if there were no men in existence?

One consideration will help us at this juncture. If we define
the words "body" and "man" in such a way that the former
denotes everything that the latter does, we are guided in doing
so by the nature of things. There exist two classes, after all,
one of which includes the other, whatever we may choose to
call them. The Frenchman and the German naturally give

them other names, yet for them also the one class includes the other.

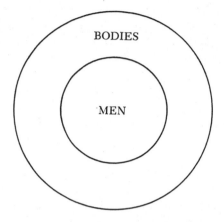

Other classes of things necessarily exclude each other. For example, there can be no things which are both round and rectangles. That these classes are mutually exclusive is readily admitted, but in other cases it is overlooked. Philosophers have talked about "incorporeal substance," Hobbes says, but it means no more than "incorporeal body" and is just as self-contradictory.

We can admit that "incorporeal body" is self-contradictory, but does it follow that "incorporeal substance" is? If it follows, according to Hobbes's own theory, then the word "substance" must, by definition, denote everything that is denoted by the word "body." But is this the case? Would it not be good English to speak of sovereignty or monarchy as entities, as things of some kind? Yet they certainly are not particular bodies in space. Would a man be using words incorrectly if he said "Absolute monarchy is an admirable institution; it is the thing that affords the greatest security to man"? Or to put the matter in a different way: Does good English require that every substance or thing be an extended body?

To ask such questions is to become doubtful of Hobbes's theory. We see that Hobbes's conclusion that "incorporeal substances" is a nonsensical expression does not rest merely on the proprieties of English usage. It is true, however, that Hobbes could give a behavioristic interpretation of a word like "monarchy." It could refer to particular human activities of a kind which distinguishes existing monarchies from other types of government. It could refer to particular activities, not to a general idea or universal. Yet would not the word have to refer to *all* these activities, and is not *all* something more than a particular thing? Does it not involve a class, an entity of some kind? And even if this difficulty could be overcome, it seems obvious that Hobbes would be giving his own special definition of "monarchy" and not relying on the common conventions, which is what he sets out to do.

When we consider Locke, in the next reading, we shall have a chance to examine another attempt to deal with the problem of universals. We shall be able to contrast Hobbes's theory that the universal is only a word with Locke's theory that it is an image of a certain kind.

V

Are fear and the desire for power the basic human passions?

The "inclination of all mankind" that Hobbes puts in the first place is "a perpetual and restless desire of power after power, that ceaseth only in death" (p. 76d). It is not that men necessarily want to acquire more pleasures than they already enjoy, but that they want to assure the possession of what they have. But if the desire for power is the ruling passion, fear of losing power, fear of death and oppression, fear of no longer having the means to live in ease and enjoyment are close seconds. In reaching this conclusion, Hobbes had certain well-known facts before him, but he also had a special motive. If men are perpetually driven by fear and insatiable lust for power, some covenant of peace and forbearance is necessary to save the race from destruction. The social contract becomes a practical necessity and the only solution.

But are there not other human passions of equal strength?

Locke and Rousseau, who also developed theories of the social contract, believed that there were. Cannot love, for example, silence fear and overcome the passion for power? This view is often taken, but here is what Hobbes says: "That which men desire they are also said to love. . . . So that desire and love are the same thing; save that by *desire,* we always signify the absence of the object; by *love,* most commonly the presence of the same" (p. 61c).

Is this altogether correct? It may be true that we do not desire what we already have, but is love otherwise the same as desire? A woman usually responds differently to a man's announcement "I love you" than she does to "I desire you," and it seems also that distance and even unattainability can "lend enchantment." It may be, then, that Hobbes's account of love is oversimple. On the other hand, he does recognize that there are, besides the sensual satisfactions, also pleasures of the mind. Would this help to remedy the matter? If desire can be of the mind and of its unique and personal qualities, desire begins to look more like love.

Hobbes does not deny what are called generous and altruistic sentiments, but he interprets them egoistically. Thus kindness is for him "love of persons for society," and love, as we have seen, is the same as desire, while desire is always desire for one's own pleasure. Similarly, pity is defined by Hobbes as "grief for the calamity of another . . . and ariseth from the imagination that the like calamity may befall himself; and therefore is called also *compassion,* and in the phrase of this present time a *fellow-feeling* . . ." (p. 63d). As is often pointed out, this definition would reduce pity for the calamity of others to pity for ourselves, and pity as a virtue to self-pity, which is regarded as weakness and a fault.

Benevolence, good will, and charity are also human traits. They are "the desire of good to another." But desire, as we have seen, is desire for one's own enjoyment. Moreover, though the benevolent man considers the good of others, it is his own good that prompts him to act. What a man calls good is simply "the object of his appetite or desire," for the words "good" and "evil" "are ever used with relation to the person that useth them" (p. 61d) and have no general meaning. But it may be asked what difference it makes whether a man is benevolent to please himself or to please those he helps, so long as he does *help* them. This brings us to our next question.

Does a man always act to promote his own pleasure?

The doctrine that a man always acts to promote his own pleasure, or "delight" as Hobbes sometimes puts it, is called "psychological hedonism." It is an old and celebrated doctrine, but it contains an equivocation which should be mentioned. Does it mean that in all our voluntary acts we think first of the pleasure we may derive from different courses of action and choose the one that promises most? Or, we must add, the one that threatens least pain? In discussing Hobbes we must be sure to keep in mind cases where we have a choice only between pains, since this philosopher takes a rather grim view of human alternatives.

Psychological hedonism, so understood, means that the mother who sacrifices herself for her child—goes without food and sleep so that the child will not go hungry or without care in sickness—always does so only after calculating that she will gain more pleasure or less pain in this way. This is so patently absurd that one wonders how it could have ever been maintained. The absurdity, however, depends on the word *always*. There are certainly many cases in which we calculate future pleasures and pains before acting, even when we intend to be outwardly very generous. That we always do, or must, is certainly false.

Can you find any evidence that Hobbes holds psychological hedonism in this sense? Does he ever say that we always calculate pains and pleasures, or "delight and trouble of mind," before taking action? Hobbes has often been criticized for maintaining this absurd proposition. Do you think the criticism is justified?

A more sensible interpretation of psychological hedonism could be put as follows: A man always acts on his strongest desire, and this is accompanied by pleasure or by relief from pain. If we decide to empty our bank account to help a friend, we do not necessarily calculate the pleasures or pains involved in doing so, but we do act on our strongest desire and doing so is pleasurable, or at least less painful than any other course open to us. We simply want to help out our friend more than we want to keep our money; it is relatively pleasant to do so, and it would be relatively painful to forgo it. But are there not cases of real self-sacrifice in which we relinquish our own interests for those of our friend? The answer, according to this version of psychological hedonism, is that, of course, we often think of the interests and well-being of the friend, but this is not enough to get us into action on his behalf. We must first desire to so act, and see ourselves able to act on our desire, which will be relatively pleasant.

Let us consider what Hobbes says about pleasure as a facilitation of action. We have seen that, according to his theory, stimulation from an external object produces motions in our sense organs. When these motions are transmitted to the heart, he says,

> . . . the real effect there is nothing but motion, or endeavour; which consisteth in appetite or aversion to or from the object moving. But the appearance or sense of that motion is that we either call *delight* or *trouble of mind* [pleasure or pain].
>
> This motion, which is called *appetite,* and for the appearance of it *delight* and *pleasure,* seemeth to be a corroboration of vital motion, and a help thereunto; and therefore such things as caused delight were not improperly called *jucunda (à juvando),* from helping or fortifying; and the contrary, *molesta,* offensive, from hindering and troubling the motion vital. (p. 62b)

Setting aside the apparent difficulty of reducing the "endeavour" and the "appearance" simply to motion, it will be evident that Hobbes is putting forth a traditional and very persuasive doctrine. Aristotle also said that pleasure eases and promotes action, and the same view is expressed by recent physiologists, such as C. Judson Herrick. If psychological hedonism means that pleasure, the pleasure of acting on or carrying out our desires, is what facilitates actions, and thus causes us to act as we do, how can anyone object to it?

Hobbes does not seem to adopt the first version of psycho-

logical hedonism, the view that we always act on the calculation of the greatest gain in pleasure, but rather the second,
which we have just described. He does take a dour view of
human nature, however. He does represent men in general as
far more egoistic and self-centered than we hope they are.
This misanthropic tendency is illustrated in the next question.

Is laughter always malicious?

"Sudden glory," Hobbes said, "is the passion which maketh
those grimaces called *laughter*." It arises in men, he says,
"either by some sudden act of their own that pleaseth them;
or by the apprehension of some deformed thing in another,
by comparison whereof they suddenly applaud themselves.
And it is incident most to them that are conscious of the fewest
abilities in themselves; who are forced to keep themselves in
their own favour by observing the imperfections of other men"
(p. 63c). Exulting laughter is naturally a very common occurrence. A man suddenly delighted with himself for some feat of
mind or body laughs aloud—sometimes even when he is alone.
But a sane man does not make a practice of this. He is much
more apt to laugh when others are present, others whom he
has worsted in some skill or competition, and here it begins
to look like malice. Whether a man is applauding his own
sudden success or the sudden failure of his companions would
be a fine point to decide. Hobbes's theory thus leaves very little
room for anything but malicious laughter.

There is no question that a tremendous part of laughter is
malicious; there is also no question that there are other kinds.
Another kind of laughter emphasized by Immanuel Kant arises
as a relief from strain. When children are released from the
long hours of discipline in school they are found to laugh
spontaneously, and the case is not much different with adults.
There is also the good-natured laughter that comes from high
spirits, good health, or good food and drink, or from sudden
embarrassment. Most important from a human and literary
point of view is the laughter which is occasioned by humor and
wit. Here, as Aristotle pointed out, we always have to do with
a perceived incongruity between what should be and what is,

an incongruity, however, which must not involve pain or moral turpitude. We laugh, that is, when the carpet is pulled out from under the feet of a sententious man, but not if he breaks his leg, and certainly not if this was intended.

Hobbes may have noted other kinds of laughter than the one or two which he describes. Perhaps he was only interested in laughter insofar as it fitted in with his leading idea. This was to show that human nature left to itself is so lamentably selfish and power-seeking that the only hope of mankind lies in a covenant, a social contract, whereby the powers of individual men are handed over to an absolute monarch for all time. Yet Hobbes depicted one type of laughter with great force and clarity, and with his word "sudden" he detected, with some originality, an essential trait of all humor.

The following questions are designed to help you test the thoroughness of your reading. Each question is to be answered by giving a page or pages of the reading assignment. Answers will be found on page 383 of this Reading Plan.

1 Did Hobbes say that experience consists of what you can remember of the past?

2 Under what circumstances do we have an after-image, according to Hobbes?

3 How does Hobbes explain the apparition which appeared to Brutus before the battle of Philippi?

4 Why did Hobbes think that witches should be punished?

5 Does Hobbes say that it is prudence that distinguishes man from beast?

6 What does Hobbes conclude from God's gift of words to Adam?

7 The Greeks, according to Hobbes, had one name for both speech and reason. What does he conclude from this?

8 How does Hobbes define "hope," "courage," and "anger"?

L O C K E

An Essay Concerning Human Understanding

Book II

Vol. 35, pp. 121-147, 178-186, 220-222

In the seventeenth century both Descartes and Locke opened doors to the Enlightenment and to modern science and the new era. Descartes undermined the authority of the past by showing that every bit of traditional knowledge can be doubted. Locke ushered in modern times by his contention that all knowledge comes from sensation and the operation of the mind on it, and can claim no other source or authority. Descartes and Leibniz demonstrated the power of mathematics which has become increasingly important in scientific method, whereas Locke, with some help from Bacon and Hobbes, opened the modern mind to the reasonableness and promise of empiricism. This was the other side of the scientific method.

Locke was also a great force for religious tolerance and individual liberty in a century marked by bigotry, persecution, and political absolutism. His moderation, common sense, and love of freedom charmed and gave hope to men weary of fanatical extremes. His gentleness and the calm air of impartiality with which he set about to examine the big questions of the time evoked affection as well as respect. He is considered one of the founders of the democratic credo. Rousseau and Montesquieu were under his sway, and so were the authors of the United States Constitution.

Although Hobbes had previously put forward the view that all knowledge is derived from sense perception, Locke elaborated the theme more thoroughly and convincingly, and his writings were ingratiating and had a wider appeal. His polemic against innate ideas and principles, which occupies Book I of *An Essay Concerning Human Understanding*, had an especially sharp impact. If Locke was right, no idea or principle could claim to be sacrosanct or immune from criticism. If men believe that $2 + 2 = 4$, that the king rules by divine right, that murder is wrong, and that God exists, these beliefs have their source in sense experience and can claim no other justification than that which experience confers. All have their origin in sensation or in the mind's reflection on sensation.

Descartes had argued that, since we never perceive anything perfect, the idea of perfection cannot be derived from perception but must have been imprinted in our minds by God. Locke, however, undertakes to show that even the most exalted ideas have their substance in experience. The infinite, for example, is simply the idea of something we can go on adding to without ever coming a whit closer to the end. (See pp. 217d-218a.) In Book IV of the *Essay*, Locke emphasizes the active power of the mind, the power to know mathematical and moral truths by intuition, yet he nowhere repudiates Book I. The source and authority of all knowledge is still experience, either outer sense, sensation, or inner sense, reflection; and it is sensation which first supplies all the materials of knowledge.

While Locke's commonsensical empirical viewpoint was shaping the whole trend of modern philosophy, it was also preparing the ground for empirical psychology and for the genetic method which looks for explanation of the complexities of passion and thought in the connection of earlier and simpler experiences. Probabilities would now become the guide and measure of theory. Locke's firm principle that the degree of assent we give to a proposition should be determined by the degree of probability it has, and by that alone, pointed out the path that psychology would have to follow.

Eighth Reading

I

The most influential of all English philosophers was born near Bristol in 1632. His mother died young, and his father, a strict but kindly attorney, took charge of John's education. The country at the time was riven with civil war and religious conflict, and the father was often away in service with the army of Parliament. "From the time that I knew anything," Locke recalled at the age of twenty-eight, "I found myself in a storm, which has continued to this time." Locke's six years at the Westminster School, where the classics were taught only by way of grammar, memory work, and Latin compositions, were anything but pleasant. His recollections, however, later furnished material for his celebrated essay, *Thoughts on Education*. At Oxford, whither he went at the age of twenty, Puritanism and Scholasticism were dominant, and neither in the context had much appeal to him. He turned rather with great avidity to the study of Descartes, Gassendi, and Hobbes. The tolerance granted at this time to all Protestants by the Chancellor of the University and also by Oliver Cromwell himself must have made an impression on Locke. This is reflected in his *Letter Concerning Toleration,* 1685.

Locke was a man of deep religious feeling, and once thought of entering the ministry. The Thirty-Nine Articles of the Church of England, however, stood in his way. Having come to believe that the required articles of faith should be reduced to a minimum and free inquiry encouraged, he gave up the idea of a career in the Church. Instead, he resolved to become a doctor, and began to study medicine and to conduct chemical experiments. In this way he was drawn into a close friendship with two famous men, the chemist Robert Boyle and the physician Sydenham. Locke warmly endorsed the empirical methods of Boyle in chemistry and of Sydenham in medicine. Although he eventually gave up medicine for philosophy, his medical studies left a lasting impression. Instead of curing men's bodies, he now sought to heal their minds and resolve their doubts and dilemmas, to promote human, i.e., humane, understanding. The bedside manner is often in evidence.

Locke's friendship with the Earl of Shaftesbury, in whose family he became secretary, tutor, and doctor, led to his warm espousal of the Whigs and his immersion in political activity. On the fall of Shaftesbury from power, he sought refuge in Holland. In 1688 came the triumph of the Revolution for which Locke had worked. William and Mary of Orange took the throne, and in the next year Locke returned to England. In the meantime he had not forgotten philosophy but had continued the composition of his great work, *An Essay Concerning Human Understanding*, which appeared in 1690. In the same year appeared also his *Two Treatises on Civil Government*. Although these short works were inquiries into the truth of things, Locke confessed that they were also actuated by a desire to defend the Revolution.

In the *Reasonableness of Christianity*, Locke portrayed Christianity as a gospel of love, and his dislike of dogmas such as that of the trinity and of eternal punishment resulted in vigorous attacks by theologians. He died in 1704 in the home of Sir Francis Masham, near London, as he wrote, "in perfect charity with all men, and in sincere communion with the whole church of Christ, by whatever names Christ's followers call themselves."

II

Book II of Locke's *Essay Concerning Human Understanding*, which is the subject of this Eighth Reading, sets out to show that all our knowledge comes from sensations, which the mind compares, organizes, unifies, abstracts, and operates on in various other ways. Locke's theory of how we get from particular sensations to general ideas or universals, will be discussed in Section III, below. Since science is made up of universals, this topic is crucial for any philosophy; it is especially so for a philosophy which says that the only materials of knowledge are sensations. Section IV deals with Locke's analysis of perception, especially with the effect of judgment and expectation, as in the perception of depth.

Starting out with sensations, such as *yellow, white, heat, cold, hard, soft, bitter, sweet,* Locke says, the mind carries out operations on them, such as *perception, memory, doubting, believing,* and *reasoning.* Our curiosity is aroused as to the nature of the mind which performs these operations. It must itself be something more than sensations or ideas. In Section V we look into Locke's theory of the mind and the problem of personal identity which it entails.

In Section VI we take up two questions which have to do with Locke's historically very important distinction between primary and secondary qualities, and one question about motivation. Primary qualities, such as bulk, figure, and number belong to physical objects, whereas the secondary qualities, according to Locke, are restricted to our own subjective experiences. The secondary qualities, such as heat and color, exist only when we perceive them—only when external things act upon our sense organs. The capability of bringing them into existence is called a "power." In the psychological sphere there are also powers, such as will and understanding. Although Locke rejected the medieval faculties, he introduced something like them, viz., "powers."

Another question to be discussed is how, according to Locke, solidity differs from hardness. Solidity is a primary quality existing in physical objects, whereas hardness is a secondary quality, which depends on the way in which external stimulation affects the organism. Unless these qualities can be discriminated in experience, the distinction of primary and secondary qualities breaks down. Lastly, we shall examine Locke's theory that there is only one instigator of thought and action, namely, uneasiness.

Before considering Book II and its account of the origin of our ideas in sense experience, we must say a few words about Locke's famous polemic against innate ideas, in Book I. The theory that some of our ideas and principles are innate, and are therefore *not* derived from sense experience, had been advanced by Locke's contemporaries, the Cambridge Platonists. Locke states the theory in his own manner, and in many ways which his own ingenuity suggests, only to find that it is always confused, absurd, or incredible. Can it be supposed, he asks, that moral principles, such as "thou shalt not kill," are known at the moment of birth, or that they are obvious to all savages?

What could "innate" mean? Could it mean that the principles are present from birth but that it takes time and experience for the individual to recognize them? Locke says that there could be no evidence for this. Moreover, having principles of which one is not conscious is not different from *not* having these principles. "To say a notion is imprinted on the mind, and yet at the same time to say, that the mind is ignorant of it, and never yet took notice of it, is to make this impression nothing. No proposition can be said to be in the mind which it never yet knew, which it was never yet conscious of" (p. 96c).

If, on the other hand, it is held that certain mathematical and moral principles are innate in the sense that they can be known by reason, Locke answers that in this case the most complicated mathematical formulae would be innate. Moreover, if reason is necessary to grasp their truth, then it is plain that they are not innate. The ability to reason is innate, but not the particular results of reasoning.

We shall have to agree with Locke when he argues that universal assent to simple mathematical and moral principles would not prove that they are innate. Even if all tribes on earth believed that $2 + 2 = 4$, and that murder is wrong, the conclusion would not follow. Similar conditions to which men are subject everywhere in the world may result in similar experiences, and similar experiences could bring about assent to the same principles. So long as there is another way to explain the universal assent to principles (and in Book II Locke shows that there is), the innateness of the principles is not proved.

Locke, however, not only denies that general assent would prove these principles innate; he also denies that there is a general assent. He begins with the contention that children and idiots do not assent to the principles supposed to be innate. This in itself "is enough to destroy the universal assent" on which the argument for innate principles depends. Idiots are a special case, since it might be held that they are not quite human. Present-day evidence with regard to children favors Locke's contention. Jean Piaget, for example, finds that young children frequently violate the law of noncontradiction. They contradict themselves without seeing that there is anything wrong in it; although they understand what they are saying they do not understand why contradictions are to be avoided. Only very gradually do they learn to observe the principle of noncontradiction; and even adults frequently return to the childish illogic. There is also some evidence that, as Locke claims, savages or preliterate peoples are not generally aware of basic logical principles. Like children, they seem to become more sensitive to self-contradictions as their education advances. On this point, then, Locke may well be right.

In the seventeenth century knowledge of primitive people was just beginning to accumulate, and Locke was much interested. He may have been right in concluding that primitive people do not always recognize simple logical, mathematical, and moral principles; he was certainly wrong in thinking they do not have abstract ideas. General ideas or universals, even the most abstract, can be expressed in languages of primitive people which have recently been studied. But general ideas or universals, though readily expressed, are strange entities. They are an especially acute problem for an empiricist like Locke.

III

We have seen that for Hobbes, universals or general ideas are only words. He conceded, however, that they are very important words, for they enable us to talk about, and deal with, men, horses, triangles, etc., which are not being perceived. The name Peter refers to only one man, whereas the universal "man" refers to each and every man. All science and practical prediction depend on universal words. But how can the word "man" be identified with the idea *man?* There is a different word for man in every language, but only one idea *man*. Locke avoided difficulties of this kind by interpreting the universal, or abstract idea, as an image. But this entailed new difficulties. What kind of an image could it be?

Could the idea of man be the image of a particular man? How then could it represent each and every man? I now have an image of General Dwight D. Eisenhower. It represents the one-time President of the United States, but it does not represent other men, for these have a different appearance. The problem is how the particular image can represent every man, every member of the class. Locke explains that

> . . . the mind makes the particular ideas received from particular objects to become general; which is done by considering them as they are in the mind such appearances,—separate from all other existences, and the circumstances of real existence, as time, place, or any other concomitant ideas. This is called ABSTRACTION, whereby ideas taken from particular beings become general representatives of all of the same kind . . . Thus the same colour being observed to-day in chalk or snow, which the mind yesterday received from milk, it considers that appearance alone, makes it a representative of all of that kind; and having given it the name *whiteness*, it by that sound signifies the same quality wheresoever to be imagined or met with; and thus universals, whether ideas or terms, are made. (p. 145c-d)

There is no doubt that we abstract from particularities in framing universals or general ideas. When we think of *man* in general, we abstract from the places and times in which individual men live. Thus we can reasonably ask the date and the locale of any particular man, but such questions would be absurd in the case of the idea *man*. *Man* has no time nor place. But *man* is also neither tall nor short, neither fat nor thin, nor smiling nor frowning, etc. How then could it be a particular idea? That is, how could it be a particular image in the mind, an image or likeness of a particular man?

Locke's answer is that we *make* the particular image a representative of the whole class. Do you think this is true in your own experience? What do you have in your mind corresponding to the word "man" when, for example, men are being contrasted with anthropoid apes? Do you have the image of a tall blond man, a short swarthy one, or some other particular semblance which somehow represents, or stands for, each and every man? Or do you have something before your mind that is not an image? If so, what could it be?

Let us take another example: What kind of image do you have in mind when someone speaks of triangles in general? Is it an image of an equilateral triangle, a right-angled triangle, a scalene or an isosceles triangle? Or is it something else? Some people have reported that they generally have a particular image of a man when the subject of man is raised, and always think of a right-angled or equilateral triangle when triangles are discussed. Some people, similarly, think of an expanse of snow—snow which has no special date or location—when white or whiteness is mentioned. Do you also tend to have some particular image when a word like "man," "triangle," or "whiteness" comes up?

If you do, then it might seem that Locke's theory is correct. But let us assume that you have an image of an equilateral triangle whenever you think of triangles. How can this particular image be what you mean by the word "triangle"? How can it represent all triangles? Suppose you are thinking of triangles and have an image of an equilateral triangle. Now change your image to a right-angled triangle, and then to triangles of other kinds, sizes, and colors. Is it not possible to go right on thinking of triangles in spite of these changes? Does the meaning of "triangle" vary with the changes of your image? Next see if you cannot eliminate all images of triangles while still attending to the definition "A triangle is a three-sided closed plane figure." Does not this definition go on making sense even when you have no images of triangles at all? If so, the image cannot *be* the sense. Finally, see if it is possible for you to keep the image of an equilateral triangle before your mind, while thinking of something else—such as the party to which you are going tonight.

If the outcome of this experiment is positive, the general idea or universal cannot be identified with a particular image. It will have been shown that the image can vary or even disappear while the universal remains unchanged. In Books III and IV, however, Locke puts forward another theory of the universal, and we must now inquire whether the same objection applies to it. Discussing the manner in which the child forms the idea (i.e., image) of *man,* i.e., by abstracting what men and women of its acquaintance have in common, Locke says:

And thus they come to have a general name, and a general idea. Wherein they make nothing new; but only leave out of the complex idea they had of Peter and James, Mary and Jane, that which is peculiar to each, and retain only what is common to them all. (pp. 255d-256a)

The universal *man* is now no longer identified with a particular image but with an image that retains only what is common to all the particular images of men. This "vague image," as it has been called, is now the universal, and the universal *man,* accordingly, will be neither tall nor short, neither swarthy nor blond, neither impressive nor insignificant, nor have any of the special qualities distinguishing one man from another. The shoulders will not be broad nor narrow, the legs neither long nor short, and so on. Bishop Berkeley, vigorously criticizing this theory of Locke, insists that there is no such thing as a vague image, for all images must be definite and particular. William James, on the other hand, is just as convinced that vague, indeterminate, shadowy images do occur and are, in fact, common features of our mental life. (See *The Principles of Psychology,* Vol. 53, pp. 480 ff.) What do you think? What do you find when you look, for example, at your image of *virtue* or *infinity?*

Berkeley, however, had another objection to vague images. He argued that even if there *were* such things as vague images, they would not have a general import. The vague image for *man* would not represent each and every man but only a vague man, as if, indeed, there could be such a thing.

In Book IV Locke himself is painfully aware of the difficulties that his conception entails. Abstract ideas, he remarks, "are not so obvious or easy to children," or even to grown men, as it might appear; for, when we reflect on them,

. . . we shall find that *general ideas* are fictions and contrivances of the mind, that carry difficulty with them . . . For example, does it not require some pains and skill to form the general idea of a triangle, (which is yet none of the most abstract, comprehensive, and difficult,) for it must be neither oblique nor rectangle, neither equilateral, equicrural, nor scalenon; but all and none of these at once. In effect, it is something imperfect, that cannot exist; an idea wherein some parts of several different and inconsistent ideas are put together. (p. 339a-b)

Although general ideas are of the greatest service to mankind, Locke seems to say, they are nevertheless self-contradictory and cannot exist. If we take the general idea of a triangle just described as an image, a kind of *picture* in the mind, it certainly cannot have sides which are both equal and unequal. This would seem to be impossible. Yet William James contended that such questions cannot be settled by *a priori* arguments. We must look to our experience. If we find that we do have vague ideas, like the idea of a triangle which is neither equilateral, right-angled, nor of any other particular kind, then that settles the matter. Such things do exist. And James might well have added: What exists cannot be self-contradictory.

It is worth noting that no trace of inconsistency appears in the ordinary definition of triangle; viz: A triangle is a plane, closed, three-sided figure. It is only when one tries to form an image or picture of a triangle in general that inconsistency seems to arise; for it is only then that there would have to be sides that are neither equal nor unequal, and an angle neither 90 degrees nor more nor less than 90 degrees. The Realist avoids this difficulty. For him the universal or abstract idea is not an image or picture of any kind but a *meaning*—a meaning which is analyzed by a definition.

IV

In his chapter "Of Perception" (pp. 138 ff.), Locke makes some points which are obvious, or obvious when you think about them, and others which are bold and controversial. He distinguishes first between voluntary and involuntary perception. "In bare naked perception, the mind is, for the most part, only passive; and what it perceives, it cannot avoid perceiving" (p. 138b-c). Yet we can turn our gaze from one object to another and concentrate on what we will. In the clanging noise and bluster of the city streets we hear only the small voice of the child we are showing the sights. Such is the power of attention. Accordingly, though external stimulation is necessary for perception, it is not at all sufficient. "A sufficient impulse there may be on the [sense] organ; but it not reaching the observation of the mind, there follows no perception: and though the motion that uses to produce the idea of sound be made in the ear, yet no sound is heard" (p. 138d).

Locke believes that children in the womb have some sensations before they are born, such as hunger and warmth. He insists, however, that such simple sensations are far removed from the abstract principles that are supposed by some writers to be innate. That the fetus has sensations is highly speculative, and it is hard to see how it could be proved, one way or the other. Some modern authorities, however, have held that conscious life before birth is quite complex. The psychiatrist Otto Rank believed that being born, i.e., being thrust from a warm safe haven into the cruel world, is such a shock that the individual often fails to recover from it. Freud himself thought this was an exaggeration.

Of special interest and importance are the sections of Chapter 9 which deal with influence of "judgment" on sensation and perception. (See pp. 139b-140b.) Although knowledge is derived from sensations, it is continually altering them. At the beginning of life we have pure sensations, but as our experience accumulates we come to expect, infer, and compute the nature of sensory objects. We say we see the hunter bring down a quail, but as far as our sensations go we experience at most only a figure with a gun pointing to the sky, a bang, and something falling to the earth. We say that we see a tall building at the end of the street, but our sensation itself is really tiny. We perceive, as we say, a four-legged table with a flat rectangular top, but our senses reveal a top that is neither level nor rectangular, and only two or three legs are really visible.

Locke gives striking illustrations of the way in which judgments involved in perception may alter sensation. He argues that although we experience a round globe by touch, what we *see* is only a flat circle. (See p. 139.) It is the shading, the differences of light and dark on the surface of the globe, which makes us judge that what we see is spherical. Having learned by touch that objects showing this variation of lighting are spherical, we even come to believe that we *see* the roundness. For proof that we do not *see* the roundness Locke takes the case of a man born blind who has learned to distinguish cubes from spheres by touch. He imagines that the blind man is suddenly made to see for the first time; and that he is presented with a cube and a sphere of the same material and of about the same size. Will he be able, without touching them, to tell which is the sphere and which the cube? Locke says he will not, for having learned how the two figures differ to the touch does not tell him anything about how they will *look,* how they will differ visually. He may well be right about this. It has been found that men who see for the first time as a result of an operation which removes cataracts from their eyes are a long time learning the difference between visual cubes and squares, though they have all their lives distinguished between cubes and squares *tactually.*[1]

Let us return to Locke's question whether we can *see* depth. If objects are close enough to us we can see part way around them. Bring a pencil close to your eyes, and you will actually see the sides of it as well as the front. This is because you are using both eyes. If you shut one eye the roundness is no longer visible, although you still seem to see the same solid pencil. Beyond a certain range we can no longer see around objects, i.e., there is no longer what is called "stereoscopic vision." Beyond the range of stereoscopic vision we have to rely on depth cues: One object is in front of another (superposition), objects are seen as smaller in the distance, their edges are shaded, their outlines and details become blurred, and color is less bright, etc.

To test Locke's view that we do not see depth we might try to remove all these depth cues and then see whether a psycho-

[1] See D. O. Hebb, *The Organization of Behavior* (New York: John Wiley & Sons, Inc., 1949), p. 18.

logical subject could still recognize a solid object by sight alone. Suppose we present a subject with two white circular shapes of the same diameter and at the same distance, one being a flat circle, the other a sphere. We must be sure that the figures are beyond the range of stereoscopic vision and that the lamps are so arranged that there is no shading on the sphere and no difference of illumination.

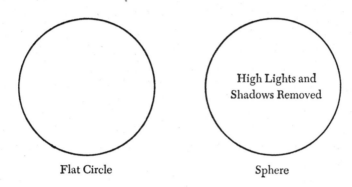

Flat Circle   Sphere

The outcome of such an experiment is well known. The subject cannot distinguish the flat circle from the sphere, and this is in accord with Locke's view. William James, while admitting, as the evidence shows, that we do not detect depth in vision except when we have the help of depth cues, insists that when they are present we do see depth, and not merely the depth cues. He maintains that when we look at a house on a distant hill, we see not only the comparative smallness of the house compared to other objects in our visual field—the shadows, the indistinctness of details and outline, etc.—but also the distance that intervenes. What would you say? Can you now, for example, see across the room, see the distance between yourself and the wall, or can you see only the wall? Do not such questions perhaps point to different senses of the world "see"?

Locke's insight that we habitually perceive far more than is given in sensation, that we perceive also what we have reason to think is in the object, what we expect is there, and even what we hope is there, has been overwhelmingly confirmed by modern psychology. Locke contends that when we see a round globe, sensation discloses only "a flat circle, variously shadowed, with several degrees of light and brightness coming to our eyes" (p. 139b). But having accustomed ourselves to the way convex objects look when the light falls upon them from different angles, we judge that the figure we see is spherical, or rather, it is *as if* we judged it to be spherical. There might have been an inference when we were first learning how tactually convex objects look 'to the eye, but it has long since been displaced by very subtle habits, habits of seeing which adjust themselves to the finest variations of shading and illumination, and to other cues without, as Locke says, "our taking notice of it" (p. 139b). Locke's recognition of the role of habit, of the part played by unconscious adjustments to cues in visual perception, was highly prophetic of future developments.

Locke, however, seldom went to extremes. He recognized that our habits, expectations, and wishes partly determine what we perceive, but he always remembered the basic role of sensation produced by stimulation of our sense organs. In fact, he balanced the subjective and objective components of perception much better than many recent philosophers have done. He pointed out that sugar may taste bitter when we have a fever, but insisted that sweetness always remains sweetness, and bitterness bitterness, and that it is beyond the power of the mind to alter them, or to change the one into the other. (See pp. 127 and 144.) Similarly, if we put both hands into lukewarm water, after one has been immersed in cold, the other in hot water, the lukewarm water will have very different temperatures for the two hands. (See p. 136.) There is nothing remarkable in this, Locke explains, if we understand that the difference is due to different motions of particles in the two hands. But here again the warmth felt by the one hand and the coolness felt by the other are unalterably distinct and different. Such sense qualities remain the basic materials of the mind.

The variations of perception with the changes of subjective conditions—such as the fever which makes sugar taste bitter, and the previous conditioning of the two hands in the other example—are employed by Locke as a proof of the subjectivity of secondary qualities. We have seen that Hobbes drew the same conclusion, and that Bishop Berkeley replied that arguments of this kind prove that the primary qualities are also subjective. In other words, all qualities are subjective; matter does not exist. Locke, however, was a man of moderation. The primary qualities disclosed in perception—motion, rest, figure, bulk, etc.—roughly agree with those in the material world, he contended, and their objectivity is essential to explain sensation, perception, and our knowledge of the external world.

V

Descartes had argued that since I think, I must exist; for the doubt that I exist implies my existence. This celebrated argument was supposed to establish the existence of the soul as a thinking substance. Unless the soul is to lapse during deep sleep and come into existence again every morning, it must continue to think day and night.

Locke, the empiricist, opposes his rationalistic deduction, and asks what evidence there is that the soul is perpetually thinking. (See pp. 123b-126c.) Why should the soul have to think always? he asks; the body does not always move. A follower of Descartes· could have replied: "Yes, but the body is always extended. Thinking, i.e., some kind of conscious activity, is as necessary to the soul as extension is to the body." But Locke denies that "*the soul always thinks*" would be generally accepted as self-evident. What does seem self-evident to him is that you cannot think without being conscious of it, and this proposition together with the fact that men do not remember thinking during the night is, in his opinion, proof that the soul does not always think.

Locke does not deny that a man during deep dreamless sleep goes on having a soul but only that we can think without being conscious of it. A man "cannot *think* at any time, waking or sleeping, without being sensible of it. Our being sensible of it is not necessary to anything but to our thoughts; and to them it is . . ." (p. 123c-d). But could not a man think during dreamless sleep, and be conscious that he is thinking at the time, but then forget about it when he wakes? This would be out of line with all our experience, Locke says. (See pp. 124c and 126a-b.) It is incredible that a man, when awakened, should have entirely forgotten what he was thinking about a second before.

Is it possible, he asks, that the soul should go on thinking during dreamless sleep, while the man who owns the soul—Mr. Jones—knows nothing about it? In this case, why say that the thinking occurs in Mr. Jones rather than in some other man? In what ways does it belong to Mr. Jones and not to Mr. Smith or Mr. Black? The proof that a man has done some thinking is his ability to recall it; and where memory fails there is no proof; it might just as well have been someone else's thinking. (See p. 124a-c.) It is memory, after all, which binds the experiences of Mr. Jones into one biography and distinguishes his from other biographies.

But if a man does not know, or remember, his thinking during the night's sleep, could not someone else know it? Locke's answer is *"If I think when I know it not, nobody else can know it"* (p. 125c). Thinking is a private operation. Fortunately, no one can know that I am thinking, or what I am thinking, unless I tell him. If I do not know myself, I could not inform another.

Locke's arguments have considerable weight and persuasiveness, but there is something to be said on the other side. It seems contradictory to claim that a man thinks without being conscious of it, but the reason may be only that we have defined thinking so as to exclude unconscious thought. A definition, however, does not settle a question of fact. Freud, as we shall see, argues that many facts of our conscious lives cannot be explained except upon the hypothesis that there are unconscious thoughts and wishes. The unconscious thoughts and wishes belong to a given person, Mr. Smith, it can be argued, because *he* reveals them by slips of the tongue and dreams, etc., and they explain *his* behavior.

Moreover, it is perhaps not surprising that we forget our nighttime thinking when we awaken, for we frequently forget dreams a moment after. William James, in discussing Locke's thesis, gives other examples of total loss of memory immediately after the event. (See Vol. 53, p. 131.) And to Locke's question what could cause a man to forget his nocturnal thoughts, Freud answered, some three hundred years later, that they are so shameful that we dare not look at them in the daylight. Lastly, it is not necessarily true that if I could not know I am thinking during dreamless sleep, no one else could. It may not be long now before electroencephalogram studies determine whether or not a sleeping man is thinking.

Locke's view that we do not think while asleep will recommend itself more to common sense. On the other hand, this view seems to imply a break in the continuity of the self, and a loss of personal identity, which is far from congenial to common sense. In what sense can I claim to be the same person when asleep as when awake, if when I am asleep I am a mere body? And how can I know that I am the same person the next morning if the stream of thought is not continuous? If a mountain stream is seen to be continuous we do not doubt its identity, but if it goes underground at one point, can we be sure that the stream that emerges some distance away is the same as that which disappeared? How is the sleeper different from this stream? Although consciousness disappears, like the stream, the sleeper's body remains, and it is a distinctive human body. Secondly, when the sleeper awakes he will be able to remember his past life but not the past life of other persons. What difference then should it make if consciousness is submerged some eight hours every day? The body of the sleeper maintains his continuity, and memory knits body and mind together in one unique biography.

Locke, however, separates the identity of man from personal identity. (See p. 220.) The identity of man, like the identity of an animal, is "one fitly organized body." It is the continuity of a unique body that makes a man the same man. For if it were the soul alone which distinguishes the man, Locke argues, the same man might inhabit the bodies of different men or even of animals. Seth, Ismael, Socrates, Pilate, St. Austin, and Caesar Borgia might conceivably be the same man who, presumably, has had several changes of heart and ideas. And who knows but that the household poodle is not really one's grandfather? Apparently with his tongue in his cheek, Locke tells the story of a parrot who conversed rationally with Prince Maurice of Brazil. His conclusion seems to be that, though such a parrot might have passed as a rational animal, he would not have been accepted as a man.

For I presume it is not the idea of a thinking or rational being alone that makes the *idea of a man* in most people's sense: but of a body, so and so shaped, joined to it . . . (p. 222a)

Is the uniqueness of a particular man, then, determined by his bodily characteristics? Do we *officially identify* him by his opinions, preferences, ideals, etc., or by his fingerprints and his picture at various angles?

Personal identity, Locke says, is something quite different. A man does not know that he is the same person by comparing his image in the mirror with his portrait the first thing in the morning. He knows that he is himself without looking in the mirror, and even though his appearance should undergo an abrupt change, although it seems likely that this would give him a shock. Personal identity consists in self-consciousness, the ability of a man to remember his past experiences. ". . . as far as this consciousness can be extended backwards to any past action or thought, so far reaches the identity of that person" (p. 222b).

Does this seem to you to be true? To test its plausibility, imagine a man who suddenly suffers a complete loss of memory, and cannot even recall who he is, where he lives, or his family and friends, while retaining, at the same time, all his other abilities. Would such a man lose his personal identity, or only his connection with the past? Although he could remember nothing of the past, he could of course begin anew to store up recollections. As a matter of fact, many persons with complete amnesia, or fugue state, as it is called, have settled down in new cities, with new jobs and new wives, and lived quite normal lives. In what sense have they lost personal identity? Or would it be in accord with Locke's definition of personal identity to say that, since they are daily building up new memories, they are aware of their personal identity in some degree? Can such a man know that he is himself, and not any other person, and still not know exactly *who* he is, nor his background and former family and friends? Would you agree with Locke that it is consciousness alone which constitutes personal identity, or would you say that similarity and continuity of contents of a biography are also important bonds of unity? In any case, is not the ability or power of a man to remember his past indispensable in knowing that he is himself? It will be seen that Locke gives considerable attention to powers in general, and to human powers in particular. They are essential to his whole system.

VI

How are powers related to primary and secondary qualities?

The primary qualities, Locke tells us, are "bulk, figure, number, situation, and motion or rest of their solid parts" (p. 137a). They are distinguished from the secondary qualities by the fact that they are in bodies whether we perceive them or not, whereas colors, sounds, tastes, and odors are subjective, i.e., exist only when our sense organs are stimulated by external bodies, in virtue of their primary qualities. The primary qualities of a body are also capable, under certain conditions, of making changes in the primary qualities of other bodies. This capability is called a power. For example, "the sun has a power to make wax white, and fire to make lead fluid" (p. 137b). The sun has the active power to melt lead, and the lead the passive power of being liquefied. It may appear to you odd that Locke should speak of a *passive* power, yet you will remember that physics refers to the melting point of lead and other metals as if it were a property. Similarly, fragility and friability seem to be regarded as properties.

What interests us, however, are powers in the psychological sphere. The clearest manifestation of power is seen in memory, will, and understanding. "That we find in ourselves a power to begin or forbear, continue or end several actions of our minds, and motions of our bodies, barely by a thought or preference of the mind ordering, or as it were commanding, the doing or not doing such or such a particular action. This power which the mind has . . . is that which we call the *Will*" (p. 179c). The power of perception, Locke says, is called *Understanding*. By it, we are able to perceive ideas, the meanings of signs, and the agreement and disagreement of our ideas.

Note how different powers are from primary and secondary qualities. We can immediately observe a man's bulk, figure, motion, etc., and also his color, the pitch of his voice, etc., but his will and understanding are hidden from view. To say that a man has a strong will or that he has reached a decision means, accordingly, that if he is in such and such a situation he will behave in such and such a way. Powers are thus not observable qualities but dispositions—dispositions to act in certain ways under stated conditions. This being so, would you say that timidity, intelligence, anger, humility, and loquacity are "powers" in Locke's sense?

What is the difference between solidity and hardness?

It is important, as previously said, to distinguish in experience the primary qualities from the secondary qualities. One of the most important primary qualities, which is often used as the acid test of the physical reality of an object, is solidity. Solidity, however, is popularly confused with hardness, which is a *secondary* quality.

Solidity, Locke says, "consists in repletion, and so an utter exclusion of other bodies out of the space it possesses: but hardness, in a firm cohesion of the parts of matter, making up masses of a sensible bulk, so that the whole does not easily change its figure" (p. 130b). Would it follow that everything that is hard is also solid? That is, does a hard object exclude every other object from the same space? What would you say about a piece of pumice stone which is hard but highly porous, i.e., admits a great deal of air? Would you say that this stone is hard but not solid?

Not all solid things are hard, of course. Air and water, according to Locke, are soft but as solid as steel, and he points out that a football and a hollow gold globe full of water both resist extreme pressures. In fact, *solidity* for Locke is a quality without degrees, whereas *hardness* is obviously something comparative, implying *harder than something else*. But is it true that solidity has no degrees? While water can be compressed scarcely at all, air and other gases have different rates of compressibility, and it is thanks to this that we have steam engines. With a gas there is no "utter exclusion of other bodies out of the space it occupies." We know that chemical elements have different rates of compressibility.

Locke went on to say that "hard and soft are names that we give to things only in relation to the constitutions of our own bodies; that being generally called hard by us, which will put us to pain sooner than change figure by the pressure of any part of our bodies . . ." (p. 130b). It might seem that Locke was completely wrong in this matter, for we speak of the hardness of metals and stones quite apart from the painfulness of exerting pressure upon them. But Locke made no mistake. "Hard," as he uses it, is a psychological term, and quite different from the term "hard" employed in physics, chemistry, geology, etc.

Is the overcoming of uneasiness the only motive to thought or action?

If a man is perfectly content and without any uneasiness, according to Locke, there will be no occasion for him to think or act, and he will remain passive and indolent. Thus our "all-wise Maker" has seen to it that men remain uneasy. (See p. 186.) But is this true? Are we not often very active—engaged in ardent and tireless pursuits—when most happy? We remain active because we seek continued or even greater happiness. Locke's answer is that the absent good that we seek produces uneasiness, and it is this which immediately determines the will, not the prospect of future enjoyment.

Let us imagine a test case. Suppose we had the prospect of winning the hand of our sweetheart but had absolutely no uneasiness of mind. Would we still put ourselves out by buying flowers and seats to the theatre when we could have gone to the ball game with the boys? Locke would probably answer No. If we had no uneasiness of mind about the prospect of winning the girl, this would mean that we think we have her in the bag already and would give ourselves no further trouble. It is the uneasiness which goads us into action, although it is the specific tastes and vulnerability of the girl which tell us *what* to do.

The following questions are designed to help you test the thoroughness of your reading. Each question is to be answered by giving a page or pages of the reading assignment. Answers will will be found on page 383 of this Reading Plan.

1 Do most simple ideas have names?

2 What sense gives us the idea of solidity?

3 How are primary and secondary qualities produced in the mind?

4 Does Locke admit it is possible that the fetus in the womb acquires some simple ideas?

5 What features of our memories fade out first?

6 What is the difference, according to Locke, between idiots and madmen?

7 Why is the understanding like a dark room lit by only two windows?

8 Why were we endowed by our Maker with pain? What is its efficacy?

9 Do animals have abstract ideas, according to Locke? Are they machines?

10 Why are secondary qualities ordinarily taken for real qualities?

HARVEY

On the Motion of the Heart and Blood in Animals

Vol. 28, pp. 267-304

T he heart has always been seen as the source and touchstone of life, in ancient times and even in primitive societies. The life processes and the tempo and tenor of existence obviously depended on the pulsing of this central organ that never sleeps. In fear and passion the heart beats stronger and faster, whereas in periods of calm it is subdued and tranquil. Courage, generosity, and love—because the heart rate varies with emotions and perhaps also because it is stronger and slower in men than in women—were understood to be qualities of the heart. The waning of the heartbeat in dying men and its final cessation were regularly noted.

On innumerable occasions also—in battles, in the sacrifice of animals, and in the examination of entrails for auguries—the interiors of live animals were exposed to view. The pulsing of the heart and of the great vessels stemming from it could be observed, but it was one thing to look and see and a very different thing to know what was going on. Many of the best minds gave their attention to the subject, but two thousand years passed before the basic mechanics were clear. Hippocrates, Aristotle, Galen, Leonardo da Vinci, Fabricius of Aquapendente, Columbus Realdus, Servetus, Vesalius, and others in the sixteenth century made important contributions, but no one up to 1628, the date of the publication of *On the Motion of the Heart and Blood in Animals,* had grasped the principle of the circulation of the blood.

"The year 1628 [wrote Sir Zachary Cope] marks one of the great dates in the history of medicine for it indicates the birth of rational physiology. Harvey's discovery compelled an entirely new orientation in medicine and set a magnificent example of the correct method to be adopted in attempting further advances. More than anyone else, Harvey introduced the scientific spirit into medicine, and his influence was widely felt. It can hardly be an accident that, immediately after the time of Harvey there should have been so many medical men interested in science that they formed 22 out of the original 115 fellows of the Royal Society, which was formally started in 1660."[1]

However impressive Harvey's own discoveries, they were eclipsed by those he made possible.

[1] Louis Chauvois, *William Harvey: His Life and Times, His Discoveries, His Methods* (quoted from *Journal of the Franklin Institute,* Vol. 261, No. 1, Jan., 1956) (New York: Philosophical Library, Inc., 1957), p. 241.

Ninth Reading

I

William Harvey, born in Folkestone on the south coast of England in 1578, had parents wealthy enough to provide him with an excellent education. After routine instruction in the Latin and Greek languages at the grammar school at Canterbury, he entered Cambridge University at the age of sixteen, and there studied the classics, logic, and a little physics. Receiving his A.B. degree three years later, Harvey began his medical studies in Padua, which was one of the greatest medical centers in the world at the time.

In the previous century the great Vesalius had lectured in Padua and carried out his anatomical investigations, making an astounding number of discoveries before his scientific career was brought to an end at the age of twenty-nine. One of his bold observations, namely, that there are no pores to be found through which the blood could seep from the right to the left ventricle of the heart, cleared away a hallowed but obstructive belief and prepared the ground for Harvey's theory of the circulation of the blood.

By the time Harvey reached Padua, Galileo had given classical demonstration of the value of measurement and had fashioned a primitive thermometer and a "pulsimeter." Harvey listened to the lectures of the famous anatomist Fabricius, who had discovered, among many other things, the valves of the veins. But the function of these valves—to prevent the blood from flowing in any direction but toward the heart—completely escaped him. The real discovery of the valves was therefore left to his pupil, Harvey. Although in his work on the circulation of the blood Harvey was obliged to disagree with Fabricius at decisive points, in his later work *On Animal Generation* he was able to show his veneration for his old master.

Back in England in 1602, Harvey began to practice medicine, but he also applied himself assiduously to field studies, dissections, and experiments. He examined with great care the hearts of living animals of eighty species—birds and mammals, eels, shrimps, snails, frogs, newts, and fish. There are great differences in the heart rate of cold- and warm-blooded animals. The frog's heart beats only about twenty times a minute, but how could the heart of a mouse be studied when the beat is between five hundred and a thousand times a minute? Harvey confessed great difficulty in distinguishing the phases of the beat of the heart, for in many species everything happens in the same instant, or "like a flash of lightning." The rapid heart beat of birds and mammals, however, is slowed down when they are in their death throes, and observation becomes easier, as it is also in the case of cold-blooded animals.

First the auricles are seen to expand and become red, and then there is a phase in which they dwindle in size and turn pale while the ventricles expand and become brighter in color. The sequence was as plain as day to Harvey. How could the great physiologists of the past have said that the auricles and ventricles dilate and contract simultaneously? They also had observed the action of the heart repeatedly, slow-beating hearts as well as rapid. Could it be that these great authorities were all wrong and Harvey alone right? Caution and the fullest confirmation were called for here and at other points, and Harvey deferred publication of his discoveries for thirteen years.

We know that by 1615 Harvey had worked out the main features of his new theory of the circulation of the blood; in that year he gave a series of lectures at the College of Physicians in London, in which he expounded and defended it. Profiting by the criticism offered by learned anatomists and physicians, and becoming more convinced of his ideas, he finally, in 1628, published his *On the Motion of the Heart and Blood in Animals*.

The appearance of this volume, which laid the foundations of modern medicine, was greeted at first with incredulity, condemnation, and abuse. Parisiani, Primerose, and Plempius made vigorous attacks on the new theory but were later converted to it. The celebrated French anatomist Jean Riolan also took the offensive, and to him Harvey replied with his two *Disquisitions,* or letters (1649), in which he refuted the many objections that had been raised.

Descartes assigns to Harvey the credit of having been the first to teach that the course of the blood in the body "is just a perpetual circulation" (*Discourse on Method,* Vol. 31, p. 57c); on the other hand, he refused to accept the muscular action of the heart, holding fast to an old doctrine that the ventricles are expanded by a sudden vaporization of the blood. Eventually many authorities came around to Harvey's position, and within his lifetime he had the satisfaction of seeing his revolutionary theory generally approved. Some schools of medicine which still held out against it were lampooned, a few years after Harvey's death, by some of the greatest literary men of France—Molière, Boileau, La Fontaine, and Racine.

Harvey's connection with the Court of the Stuarts, which had been formed during the lifetime of James I, continued and grew stronger under Charles I. He was physician to the King, served him at home and abroad, and remained with him in Oxford in 1646, the year of his final defeat. Owing to his close association with the King, Harvey's house was plundered and valuable notes were stolen. Harvey nevertheless lived the last ten years of his life in studious retirement and, free from financial cares, was able to give himself to biological investigations. In 1651 his *Exercitationes de Generatione Animalium* appeared, a book that aroused none of the violent controversy that had attended his little volumes on the circulation of the blood. Full of honor, both at home and abroad, he died in 1657 at the age of eighty.

II

A glance at the headings of the chapters of Harvey's *On the Motion of the Heart and Blood in Animals* will show that he is concerned to refute the errors of his predecessors and to expound, demonstrate, and defend his own theory. It is best

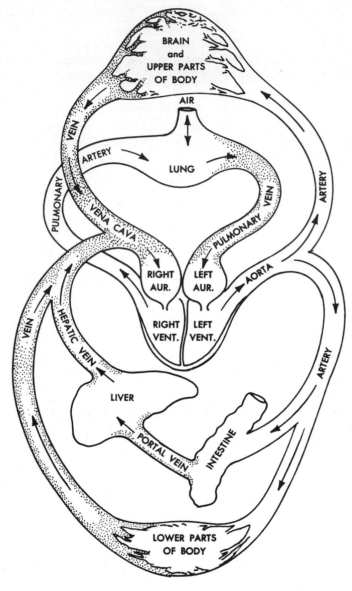

FIG. 1

Circulation of the blood according to Harvey

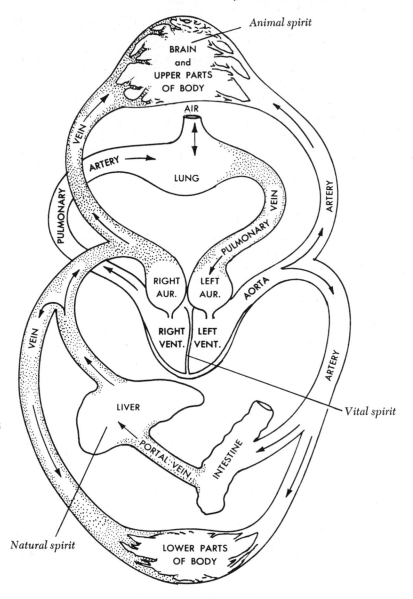

FIG. 2

Movement of the blood according to Galen

to focus first on the central, most original feature of his innovation, i.e., the *circulation* of the same blood (a) throughout the body, and (b) to the lungs, and back to the heart, where the whole process repeats itself.

In the diagram (Fig. 1) on page 160 we can trace the two circuits involved in the circulation of the blood, the systemic circuit, in which the blood is carried to the tissues throughout the body and back to the heart; and the pulmonary circuit, in which the blood is propelled to the lungs, where it is aerated and purified, and then back to the heart. Beginning with the left auricle of the heart, we can see that when this auricle contracts, the blood will be driven into the left ventricle. When the left ventricle is filled it will in turn contract, propelling the blood into the aorta and other tributary arteries which eventually branch out into tiny vessels supplying the tissues of the body. Other small vessels in the tissues now carry the impure or venous blood back through the veins to the right auricle of the heart. The right auricle, now being distended, contracts and sends the blood into the right ventricle, which in turn contracts, sending the blood along the pulmonary artery to the lungs, and from there it is returned via pulmonary veins to the left auricle.

It will be observed that the aorta divides, one branch supplying the lower parts of the body, the other the higher parts. Similarly one branch of the vena cava carries the venous blood back from the upper parts of the body. One branch of the aorta carries blood to the intestine, where nutriment is absorbed, and then to the liver, and finally, via the hepatic vein, back to the heart.

A diagram (Fig. 2) of the movement of the blood as Galen conceived it is shown on page 161. By comparing the two diagrams we shall be better able to understand the extent of the contribution that Harvey made.

According to the old theory of Galen, the blood flows through the arteries and the veins, but it does not *circulate*, i.e., it does not travel in a circle. The process rather starts in the liver, which receives, through the portal vein, foodstuff from the intestine in the form of "chyle." The liver transforms this chyle into blood and invests it with "natural spirit." Some of this blood then flows to the right ventricle and thence to the lungs, where it is freed from impurities, and thereupon moves back and forth in the arteries and veins in a manner likened to the ebb and flow of the tide, carrying nutriment to tissues and organs. Some of this blood oozes through the thick wall or septum dividing the right from the left ventricle, and is endowed with "vital spirit," the principle of life. It is this vital spirit in the blood, ebbing in the veins, which endows the organs of the body with their functions. The part of this superior blood which reaches the brain acquires the "animal spirit" which, transported by the nerves, initiates the higher functions such as sensation and reason.

There is no sign of a circuit in this development. The same blood does not get back to its starting point to repeat a circular motion. The blood is rather consumed in the process of giving nutriment and activating the functions of the body, and must be continually recreated in the liver to supply the loss.

Harvey combats this old theory with great energy, employing the quantitative method which his contemporary Galileo had just put to use in discovering the law of falling bodies. He argues that the blood which incessantly flows into the arteries is far greater in amount than could be supplied by the food we eat, and it is therefore necessary to suppose that the blood is not consumed by the body but returns to the point whence it set out. But how much blood does flow out into the arteries? Harvey reports that in a dead body he has found upward of two ounces remaining in the left ventricle.

If we assume that only two ounces are expelled into the aorta at every beat, then, since we know that the heart beats at least a thousand times in a half hour (and, in fact, even up to three thousand and four thousand times), we can conclude that in that short time 125 pounds of blood are expelled, "a larger quantity . . . than is contained in the whole body" (p. 286d). But even if the heart propelled only a tenth of this amount in half an hour, it is perfectly obvious that we do not eat enough food to furnish such a supply. A large part of the blood in the body—almost all—must circulate, i.e., must return to its source and make the same circuit again. What other explanation could there possibly be?

This argument sounds very conclusive, but Harvey is concerned to stop all possible loopholes. In the first place, it might be objected that some of the blood that the left ventricle pumps into the aorta regurgitates, i.e., eddies back into the ventricle. In this case less blood would flow out into the body than had been supposed. The answer to this is that the semilunar valves located at the mouths of the aorta and the pulmonary artery prevent the blood from regurgitating. When the ventricles contract the valves open; when the ventricles relax the valves are effectively closed. That the biscuspid and tricuspid valves guarding the entrances of the ventricles play the same role can be seen from the diagram (Fig. 3) on the opposite page. Harvey shows that even Galen concedes this at times, as when he says of the valves of the heart in general:

"That they have all a common use . . . and that it is to prevent regurgitation or backward motion . . ." (p. 284b)

Galen makes several admissions of this kind, although, as we have seen, they are contrary to his own theory of the ebb and flow of the blood. Harvey goes on to argue that if the valves did not effectively close and prevent regurgitation, the blood would dam up in the ventricles, and then in the auricles, and eventually the veins would become glutted and burst.

Harvey also considers the possibility that "the heart in contracting sometimes propels and sometimes does not propel, or at most propels but very little . . ." (p. 287a). If this should turn out to be the case, the amount of blood expelled by the heart in a given period of time need not be as great as had been calculated. Harvey's reply to this objection is that the amount of blood expelled by the ventricle is in proportion to its total capacity when dilated. He does not undertake to say just what the proportion is. For the purpose of the argument it could be a third, a sixth, or an eighth of its total capacity. What he insists on is that *if* one ounce only is ejected by one stroke of the heart and there are a thousand strokes in a half-hour, 62½ pounds will be ejected in this time. *If* two ounces are expelled by one stroke, then the total for a half-hour will be 125 pounds. The proportion, in general, remains the same. (See p. 287b.) The left ventricle, for example, does not expel two ounces at one stroke, and then nothing or very little the next few strokes, for in this event it could not hold the excess that would accumulate. Moreover, when the artery near the heart is perforated one can see a spurt of blood for every pulse of the heart.

Does this train of argument for the circulation of the blood seem to you conclusive at this point? Does it not presuppose a

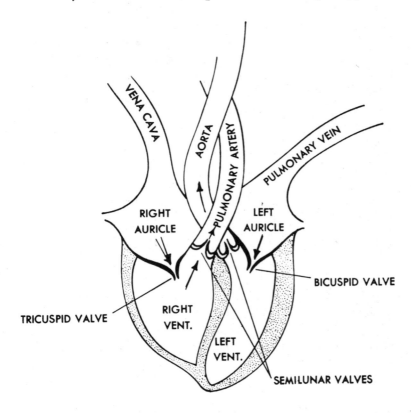

Fig. 3

The valves of the heart

regular one-way flow of the blood into the auricles of the heart, which has not yet been proved? If the blood is said to go out from the heart in two big circuits—to the organs and tissues of the body and to the lungs, could not objections be raised to the feasibility of the flow at any point in the two circuits? Harvey may have shown by his quantitative argument, which we have been discussing, that the blood, since it cannot renew itself in sufficient quantities, cannot do anything but circulate; but to establish his theory that it *does* circulate in a particular fashion, he is obliged to show that it is feasible at every sector of its course, and to answer objections.

III

It will help to understand Harvey's contributions if we briefly review some of the opinions of his predecessors. Every great discoverer stands on the shoulders of men who did not see so far, and would not otherwise be understood. Hippocrates, in his book *The Heart*,[2] described the chambers of that organ and the large vessels stemming from it with some accuracy. He noted the valves which lie between the auricles and the ventricles (the bicuspid and tricuspid valves), and those which lie between the ventricles and the arteries (the semilunar valves). (See *The Heart*, Ch. 10, p. 68.) It was not until Harvey, however, that their function was understood. "The father of medicine" also recognized the heart as a "powerful muscle," and described the movement of the blood to the lungs and back again to the heart. The function of the movement of the blood out into the body was to supply nourishment.

Other views of Hippocrates were popular down to the time of Harvey, but not beyond. For example, he regarded the heart not only as a pressure pump, but also as a suction pump. While it impels the blood into the blood vessels it also sucks in the air from the lungs, working like a bellows. The air has . the effect of cooling the blood, which has been heated or overheated by the heart. In the left ventricle, where the natural

[2] Richard Kapferer (ed.), *Die Werke des Hippokrates.* Die hippokratische Schriftensammlung in neuer deutscher Uebersetzung (Stuttgart-Leipzig, 1936), Part 16.

heat is said to be greatest, the blood becomes invisible. In support of this last contention was the fact that when an animal was sacrificed, no blood was to be found in this chamber of the heart.

Aristotle recognized that the heart is "the origin and fountain, or primary receptacle, of the blood" (Vol. 9, p. 193d), from which blood is supplied to the organs of the body. This must be so because elsewhere in the body blood is confined to blood vessels; only in the heart is it found outside the vessels. Moreover, "the vessels manifestly issue from [the heart] and do not go through it" (Vol. 9, p. 193c). This organ is also the first to be formed, as becomes clear from observation of the embryo, and "no sooner is it formed than it contains blood" (Vol. 9, p. 194a). It is through the flow of the blood from the heart that the organism receives all its nourishment, and from it the organs are formed. Hence the liver cannot be the source of the blood. The heart is well supplied with "sinews," and its beat is the direct cause of the pulse of the arteries.

Other Aristotelian ideas about the heart, though influential for centuries, were also opposed and finally overturned. The prime example is the view that the heart is the seat of the soul. Whereas Pythagoras and Plato had held that the brain was the organ of intelligence and the seat of the soul, Aristotle argued that sensation, movement, and the higher functions have their source in the heart. (See Vol. 9, p. 194a and c.) Even here Aristotle was not entirely on the wrong track, for the important role he assigned to the heart in fear and emotional states has been well confirmed.

Galen's views of the movement of the heart and blood have already been touched on. He held, as a general principle, that the organs of the body have a power or faculty of attracting the blood that they require, another faculty of retaining the blood a sufficient time for assimilation of its nutriment, as well as the faculty of assimilation. Such natural faculties seemed to exclude mechanical explanations of the action of the heart. If the organs naturally attract the blood that they require, what need would there be for a muscular heart which pumps it to them?

Galen, as we have seen, implemented the faculty of attraction by the theory that the heart and blood vessels alternately dilate and contract. (See Vol. 10, p. 213a.) The blood is drawn through the vena cava to the right side of the heart because it forms a vacuum as it dilates. Dilation is followed at once by contraction. When the heart contracts, most of the blood that has been sucked in is forced out again along the vena cava to the organs and tissues.

There is thus a constant ebb and flow of blood carrying nutriment to the body, and the blood is required to flow both ways in the vessels. The valves of the heart permit the blood to be sucked into its cavities but do not prevent some of it from running back into the blood vessels. The valves work, but imperfectly. There is thus a rhythmic flux and reflux of blood, from the vessels to the heart and then from the heart to the vessels again. It is important to recognize, Galen says, that "every thing possessing a large and appreciable cavity must, when it dilates, abstract matter from all its neighbours, and, when it contracts, must squeeze matter back into them" (Vol. 10, p. 213a-b). The principle involved is nature's "horror of the vacuum," and the heart acts like a bellows. Its action is not contraction but dilation, caused by the heat of the blood. It is active when it dilates and not when it contracts. That this would make it very different from other muscles, Galen was fully aware. But the heart, Galen says, differs from other muscles in this as in other respects. It is also involuntary and continually in action. Moreover, "the power of pulsation has its origin in the heart itself,"[3] so that when it is removed from the thorax it continues to beat for some time.

There is still another feature of Galen's system that Harvey had to overcome in establishing his own. This was the doctrine, already mentioned, that some of the blood sucked into the right ventricle finds its way through supposed pores in the septum (which divides the ventricles) into the left ventricle, where it is invested with vital spirit, and flows out to the body and its tissues, carrying with it this activating principle. Somehow the

---

[3] Galen, *On Anatomical Procedures*, trans. Charles Singer (New York: Oxford University Press, 1956), p. 184.

blood, in Galen's system, must get from the right side of the heart to the left. Otherwise it cannot perform its function. The trouble was that the pores were invisible and there was only the word of the master to prove that they were there at all.

So great was the authority of Galen, however, that it was not until the sixteenth century that an anatomist, Vesalius, dared to challenge their existence. Vesalius himself was at first very reluctant to take this bold step, for did it not mean a repudiation of Galen's whole theory of the movement of the blood? It was not quite as serious as this, for Galen had provided for other connections (anastomoses)—those between the veins and arteries. (See Vol. 10, pp. 213d-214c.) Through these connections some blood could have made its way from the right side of the heart to the left. The denial of the existence of the pores leading through the septum from the right to the left ventricle was, nevertheless, a great blow to the Galenic system, and prepared the ground for Harvey's epoch-making theory.

In other respects, however, the great Vesalius followed the physiology of Galen closely. He thought the heart was like a bundle of reeds, forming a pyramid, so that the sides can be made to bulge. The chambers of the heart accordingly dilate and the ventricles act like a cupping glass,[4] sucking in the blood.

Another stepping stone to Harvey's theory of circulation was the discovery of the valves in the veins by Fabricius of Aquapendente, Harvey's instructor in anatomy at the University of Padua. The book announcing this discovery—*On the Valves of the Veins*—appeared in 1600, while Harvey was a student at the University. Fabricius showed that the valves are so constructed as to permit the flow of blood toward the heart in all cases, but never away from it. He thereby provided a necessary link in Harvey's theory of circulation, but he himself remained faithful to Galen's thought, and he did not suspect the real function of the valves.

Still another link in the chain of Harvey's argument was re-

[4] The cupping glass was used to draw blood to a certain position of the skin by creating a partial vacuum.

inforced by Carlo Ruini, a Senator of Bologna. In a book published in 1598, he argued that there are two contractions of the heart; first the auricles contract, then the ventricles.[5] Harvey himself had often observed this sequence, especially in cold-blooded animals such as eels, squid, and fish bought in the market at Padua, for in them the pulse of the heart is much slower, and it is easy to distinguish the successive beats. In mammals and birds the beat is much faster, as has been pointed out, but even here it is possible to observe the sequence of beats when the animal is in its death throes and the beat is greatly retarded. This was an essential part of the story that Harvey was piecing together, for the auricles must contract first if the ventricles are to become engorged with blood and by their contraction impel it into the arteries.

We have considered a few of the ideas about the motion of the heart and blood which Harvey had to disprove to establish his own theory, and a few of the discoveries by his predecessors which fitted into his theory and served his purpose.

First, Harvey rejects the revered Galenic view that the arteries transport not only blood but air, which they suck in from the lungs. From one of Galen's own experiments it becomes evident that this cannot be so. The experiment, in Galen's words, is as follows: " 'If you include a portion of an artery between two ligatures, and slit it open lengthways, you will find nothing but blood'" (p. 270a). The two ligatures stop the movement in or out of the segment of artery, which becomes like a closed sack. When it is opened, " 'you will find nothing but blood,'" as Galen says. Harvey thus concludes that Galen has proved, against his own theory, "that the arteries contain blood only" (p. 270a).

Do you think that Harvey, by this *ad hominem* argument, has completely disproved the ancient theory that the arteries contain air as well as blood? Suppose Galen had made a mistake—had failed to detect the air emerging from the severed artery. Harvey, of course, had repeated Galen's experiment many times and obtained the same result. He had confirmed

---

[5] See Chauvois, *op cit.,* pp. 85-86.

also that only blood is to be found in the veins, and had discovered that the blood in the veins is not different from that in the arteries. But could Harvey be sure of this, having no means of chemical analysis and only a crude microscope at his disposal? This may be contended, but would not Harvey have been right in putting the burden of proof on those who maintain that the arteries contain air?

Another strand of Harvey's argument is as follows:

And how should seals, whales, dolphins, and other cetaceans, and fishes of every description, living in the depths of the sea, take in and emit air by the diastole and systole of their arteries through the infinite mass of waters? (p. 269b-c)

Would this particular argument of Harvey's stand up after the discovery of oxygen by Priestley (1774), the discovery of respiration by combustion by Lavoisier (1777), and the discovery of the chemical composition of water by Cavendish (1785)? Do you think the argument had a certain logical force at the time Harvey expressed it? Another question of logic about which there should be no mistake is that the discovery that an *argument for* a theory is wrong does not show that the theory itself is wrong. Could not some of Harvey's arguments be invalid without weakening his theory in the least?

The reader will have noted that Harvey has a whole battery of arguments on particular points of his theory, but these do not stand or fall alone. They derive some of their plausibility from the over-all conception into which they fit. How can the arteries inspire or draw in air from the lungs, he says, precisely when they are supposed to be filled with blood sucked in from the heart? They cannot suck in the air from the lungs in their diastole, their distended phase, because by this distention they are supposed to suck in the blood from the heart. Could they fill up with air and blood at the same instant? Nor can the arteries draw in the air during their systole—when they are in contraction—for when they are contracted they hold less and not more. (See p. 270b.) During their contraction they could not draw in blood either; their capacity is simply less than before. The argument thus runs as follows: (1) If air is drawn into the arteries, it must be during their diastole or their systole. (2) But it cannot be during either, and therefore (3) the air is not drawn into the arteries. Do you see anything wrong with this argument? If (1) and (2) are true, must (3) be true? Could you challenge (1) or (2)? You know, of course, that (3) could be true even though the argument were invalid. We have already seen that Galen himself found only blood in the arteries.

In Galen's theory the arteries draw in the air from the lungs and the blood from the heart, but how does the heart get its blood? It comes from the liver by way of the vena cava and is sucked into the right ventricle when this chamber distends, acting like a bellows. But Harvey denies

. . . that the heart by any dilatation or motion of its own, has the power of drawing the blood into the ventricles; for when it acts and becomes tense, the blood is expelled; when it relaxes and sinks together it receives the blood . . . (p. 275c)

The Galenic theory was that the beat of the heart is felt when the ventricles dilate: it is in their distention that they strike against the breast. This cannot be true, according to Harvey, for observation of the hearts of living animals shows that the beat is simultaneous with the contraction of the ventricles, not with their dilation. This was plain as day to Harvey, and could be seen most clearly in eels and other cold-blooded animals in which the heart rate is slow. It was obvious not only to the eye but also to the touch, for "the heart being grasped in the hand, it is felt to become harder during its action. Now this hardness proceeds from tension, precisely as when the forearm is grasped, its tendons are perceived to become tense and resilient when the fingers are moved" (p. 274c-d).

When the heart dilates (as in diastole), on the contrary, it is found to be soft, inert, and flaccid (see p. 274c); it is like a sack passively filled with blood.

The muscles of the heart, like other muscles, become tense when they contract, not when they relax; and the contraction (the systole) coincides with the expulsion of the blood, not with the filling up and repletion. The muscle fibers of the heart, described by Aristotle, also indicate that the action of the heart is contraction, not the bellowing out to suck in blood. "The true effect of every one of its fibres is to constringe the heart [ventricle] at the same time that they render it tense; and this rather with the effect of thickening and amplifying the walls and substance of the organ than enlarging its ventricles" (p. 275b). Galen and his followers have been misled. The effect of muscular action is to shorten and thicken the muscle fibers. On the contraction of the circular fibers, they become shorter, the cavities are constricted, and there is less and not more space for the blood. (See p. 275b.)

The strongest proof for the propulsive function of the heart, and against the bellows theory, is the result obtained when the aorta of a still living animal is punctured and a tube is inserted into the wound. The blood is then seen to spurt out with great force at every contraction of the ventricles. The closer the perforation is to the heart, as would be expected on Harvey's theory, the stronger is the gush of the blood.

IV

We have so far considered how Harvey's theory of the motion of the heart and the blood differs from those of his predecessors, and some of his main arguments for this theory. We shall now recapitulate the arguments already discussed and add a few others in order to assess his line of proof. We shall try to understand why his ideas so quickly triumphed over doctrines which had stood for fifteen hundred years.

(1) The blood must circulate, as we have seen, for the amount the heart pumps into the aorta is far greater than could be supplied by the food we eat.

(2) Various objections to this conclusion are answered. For example, blood ejected by the left ventricle into the aorta cannot flow back into the ventricle. It is prevented from regurgitating by the semilunar valve. Similarly, the bicuspid valve, between the left auricle and the left ventricle, prevents the blood in the latter from flowing back into the former. It can move only to the ventricle. And the same is true, analogously, of the right side of the heart. There too the semilunar valve at the

opening of the pulmonary artery, and the tricuspid valve between the two chambers, keep the blood flowing in one direction only, as is called for by Harvey's theory. (See Fig. 3.)

(3) Experiments show, as we have seen, that the arteries do not transport air as well as blood, but only blood. That air is conducted from the lungs to the heart by the pulmonary veins was a pivotal element in Galen's theory, and if Harvey did not eliminate it once and for all his own theory could not gain acceptance. He argues, in part, that Galen's own experiments show that no air is present in the arteries. Some of these experiments we have already discussed. Another might be mentioned: The lungs of a living dog are inflated and the trachea or windpipe tied to prevent the air from escaping. Under these circumstances we should certainly expect to find an abundance of air in the pulmonary veins and the left auricle, if Galen's theory were true; but in fact we find only blood. (See p. 272b-c.)

(4) Harvey calls attention also to some gross improbabilities. For example, he asks how it is that the huge pulmonary artery, on Galen's theory, has only one function, to supply the lungs; whereas the pulmonary vein has no fewer than three conflicting functions: (a) it conducts air from the lungs to the left ventricle; (b) it transports impure vapors in the opposite direction, from the heart to the lungs, and (c) it carries some blood endowed with vital spirit for the use of the lungs. (See p. 272a.) Moreover, if the pulmonary vein is designed to transport air, why is it constructed like a blood vessel? Why is it not firm and noncollapsible like the trachea? (See p. 272c.)

(5) The fact that in excitement or exercise the heart rate and rate of breathing both increase, Harvey says, does not mean that "the uses of the pulse and the respiration are the same" (p. 271a). For there are times when the one is fast and the other slow.

Does not Harvey, owing to the fact that the role of oxygen in respiration had not yet been discovered, miss something very important here? Is there not in fact a very basic relation between the amount of blood sent to the heart and the amount of air taken into the lungs?

(6) Another Galenic idea that had to be eliminated if Har-

vey's theory were to prove itself was that the pulse of the heart is extended to the arteries through their walls, so that it is really the walls of the arteries which pulse, and the blood only secondarily. This is disproved, Harvey claims, by the way the blood spurts when arteries are cut. It is thrown out periodically in strong jets, and the jets are simultaneous with the diastole of the arteries, i.e., the phase in which they are dilated, but never the systole. By which it is clear, Harvey says, "that the artery is dilated by the impulse of the blood; for of itself it would not throw the blood to such a distance" (p. 270d). Does this mean that if the walls of the arteries caused the vigorous jets of blood, these would have to occur when the arteries were contracted—when there was accordingly more pressure on the blood? Can you think of another experiment which might establish the same point?

(7) The old doctrine of pores leading through the thick wall, or septum, separating the right and left ventricles also had to be swept away. Harvey points out in argument with Vesalius that the pores are not to be seen and are most improbable. He might have added that they are also unnecessary. Even in Galen's system the blood can get from the right side of the heart to the left without their help.

(8) The relative thickness of the walls of the arteries and veins favors Harvey's theory. The walls of the arteries are much thicker than those of the veins because they must sustain the shock of impelling the blood. Hence, the nearer the heart the arteries are, the greater their difference from the veins. And since the impact of the blood is less in the pulmonary artery than in the aorta, it has a much thinner coat. (See pp. 303a-304c.)

But does not the pulmonary artery transport as much blood as the aorta? Should not its tunic or coat be just as thick and strong? The answer here would be that the blood, though no more in quantity, is pumped into the aorta with greater force, since it must travel a greater distance. Everywhere the thickness of the coat of vessels corresponds to the pressure they must withstand, if the blood circulates as Harvey claimed it does.

In the Galenic doctrine, the huge pulmonary artery can have

no other function than to supply the lungs with blood. Never plausible, this idea now becomes superfluous. This artery must be large. in Harvey's conception, because it carries even more blood than the aorta.

(9) We see now also why the right ventricle has a greater capacity than the left: it propels all the blood that the aorta does, but also an additional amount—that which supplies nutriment to the lungs. Yet the left ventricle is much stronger than the right, its muscular walls being, as Aristotle had noted, three times as thick. This is easy to understand (see p. 300a-b), for it must propel the blood throughout the body, from the top of the head to the soles of the feet. (See p. 301a.)

(10) To explain why organs get the quantity of blood they need, Galen resorted to his attractive faculty—the faculty of the organ to attract the blood it needs. Harvey, on the other hand, contended that the quantity of blood is determined by the size of the arteries supplying the organ. (See p. 297a.) Does this strike you as a better explanation? If so, why? But can Harvey account for the particular substances that a given organ extracts from the blood? Would something like Galen's attractive faculty be required here? Or do you think the explanation would lie in the field of organic chemistry, which in Harvey's time was still to be developed?

(11) Galen had noted that after the rest of the heart has ceased to beat and all movement has ceased, the right auricle continues to beat. (See pp. 276d-277a.) It is indeed "'the first to live, the last to die'" (p. 301d). Harvey confirmed this fact by close observation, and it fitted his theory beautifully. The right auricle *could not* die before the right ventricle, because the latter can beat only when the former is beating, and thus supplying it with blood. For the same reason the left side of the heart is dependent on the action of the right auricle; it too could not live without the pulse of this prime mover. The order of the chambers of the heart in dying is, in fact, as we should expect on Harvey's theory, the reverse of the order in which the blood streams through them, viz:

Flow of Blood: R. Auricle → R. Ventricle → L. Auricle → L. Ventricle

Order of Dying: L. Ventricle →L. Auricle → R. Ventricle →
R. Auricle

It will be noted that Harvey had independent proof of both
series. For example, on cutting a living heart on a line dividing
the right auricle from the right ventricle, the blood was seen
to gush from the opening of the auricle, not from that of the
ventricle. (See p. 277a.) On the other hand, observation of the
hearts of dying animals exhibited the order in which the chambers ceased to pulse. Does not the *independence* of the proof
of these two series add further support to Harvey's theory?
Why?

(12) Yet it is a fact, observed by Harvey and attested to by
modern physiology, that the two auricles beat in unison, followed by the simultaneous pulse of the two ventricles. This
simultaneity, of course, does not conflict with the order of the
flow of blood through the chambers of the heart. The two
auricles beat together and the blood embouches into the two
ventricles; then the two ventricles beat simultaneously, although the blood the one expels is destined for the lungs, that
of the other for tissues and organs of the body.

The finding that they beat in unison is in harmony with their
structural interconnection. Since the two chambers have a
thick muscular wall in common, would it not be difficult for
one to contract while the other is relaxing?

(13) The fact that the veins have valves whereas the arteries
do not is also in accord with Harvey's theory. The arteries do
not need valves, except at their mouths, because the contraction of the ventricle produces relatively high pressure in them,
thus preventing a backward flow of the blood; whereas in the
veins the pressure is lower, as would be expected, and the
valves are needed to keep the stream moving in the direction
of the heart. The evidence for this function of the valves of the
veins will be found in Chapter 8.

(14) Harvey is able to agree with Aristotle, and support his
own ideas as well, in maintaining that the heart is the arbiter
of life and death of the organism. A man afflicted with disease
always has a good chance of recovery unless the heart becomes
affected, but once the heart is smitten and chilled the whole

organism falls into decay. (See p. 296d.) Similarly, poisons can exist in the blood stream and be carried here and there in the body, but if they reach the heart, the infection passes into a critical stage, and the patient soon dies. (See p. 297b-d.) This is what would be expected if the blood is circulated by the continuous action of the heart, and the bodily organs depend from minute to minute on the nourishment it supplies.

These fourteen considerations supporting Harvey's theory of the circulation of the blood are not by any means all that he offers. Some readers may wish to sift the text to see how many more they can find.

V

How does the blood circulate in animals which have no lungs?

In fish, which have no lungs, Harvey explains, the heart consists of a single auricle and ventricle. The auricle, he says, "plainly throws the blood into the heart [ventricle], and the heart, in its turn, conspicuously transmits it by a pipe or artery . . . ; these are facts which are confirmed by simple ocular inspection, as well as by a division of the vessel, when the blood is seen to be projected by each pulsation of the heart [ventricle]" (p. 280d).

Since fish have no lungs, Harvey was led to believe that they have no pulmonary circuit but only a systemic circuit of the blood. The one ventricle, corresponding to the left ventricle in human beings, pumps the blood out into the body of the fish, whereupon it returns by way of the intestines and liver to the heart again. That is all. From the fact that fish have no lungs it seemed to follow that they have only a left heart (i.e., left auricle and left ventricle), and this appeared to be confirmed by observation, for when the large vessel leading from the ventricle is divided, "the blood is seen to be projected by each pulsation of the heart" (p. 280d).

Harvey reached the wrong conclusion only because certain things were not known at the time, viz: the function of the gills of fish, the role of oxygen in respiration, and the presence of oxygen in the water. His clear statement of a mistaken view called attention to the problems involved and helped later investigators to the right conclusion, which was that the fish has only a right heart (right auricle and right ventricle). The arterial circulation really begins at the gills, from which the oxygenated blood flows through the aorta to organs and tissues, and the heart serves merely to pump exhausted blood back to the gills.

Could one experiment alone prove the circulation of the blood?

We have already raised the question whether the mere quantity of blood discharged into the aorta every half-hour does not by itself prove the circulation of the blood. Could this be explained any other way? The question which we wish to raise now is whether one experiment could by itself establish this circuit—the arterial flow to the body and the corresponding return of the blood to the heart. Writers on scientific method have spoken of the possibility of a crucial experiment, i.e., an experiment which, if successful, would establish a hypothesis singlehanded. The experiment we have in mind is discussed in Chapter 10. In serpents, Harvey says,

. . . by tying the veins some way below the heart, you will perceive a space between the ligature and the heart speedily to become empty; so that, unless you would deny the evidence of your senses, you must needs admit the return of the blood to the heart.

. . . .

If, on the contrary, the artery instead of the vein be compressed or tied, you will observe the part between the obstacle and the heart, and the heart itself, to become inordinately distended, to assume a deep purple or even livid colour, and at length to be so much oppressed with blood that you will believe it about to be choked; but the obstacle removed, all things immediately return to their pristine state—the heart to its colour, size, stroke, &c. (p. 289a-b)

How account for the emptying of the vein when, and only when, it is tied? The only explanation possible seems to be that the blood normally runs through a vein to the heart but is now prevented by the ligature. That is, the cord that has been tied around the vein prevents the normal flow of blood to the heart. Similarly, what could be the reason for the abnormal distention of the ligatured artery and the heart itself except the simple and plausible one that Harvey gives? The function of the arteries is to conduct the blood into the body, but when the artery is tied the blood dams up in the segment of the artery and also in the heart.

This experiment might seem sufficient in itself to establish the circulation of the blood, but Harvey knew it was not, and he added many other supporting arguments. In the first place, it would have to be repeated using other species of animals and especially human beings. Moreover, the new theory could not win general assent until the circulation of the blood had been proved or rendered plausible at every sector of the two circuits. How, for example, does the blood get from the arterial system to the veins? As a matter of fact, Harvey was hard pressed at this point, for the magnifying glasses at his disposal were too weak for a close study of the capillaries. A moot question was how the blood could pass through the meshes of the lungs. No single experiment could establish the circulation of the blood, because what was needed was a mechanical model of the whole process, proved or plausible at every point.

A single experiment, however, might *disprove* an earlier theory of the movement of the blood. Thus a clear demonstration of the way in which the valves of the veins work would be sufficient to destroy the old doctrine of the ebb and flow of the blood in the veins.

How do changes of pressure affect the flow of blood through the chambers of the heart?

(1) When the auricular muscles contract, pressure in the auricles is increased.

(2) As a result, the flaps of the bicuspid and tricuspid valves (between the auricles and the ventricles) open up, and the blood can flow into the ventricles. (See Fig. 3.)

(3) The ventricular muscles are now excited, and their contraction raises the pressure in the ventricles above that in the auricles.

(4) The flaps of the valves just mentioned are thus closed, preventing the backward flow of the blood.

(5) The pressure in the ventricles is now also greater than the arterial pressure, and as a result the semilunar valves (between the ventricles and the arteries) open up, and the blood is expelled into the arteries.

(6) Pressure is consequently built up in the arteries, causing the semilunar valves to close, which prevents regurgitation of the blood into the ventricles.

(7) In the meantime, however, the auricular muscles are again excited, and the cycle repeats itself.

Harvey did not himself describe the role of changing pressures in the action of the heart, but he was close to doing so. Interest in the relation of volume and pressure was much aroused, and Robert Boyle was soon to discover his famous law of gases that, at a given temperature, volume, and pressure, have a constant inverse relation, the increase in one causing a proportionate decrease in the other, and vice versa. Harvey, who made so many discoveries, was often on the verge of making more, and often held the light for his successors.

The following questions are designed to help you test the thoroughness of your reading. Each question is to be answered by giving a page or pages of the reading assignment. Answers will be found on page 384 of this Reading Plan.

1 Did Harvey believe that others might be more successful in their inquiries about the heart than he had been?

2 Did he deny that seals, whales, and dolphins absorb air from the water?

3 Does the heart, according to Harvey, become hard, erect, and smaller during its contraction?

4 How did Harvey explain the fact that when the hearts of eels are taken out of the body, the ventricle can be seen to beat without the auricle?

5 Do all animals having a heart also have an auricle, according to Harvey? And if they have two ventricles, do they have two auricles as well? Is the converse true?

6 In what respect is the heart's delivery of blood to the arteries like a horse drinking water?

7 How is the action of the heart like the chain reaction in firearms?

8 How is it comparable to deglutition, or the process of swallowing?

9 When the windpipe and an artery are divided, very different things happen. What ancient theory is rendered improbable by this result?

182

DARWIN

The Origin of Species

Ch. 3-4

Vol. 49, pp. 32-64, 152-153

Only a few times in history has the work of one man upset the foundations of a science and changed the whole direction and velocity of its development. In the seventeenth century Newton, aided by the discoveries of Galileo and Kepler, applied mathematical knowledge to all motion, and in the nineteenth century Darwin put forward his revolutionary theories in the biological sciences, supporting them with a massive accumulation of facts and arguing on their behalf with great persistence, skill, and personal disinterestedness.

The influence of Darwin was perhaps as profound as that of Newton, yet it was very different in quality. Newton's main discoveries became the firm, unchallenged foundation of the physical sciences, which even Einstein's revolutionary Theory of General Relativity, in the twentieth century, left practically intact. Darwin's theory of the origin of species, and especially of *Homo sapiens,* on the other hand, has been subject to continuous attack not only by theologians and moralists but also by biologists of various schools and methods. There is still much dispute as to how far Darwin was right. There is no question about the immensity of his contribution to knowledge.

The theory of organic evolution—the theory that all present-day species have evolved from simpler forms—was not original with Darwin, but it was Darwin who first demonstrated it and convinced the scientific world. Biologists now accept organic evolution as a fact. It is the question of *how* species evolve which is still disputed and which has sparked investigations continuously for the past hundred years, ever since the publication of *The Origin of Species* in 1859. The theory of natural selection put forward in this famous book has had to be modified in the light of advancing knowledge, yet the surprising thing is how much of it modern Darwinists, such as Julian Huxley, J. B. S. Haldane, and T. H. Morgan, have been able to retain. All modern biologists are, in great measure, Darwinists.

For all its breadth and power, Darwin's idea of natural selection would have had little impact without his vast accumulation of facts to support it. Given this support, the idea had consequences far beyond the biological sciences and geology, to which it gave a new outlook and direction, extending to psychology, anthropology, sociology, history, philosophy, and even to the thought ways of the man on the street. Every aspect of life was now seen to be in flux and development, and the question of antecedent causes and outcome of phenomena became focal. The progress of the experimental method was greatly accelerated.

Tenth Reading

I

The childhood of Charles Darwin gave no hint of his later renown as a naturalist, and it seemed more likely that he would settle down as a doctor or a country clergyman or become an idle sportsman. Born at Shrewsbury, England, in 1809, he received the customary English education, devoted chiefly to classical languages, in which he took little interest. In 1825 his father, a physician, sent him to Edinburgh to study medicine. It turned out, however, that Darwin had no taste for the instruction offered at Edinburgh, nor for the medical profession, and broke off his studies three years later, before receiving the training in anatomy which would have been a boon to him in his life work—a fact which he never ceased to regret. His father, "properly vehement against my turning into an idle sporting man," as he relates in his autobiography, proposed that he become a clergyman.

Young Darwin felt no objection on doctrinal grounds, and soon began his studies at Christ's College, Cambridge. Although he took his A.B. in 1831, with a respectable if not distinguished standing, he confesses that most of his time at Cambridge was deplorably wasted at hunting and sport and in frivolous company. Perhaps he exaggerated. He did receive basic training in geology under Adam Sedgwick and accompanied him on instructive field trips, listened to lectures on botany, and made his own collections of beetles and other animals and plants. It is notable too that so young a man should have gained the friendship of scientific men such as Henslow, Grant, MacGillivray, and Sedgwick himself.

In preparing for the ministry, Darwin had committed to memory Paley's demonstration of the existence of God from the purposiveness displayed throughout nature, and had greatly admired the logical force of Paley's argument. In the career into which he was now to enter he gathered impressive evidence that the appearance of purposiveness in the world could be otherwise explained, and his early faith was gradually and reluctantly transformed into agnosticism—the view that God may or may not exist. Suddenly, in 1831, he was offered a post as naturalist on the government ship *Beagle,* bound on a surveying expedition. He spent the next five years investigating geological formations, fossil remains, and endless varieties of plant and animal life. The voyage took him to various islands in the Atlantic, to the coasts of South America where a number of expeditions were carried out, to New Zealand, Australia, Tahiti, Tasmania, and many other islands from which he assembled a rich store of notes and deductions. He later wrote:

> The voyage of the *Beagle* has been by far the most important event in my life, and has determined my whole career . . . I have always felt that I owe to the voyage the first real training or education of my mind; I was led to attend closely to several branches of natural history, and thus my powers of observation were improved, though they were always fairly developed.[1]

Whereas Darwin set off on the voyage a firm believer in the immutability of species, he returned with his general theory of natural selection pretty well established in his mind, though as yet many things were unclear.

Back in England Darwin saw a great deal of Sir Charles Lyell, the famous geologist whose *Principles of Geology* had been his constant companion on the *Beagle.* He continued his investigations of the record of the variations of plant and animal life, and gave especial attention to variations of domestic species. In 1838 he read Malthus on *Population,* which argued that since population increases at a geometrical rate and the food supply only at an arithmetical rate, population is bound to exceed available food resources. He was greatly impressed. "Here then," he said, "I had at last a theory by which to work." His notebook of 1837, however, shows clearly that he owed to

[1] Francis Darwin (ed.), *The Life and Letters of Charles Darwin* (New York: D. Appleton & Company, 1898), Vol. I, pp. 51-52.

Malthus not the idea of natural selection but only an unexpected confirmation of it.

Marrying his cousin Emma Wedgwood in 1839, Darwin remained in London until 1842 and then settled down to live and work in Down for the rest of his life. In 1858, while composing a large volume setting forth his new theory of natural selection, he received a manuscript from a young scientist, A. R. Wallace, expounding in effect the same theory. Darwin immediately put his predicament in the hands of his friends Lyell and the botanist Hooker, and the result was that Darwin and Wallace sent a joint communication to the *Linnean Society Journal,* sharing the honors of the discovery amicably and with great mutual esteem. In the following year Darwin's *Origin of Species* appeared. So great was the anticipation that the whole edition was sold out on the first day.

I I

The struggle for existence throughout nature will be admitted by everyone, but not always remembered. People are surprised that animal forms that once ruled the earth, such as the monstrous reptiles called dinosaurs, should have become extinct, and invent catastrophes to explain their disappearance. Because the surface of nature remains calm, it is forgotten that the life-and-death struggle is incessant and that the balance of forces is often so delicate that it is touch-and-go which individual, which variety, which species or genus will succumb and which survive. The slightest change in climate or in the populations of other species sometimes makes all the difference. The very size and strength which renders one group dominant over other animal forms may intensify the intragroup conflict for the limited supplies of food. Darwin remarked:

Nothing is easier than to admit in words the truth of the universal struggle for life, or more difficult—at least I have found it so—than constantly to bear this conclusion in mind. Yet unless it be thoroughly engrained in the mind, the whole economy of nature, with every fact on distribution, rarity, abundance, extinction, and variation, will be dimly seen or quite misunderstood. We behold the face of nature bright with gladness, we often see superabundance of food; we do not see or we forget, that the birds which are idly singing round us mostly live on insects or seeds, and are thus constantly destroying life; or we forget how largely these songsters, or their eggs, or their nestlings, are destroyed by birds and beasts of prey; we do not always bear in mind, that, though food may be now superabundant, it is not so at all seasons of each recurring year. (p. 32d)

Even where the land is very poor and the yield of food meager, there are still a few species which compete among themselves and with other groups for survival. "Not until we reach the extreme confines of life, in the Arctic regions or on the borders of an utter desert, will competition cease" (pp. 38d-39a). Geographical isolation of a species, or exceptional adaptive ability, such as that of the beaver, may greatly reduce the competition with other groups but not that among members of the species itself.

The universal struggle for existence is a matter of observation, but it can also be deduced. Even where we do not know the specific checks to population increase, we know that they must exist. We can infer that most of the progeny of a species succumb to the life-and-death struggle for food and with the inimical forms of life which surround them. We can infer this because, as Darwin explains:

There is no exception to the rule that every organic being naturally increases at so high a rate, that, if not destroyed, the earth would soon be covered by the progeny of a single pair. (p. 33c)

This is true even of slow-breeding man; in less than a thousand years there would not be standing room on the earth. Fish, which lay thousands or millions of eggs, if not devoured or destroyed, would soon fill up the ocean. The only difference between the slow breeders and the fast breeders, Darwin tells us, is that it would take the latter a shorter time to glut the whole world.

The British clergyman and economist Malthus had startled the world in 1798 by his theory that poverty and distress are inevitable, since human population increases in a geometric ratio, whereas the means of subsistence increases only in an arithmetic ratio. Thus population, he said, tends to expand in a geometrical proportion 1, 2, 4, 8, 16, 32, 64 . . . , whereas the means of subsistence increase only at the rate 1, 2, 3, 4, 5, 6. . . . In subsequent statements of his theory, he dropped the idea that the population increases in geometric ratio, for it was obvious that the rate of increase is not always the same—is not always to be obtained by multiplying by 2 or any other fixed multiple. His point remained, however, that population, in view of "the sexual passion" and the limited yield of the soil, tends always to outrun subsistence, the only checks to increase being moral restraint, vice, and misery. The decisive factor he omitted was birth control, and population trends have not in general borne out his predictions. There is a world population problem today, but it lies in technically backward areas where medicine has curbed mortality but family limitation has not yet been adopted.

Man is the only species which can, and sometimes does, live within its means. In the world of plants and animals, where there is no question of voluntary control, population regularly outruns subsistence, and individuals devoured, starved, or crowded out usually far exceed those which manage to survive and reproduce. As to the universal tendency to overpopulation, all biologists agree, and it is a point clearly consistent with Darwin's "red in tooth and claw" naturalism rather than with divine providence. From it the struggle for existence at once follows, and here again there could be little disagreement.

But what are the factors which check the prodigality of nature? It is easy to see that rabbits and deer are destroyed in great numbers by wolves, men, and other predatory enemies, but Darwin warns us not to overestimate this factor. The real struggle for existence for these timid animals may be hidden. The most deadly enemies may be vermin and parasites. Predatory animals, while destroying individuals, may actually preserve the group. Wolves have recently been imported into remote islands of the Great Lakes to preserve the elk which, without this check on their natural increase, would soon completely exhaust their food supply and disappear. On the other hand, the kings of beasts, the lion in Africa and the elephant in India, which no other species dares to attack, are just as effectively curbed in other ways.

Weather is also a most important check on populations, but Darwin warns us not to overestimate this factor either. Cold may kill birds and heat wither plants, but very often change in the weather is only an indirect cause. Plants adapted to a temperate climate may survive the climatic change when transplanted to a warmer or a colder region, but cannot compete with other species which are better adapted to it.

That climate acts in main part indirectly by favouring other species, we clearly see in the prodigious number of plants which in our gardens can perfectly well endure our climate, but which never become naturalized, for they cannot compete with our native plants nor resist destruction by our native animals. (p. 35c)

In this connection Darwin call our attention to an interesting phenomenon. Where a rare species does exist, it frequently exists in one area in great numbers. Why should this be? The answer is that if a rare species were spread thin wherever it existed, it would most likely be wiped out by unfavorable climatic conditions, which occur periodically, whereas when it is numerous in a certain area, there is more chance for the sturdier specimens to survive. There is also more opportunity for intercrossing to occur, Darwin adds, producing a hardier race. (See p. 36a.) That the more numerous a plant is in a certain area, the greater in general its chance to survive drought, storm, extremes of heat and cold, etc., is pretty obvious. The increased hardihood and fertility produced by the intercrossing of plants, as contrasted with self-fertilization, is also a favorite theme of Darwin (see p. 47ff.), and subsequent studies bear him out.

The prodigality of nature, i.e., the tendency of all living forms to multiply far beyond subsistence, is clear and uncontested. The nature of the ensuing process, the struggle for existence, on the other hand, requires some discussion. Although the examples Darwin gives are usually of conflict where one organism survives only through the death of others, his definition of the *struggle for existence* includes cooperation as well as competition.

. . . I use this term in a large and metaphorical sense including dependence of one being on another, and including (which is more important) not only the life of the individual, but success in leaving progeny. (p. 33a)

He goes on to give examples of species which depend upon others without really struggling with them. Thus the mistletoe depends on the apple tree and a few other trees on which it lives, and on birds which disseminate its seeds. There are also numerous instances in which the dependence is to some degree mutual. For example:

Nearly all our orchidaceous[2] plants absolutely require the visits of insects to remove their pollen-masses and thus to fertilise them. I find from experiments that humble-bees are almost indispensable to the fertilisation of the heartsease (*Viola tricolor*), for other bees do not visit this flower. I have also found that the visits of bees are necessary for the fertilisation of some kinds of clover . . . (p. 37a)

It should be remembered, then, that for Darwin the struggle for existence includes dependence of one species on another. Yet this is certainly not his emphasis, and the casual reader can easily overlook this more benign aspect of the "struggle" altogether. In general Darwin depicts a ruthless warfare in which the more vigorous and fertile survive only through the extinction of numerous rivals—a conflict all the more intense and cruel when it is fraternal, i.e., between members of the same species or variety.

In 1888, six years after Darwin's death, the philosopher and anarchist Prince Kropotkin brought out his *Mutual Aid,* a book which challenged Darwin's "gladitorial" view of evolution and maintained that mutual aid and cooperation are the most important factors in survival. "Competition," he wrote, "is always injurious to the species," and combination and mutual aid give "the best guarantee of existence and progress." He gave numerous examples of mutual dependence and cooperation and thereby corrected the one-sided grimness of Darwin's portrayal. The reader will remember that highly successful insects such as ants and bees do combine and cooperate, though not of course with conscious intention; that many insects and plants are mutually dependent, and that many birds

[2] Of the family of orchids.

and mammals would perish without maternal care of helpless offspring, etc.

Although Kropotkin sometimes exaggerated, he did not mean to say that competition does not play a major part in natural selection, but only that cooperation plays an even greater role. Moreover, competition itself can benefit the whole group. When the living space of a species becomes too small for it, some members may adapt themselves to conditions elsewhere, with the result that the larger resources of nature are utilized and no one is the loser.

Many authorities now recognized the important place of what Kropotkin called "mutual aid" in the evolutionary process. A recent book by the anthropologist Ashley Montagu, *Darwin, Competition and Cooperation*, gives a good account of these developments. The judgment of two well-known zoologists will indicate the trend. Professor Warder C. Allee and his collaborators assert:

"We may thus summarize the section on Ecology and Evolution—and indeed the book as a whole—by repeating . . . : The probability of survival of individual living things, or of populations, increases with the degree with which they harmoniously adjust themselves to each other and their environment."[3]

Professor Marston Bates writes in the same vein:

"The basic theme in nature is cooperation rather than competition—a cooperation that has become so all-pervasive, so completely integrated, that it is difficult to untwine and follow out the separate strands."[4]

But what would Darwin have said of this emphasis on cooperation in the evolutionary process? We have seen that he assigned a certain role in evolution to the interdependence of species but did not give much weight to this factor. The reason may well have been that he regarded the cooperation *within* a species as a means of competing with other species

---

[3] Warder C. Allee and collaborators in *Principles of Animal Ecology,* as quoted by M. F. Ashley Montagu in *Darwin: Competition and Co-operation* (New York: Henry Schuman, Inc., 1952), p. 59.

[4] Marston Bates in *The Nature of Natural History,* as quoted in *ibid.,* p. 58.

the more successfully, and the cooperation between species as a way of obtaining subsistence which otherwise would be enjoyed by other species less successful in the struggle for existence. The tendency of all species to overproduce themselves and to far exceed their means of subsistence would remain the basic fact. The struggle was essentially competition for the means of survival, whereas cooperation was only one form that the competition could take.

I I I

The struggle for existence, Darwin argues, is most severe among individuals and varieties of the same species. (See pp. 38b-39d.) A species survives to a great extent through the elimination of its less well-adapted members and varieties. This weeding out of the unfit may result from predations or preemption of available food by other species, but also from conflict and pressure within the species. Sometimes, it is true, adaptations which favor the survival of the individual are hurtful to the species, as when the energies of the male are drained off in excessive ornament to stimulate the female, or in immense horns and antlers useful mainly against rival males. But Darwin assumed that adaptations advantageous for the individual tend to be so also for its species. This, in the light of present-day knowledge, seems reasonable.

The struggle for existence might still ensue if the members of a species were all alike, but there could be no natural selection, i.e., survival of the *fittest*. Evolution, in Darwin's view, is absolutely dependent on the existence of slight variations among the members of a species, for he held that advantageous variations in a species are sometimes inherited, so that new species are eventually formed, and that evolution is the result. There is no question about the existence of these slight variations. We all know that in a litter of puppies or kittens there are no two which are exactly alike, and this holds true even for pure breeds, where every effort has been made to eliminate variations. There is no dispute about the fact, but only about its causes, and its significance in evolution.

What were the causes of these variations, according to Darwin? If the parents are the same, why should not the offspring be identical? Darwin's answer is as follows:

We see indefinite variability in the endless slight peculiaities which distinguish the individuals of the same species, and which cannot be accounted for by inheritance from either parent or from some more remote ancestor. Even strongly marked differences occasionally appear in the young of the same litter, ad in seedlings from the same seed-capsule. At long intervals of time, out of millions of individuals reared in the same country and fed on nearly the same food, deviations of structure so strngly pronunced as to deserve to be called monstrosities arise; but monstrosities cannot be separated by any distinct line from slighter variations. All such changes of structure, whether extremely slight or strongly marked, which appear amongst many individuals living together, may be considered as the indefinite effects of the conditions of life on each individual organism, in nearly the same manner as the chill affects different men in an indefinite manner, according to their state of body or constitution, causing coughs or colds, rheumatism, or inflammation of various organs. (pp. 9d-10a)

Variability may also have an indirect cause: altered environmental conditions may affect the reproductive system, which is very sensitive to changes. Many plants and animals do not propagate themselves at all under confinement and, if they do, produce 'offspring somewhat unlike their parents" (p. 10b). But Darwin says this hardly ever occurs in a state of nature; unnatural conditions in which mating occurs would not help to explain variations in general, but only under domestication.

What then is the source of the individual differences which natural selection presupposes? Darwin acknowledged the occurrence of sports or mutations, but he regarded them as only strongly marked variations and believed that they occur rarely if ever in nature. There role in the formation of new species is, in any case, minor compared with that of slight variations. But could we not say that variations among the members of a species would be expected to occur when the species is dispersed over large areas where soil, climate, and the food supply differed markedly? The trouble with this proposal was that similar variations were also found in animals living under the same conditions.

That Darwin was himself dissatisfed with his account of the

origin of variations seems certain. Why else should he have fallen back on the explanation of his chief adversary, Lamarck? Under the title "Effect of Habit and of the Use or Disuse of Parts; Correlated Variation; Inheritance" (pp. 10-12), we find him arguing that the difference between the proportions of the bones in wild and domestic ducks is due to the fact that the latter fly less and walk more than their wild parents do. The effects of use also account for the large udders of domestic cows and goats found only in countries where they are regularly milked.

Everyone admits that animals are modified to some extent by the use and disuse of parts. Habitual disuse of an organ can lead to atrophy, as in paralysis, and the muscles of a wrestler may be greatly developed through long training. The only relevant question is whether changes of this kind can be passed on to the next generation. Only if they are inherited in some degree could they have any influence on the formation of new species. Lamarck had held that many generations of giraffes stretching their necks for leaves of high trees had gradually built in an inheritable trait of the species, and many biologists following Lamarck, the so-called neo-Lamarckians, made the inheritance of characters acquired through use and disuse the fundamental principle of evolution. Unfortunately for Lamarck's theory, the most careful investigations carried on for decades failed to prove that acquired characters are ever inherited.

This attempt to account for the appearance of slight variations in the members of a species must therefore be regarded as a failure. It was also inconsistent with Darwin's principle of natural selection, for this principle excluded purpose as an explanation of evolution, whereas Lamarck assumed that the will or striving of animals for certain ends produced the modifications which were then inherited, and that purpose was thus essential to the evolutionary process.

Since Darwin there have been vast developments in evolutionary theory, and especially in our knowledge of heredity, but has the particular problem of the origin of variations been resolved? Theodore Dobzhansky, a distinguished geneticist, remarks:

In a sense we are, then, in the same position in which Darwin was: The intimate nature of the hereditary variation is still unknown.[5]

Once hereditary variations have occurred, and are known to exist in a population, the modern geneticist can bring to bear various laws and a great accumulation of knowledge toward the explanation of what will ensue. But the causes of the original emergence of variations—whether slight or large-scale and abrupt, i.e., mutations—are still much of a mystery.

One distinction here is important. Variations are now known to be of two kinds, phenotypic and genotypic. Early in the century the Danish scientist W. L. Johannsen selected pure lines of beans and raised beans from the large, small, and intermediate bean seeds, expecting that the plants would yield a series of different norms of size. But instead of this, the *one* norm of size remained, with all the bean progeny clustered about it. The size of the bean had been merely phenotypic and not genotypic. As a result, the beans raised from the large seeds did not tend to be larger than those raised from small ones. The seeds differed phenotypically (in size) but had the same genotype—the same pattern of genes.

It is well known, on the other hand, that domestic varieties of plants and animals are easily produced by selective breeding. The fruits and vegetables we eat have been developed, from wild stocks, by selecting those qualities such as size, taste, and marketability which are desired. It is common knowledge also that racehorses, heavy draft horses such as the Percheron and Clydesdale, and all the many breeds of dogs have been gradually developed by mating animals with the desired qualities for successive generations. Starting off with a supply of rats used in psychological experiments, which are a relatively pure breed, it is possible by mating the smartest with the smartest, and the stupid with the stupid—as judged by the length of time it takes them to learn a maze run—to

[5] T. Dobzhansky, *Genetics and the Origin of Species* (New York: Columbia University Press, 1937), p. 119.

produce a bimodal distribution of the population. Most of the rats will fall into one of two modes or groupings—the smart and the stupid—whereas at the beginning most of the animals were intermediate—neither smart nor stupid. The first distribution of smart and stupid in the population could be represented by the curve

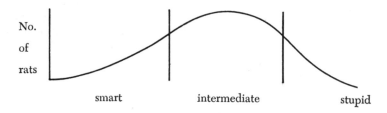

| smart | intermediate | stupid |

whereas the second distribution which results from selective breeding is shown in a bimodal curve

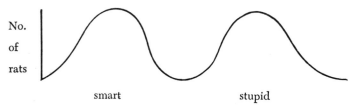

| smart | stupid |

"Darwin's works have had a profound influence on the breeding of domestic animals," says the Cambridge scientist John Hammond, "and his theories on selection still form the main basis for the improvement of livestock." Utilizing the small variations that crop up in domestic stocks, the kind that Darwin considered most important, animal breeders can accomplish far more than they can with sports or mutations. For one thing, although a bull calf born without horns could be useful, sports occur rarely and the deviations are not usually in a desired direction. "Darwin's dictum, that like begets like," Hammond continues, "is in general true for the commercial qualities of livestock, although there are many exceptions. . . ."[6]

[6] "Darwin and Animal Breeding" in *A Century of Darwin*, ed. S. A. Barnett (Cambridge, Mass.: Harvard University Press, 1958), p. 85.

What are the exceptions? We have already seen that characters observed in plants and animals may not be genotypical but only phenotypical, i.e., not represented in the genes of the organism which determine inheritance. Only genotypical characters are transmitted to the next generation, and the breeder does not know in advance whether a character is genotypical or only phenotypical. Thus, though Darwin's methods of producing varieties were usually successful, they were not always so. The clarification of the hereditary mechanism in recent times has not diminished Darwin's stature but has facilitated a better understanding of his contributions.

But how could Darwin have been so far right in practice when he was so far wrong in theory? He was wrong in accepting "blending inheritance," rather than the "particulate inheritance." This he understood in part from the work of Naudin, but it was only developed in all its plausibility by Mendel and his followers, of whose work Darwin knew nothing. Blending inheritance occurs when animals are crossed which possess some marked quantitative difference, as in weight, size, length of limbs, etc., with the result that in successive generations most of the progeny are intermediate between the parents. In Darwin's *Variation of Animals and Plants* (of which Chapter 1 of the *Origin* is a condensation), there is a striking passage on blending inheritance:

When two commingled breeds exist at first in nearly equal numbers, the whole will sooner or later become intimately blended, but not so soon, both breeds being equally favoured in all respects, as might have been expected. The following calculation [White, "Regular Gradation in Man," p. 146] shows that this is the case: if a colony with an equal number of black and white men were founded, and we assume that they marry indiscriminately, are equally prolific, and that one in thirty annually dies and is born; then "in 65 years the number of blacks, whites, and mulattoes would be equal. In 91 years the whites would be 1-10th, the blacks 1-10th, and the mulattoes, or people of intermediate degrees of colour, 8-10ths of the whole number. In three centuries not 1-100th part of the whites would exist."[7]

In particulate inheritance, on the other hand, the results are very different. It will be remembered that when Mendel

[7] *The Variation of Animals and Plants Under Domestication* (London: John Murray, 1921), Vol. II, p. 64.

crossed smooth and wrinkled peas, the first filial generation was always smooth. A like result was obtained in other cases: the first generation invariably had the character of one of the parents. In the second filial generation the ratio was 3 to 1, i.e., three smooth to one wrinkled. When a second pair of characters, yellow and green, were selected, along with the first pair, the proportion in the second generation was as follows: 9 smooth yellow, 3 smooth green, 3 yellow wrinkled, and 1 wrinkled green. Such results are related in every biology textbook. What interests us here is that the genes determining the four characters remain distinct and unchanged by their combination. Even when they combine in complex clusters to form hybrids intermediate between the parent forms, the genes remain (relatively) discrete, separate, and unchanging. According to the theory of blending inheritance, on the contrary, the genes of the parents typically fuse in the hybrid to form a new gene, while the parent genes tend to disappear. This theory thus obviously favored the formation of new varieties and species, whereas the theory of particulate inheritance, which is now accepted by all authorities, explains the *stability* of species. But is it consistent with the *origin* of species?

Particulate inheritance is quite consistent with the origin of species, with Darwin's observations and experiments, and with the great practical success in breeding new varieties of plants and animals. Hybrids can be formed with characters intermediate between their parents, and desired qualities can be intensified in successive generations by selective breeding. Improved racehorses and milch cows can be evolved. But it comes about by the isolation and recombination of many genes, each having only a minor effect. Each of these genes can follow Mendel's laws, in accord with the particulate theory of inheritance, and yet their combination and recombination could account for the well-known facts of hybridization.

On another great issue about the importance of variations, Darwin seems to come out with flying colors. This is the issue as to whether slight variations or mutations are most important in the evolutionary process. The great geneticist H. J. Muller reaches the following conclusion:

As the century progressed, biological thought swung around to the opinion that however wrong Darwin may have been in certain details, he had been justified in his view that small changes are less apt to be detrimental to the organism and are the more likely mode of evolutionary change.[8]

IV

The problem now is how the struggle for existence can result in natural selection, or the survival of the fittest, and the formation of new species. It is undeniable that man can produce new varieties of plants and animals by selecting the parents through successive generations, but can nature do the job of selecting? Darwin shows that the slight variations formed in domestic breeds also occur in nature, but how can these variations in nature add up to new varieties or species as they do in the hands of the breeder? Darwin faces this question directly when he says:

Can it, then, be thought improbable, seeing that variations useful to man have undoubtedly occurred, that other variations useful in some way to each being in the great and complex battle of life, should occur in the course of many successive generations? If such do occur, can we doubt (remembering that many more individuals are born than can possibly survive) that individuals having any advantage, however slight, over others, would have the best chance of surviving and of procreating their kind? On the other hand, we may feel sure that any variation in the least degree injurious would be rigidly destroyed. This preservation of favourable individual differences and variations, and the destruction of those which are injurious, I have called Natural Selection, or the Survival of the Fittest. (p. 40b)

But let us ask ourselves how a slight variation could give an animal such a mortal edge over its fellows. Suppose, to borrow one of Darwin's examples, that the rabbit population in a region declined and the hares became more numerous. This would give the hounds with slightly longer legs and a trifle more speed a certain advantage, but would the advantage be sufficient to ensure their survival and that of their offspring—the necessary first step in the formation of a speedier race of hounds?

[8] Loren Eiseley, *Darwin's Century* (Garden City, N.Y.: Anchor Books, Doubleday & Company, Inc., 1962), p. 229.

Darwin's answer is that, given enough time—and nature has all the time in the world—even a very minor advantage would count. In the long run, the *probabilities* of survival would lie with animals possessing a favorable variation, however slight. Faster hounds would be more likely to live and reproduce. The tendency set in motion would have a natural limit, however. At a certain point, the asset would turn into a liability: the advantage of speed would be offset, for example, by the larger food requirements of the larger, speedier animal.

But would not slightly favorable characters in a species be eliminated by indiscriminate interbreeding with individuals not possessing them? It has been pointed out that nature sometimes imitates the breeder of animals by segregating favorable variations or mutations. Suppose that animals possessing some differential asset—in speed, size, strength, or whatnot—were to be cut off from most of the species by a flood, a landslide, or a glacier. In this case the favorable trait would be more apt to survive and need not be swamped by interbreeding. If it is objected that such segregation of favorable traits would seldom occur, the answer could be, as before, that nature has plenty of time and can afford to wait.

A more serious objection is that Darwin's "blending inheritance," which we have briefly discussed, implies that divergent types would eventually reduce to a uniform average, and all evolution would cease. If the hereditary traits of the parents blend in the offspring, forming a new pattern intermediate between the two, and the population interbreeds at random, would not all divergence in the species eventually disappear, leaving only a uniform neutral average of characters? This trend could be counteracted only if divergences or variations kept appearing in the species spontaneously. Only by this means could natural selection have anything to select. We have seen that Darwin wrestled with the problem of the origin of variations without ever reaching a satisfactory answer and that, as regards this particular question, even the most advanced biology and genetics of today have not done much better.

Darwin's phrase "the survival of the fittest," which he takes to be synonymous with natural selection, has occasioned much controversy. There are two main objections. First, it is claimed that "fittest" means physically, mentally, or morally superior. Darwin did sometimes talk as if this was what he meant, and he unquestionably believed that, in the long ascent from monocellular organisms to man, there had been much progress. What did he mean by "progress"? In the section of Chapter 4 "On the Degree to which Organisation tends to advance," he argues that there is a "gradual advancement of the organisation of the greater number of living beings throughout the world" (p. 60b). By this he meant that the trend of evolution is toward a greater division of physiological structure and function, a specialization of organs. There is, accordingly, greater sensitivity and more selective response. Could it be that there is also a tendency to lower mortality rates in the higher species, whereby the life and health of the individual, if not of the species itself, becomes more secure? Could this too be called progress?

But Darwin is far from denying that there are reverse trends or retrogression in the evolutionary process, and cites in particular organisms which adapt themselves by becoming parasites, with simplification of organization and loss of sensitivity, which is, of course, no longer needed. Thus, though Darwin readily admits that evolution *sometimes* involves a loss of organization and specialization, he rightly insists that, however numerous the examples may be, they are only exceptions to the general rule. But this is far from claiming that individuals who are "fittest" to survive are the most worthy, the most deserving of survival. It is true, however, that Darwin sometimes *suggests* such a view. Speaking of the ruthlessness of the struggle for existence, he remarks that

. . . we may console ourselves with the full belief, that . . . the vigorous, the healthy, and the happy survive and multiply. (p. 39c)

Some of his followers, the so-called Social Darwinists, who carried over the struggle for existence and the survival of the fittest from the biological world to human history, in a way that Darwin himself hardly endorsed, did not hesitate to interpret the *fittest* as the *best*. Dominant races and classes were on top because they had proved their superiority on the great testing ground of evolutionary competition. A good account of this cult, which flourished in the first decades of this century, is to be found in Richard P. Hofstadter's *Social Darwinism in America*.

Can there be any doubt that the Social Darwinists were wrong? Man has advanced through human history, but the progress has been neither evolutionary nor biological but social, technological, and cultural. The *prehistorical* progress of man and various forerunners of man is a different story. This we reserve for the next section. ·

The second objection to the "survival of the fittest" formula is that it is a mere truism. It can mean only that those which survive are those which survive. Is this very popular criticism valid? It is obvious at once that Darwin's phrase is not like *A is A*, for *A is A* could not be false, whereas "those which survive are the fittest" *could be* false if only the variations which plants and animals possess have no survival value. Darwin recognized that survival may depend on accident. Which members of a species die sometimes depends on which happen to stray into an arid region or are caught in a landslide or some other natural catastrophe. If death for the individual were *always* accidental, then Darwin's formula would be false; it is therefore not a tautology like *A is A*.

We have seen that fitness, according to Darwin, involves something more than survival, namely, increasing organization and specialization. But can "organization" and "specialization" be defined independently of "survival"? Does *all* increase of organization result in survival, or only *some kinds*? If so, can the latter be specified? This line of questioning may be reasonable; it often amounts to a demand that Darwin reveal the secret of natural selection at every conceivable turn, or confess that he is not saying anything at all. The phrase "survival of the fittest" is packed with meaning and implications which are being greatly extended as the details of the evolutionary process become better known.

One minimum meaning is as follows: the fittest are those

which have a relatively high probability of surviving after one, two, or (let us say) a hundred generations, and are thus capable of adapting themselves successfully to environmental changes. Army ants have a collective stability of organization which has enabled them to survive for thirty million years. Man, who adapts to nature by adapting nature to himself, has a very different sort of fitness. Both species survive because they can withstand environmental change better than their rivals can. The "survival of the fittest" formula thus points to the adaptive features of species in relation to environmental change as the key to evolution and to progress in evolution.

V

It will be remembered that Darwin not only put forward a theory of how new species arose (i.e., through natural selection involving the extinction of intermediate varieties) but also demonstrated for the first time the fact of organic evolution. Natural selection cannot be true unless evolution is, but evolution can be accepted even though natural selection is rejected. Let us pause for a moment to consider some of the evidence for the evolutionary theory. The most spectacular evidence comes from geology and embryology.

Readers of Chapter 10 of the *Origin*, "On the Imperfection of the Geological Record," will be surprised by the defensive tone that Darwin adopts, especially in view of the strength of the evidence that he is able to produce. The explanation is that, though supported in his contention by many facts, he had no support from the ablest geologists of the time and was waging an uphill battle. The data of the argument are of the utmost complexity, but the bare outline is easily understood. As deeper and deeper levels of geological strata are explored, fossil remains are found of (a) many extinct species (b) forming a rough continuity, though with many gaps, and (c) progressing in the order of time from simpler to more complex forms.

(a) The evidence for extinct species was not in question. In South America, during his voyage on the *Beagle*, Darwin had found fossils of a primitive horse, monstrous ungulates, and ground sloths, giant relatives of the armadillo, and other marsupial ancestors of the present-day opossum and porcupine, all long since extinct. Some of these extinct species were clearly ancestors of forms now living in South America but not found elsewhere, unless in Australia. This could be explained on the evolutionary theory if South American species had been cut off from other areas in a far-distant geological epoch and had developed in their own way, unmolested by the deadly carnivorous mammals which developed elsewhere. But how would the theory that each species came into being by a special creation account for this restriction of species and larger groupings to South America? Darwin asked himself a similar question when he found closely related species of finches confined to single islands in the Galápagos group. Had the Deity created special species for different islands? Questions of this kind helped to shake his original faith in creation.

(b and c) Darwin's accumulation of data exhibiting the continuity of plant and animal life is sometimes regarded as his greatest contribution to science. But Darwin himself was disturbed by the incompleteness of the record and thought his argument would be much stronger if only more facts were available, which turned out to be true. But to a great extent, he explained, the gaps in the record were to be expected. Why did species usually appear abruptly in the geological strata, without intermediate forms? What about the connecting links? Darwin gives a good general answer in Chapter 6, where he says:

As natural selection acts solely by the preservation of profitable modifications, each new form will tend . . . to take the place of, and finally to exterminate, its own less improved parent-form and other less favoured forms with which it comes into competition. Thus extinction and natural selection go hand in hand. Hence, if we look at each species as descended from some unknown form, both the parent and all the transitional varieties will generally have been exterminated. . . . (p. 80b-c)

Moreover, it is a mistake to think we must always find intermediate links between similar forms, such as, for example, the tapir and the horse. It is likely, Darwin said (see p. 152d), that they both descended from a common remote ancestor, and the

intermediates in the fossil remains would lie between this remote ancestor and the two descendants, not between the two
descendants themselves. In recent times, Darwin's surmise has
been substantiated by discovery of a number of these intermediates, and the common remote ancestor of the modern
horse and the ungulate tapir has been pretty well identified.

Darwin cited plenty of reasons for the incompleteness of
the fossil record. Only a very small part of the earth's surface
had been geologically explored at the time, and the specimens
representing extinct species were usually fragmentary and
broken. Moreover, unless a deposit of sediment is quickly laid
down over the shells and bones of animals, they rapidly decay
and are lost forever. Traces of animals having neither shells
nor bones are even more fragile and ephemeral. It was inevitable that the "phylogenetic tree," representing the elaboration of present-day species from the simplest ancestral forms,
should not be fully represented in the fossil record and that
many segments of trunk, branch, and twig should be missing.
Within a given geological formation one might expect to find
evidence of a gradual evolution of species, but in Darwin's
time this evidence had not yet been found nor confirmed.

Shortly after the first edition of the *Origin*, the fossil *Arch-
aeopteryx* was discovered, a fabulous reptilelike bird which
lived some 150 million years ago; it represented the link between reptiles and advanced birds. Other discoveries have
closed other gaps in vertebrate evolution from reptiles to mammals, and the record in general is now far more complete.
Darwin, relying on the fragmentary materials known at the
time, still had a strong argument. He was in a position, however, like that of the paleontologist who pieces together a few
fragments of broken bones, with large sections of plaster, into
a huge dinosaur. When a visitor to the museum asks him,
"What makes you think it was like this?" he replies, "Well,
given all the known facts, what else could it be?"

The fossil findings could not be completely explained by
Darwin. How could the evolutionary hypothesis account for
the sudden, abrupt appearance of whole groups of new species
in the same geological formation? Evolution was supposed to

be a gradual process. Darwin's answer was to deny the fact; there was nothing to support it but the failure *so far* to find earlier forms. There were other objections. How, for example, could evolution account for groups of allied species on the lowest fossiliferous strata, those of the Cambrian (now dated about 500 million years ago)? Here Darwin confessed he had no satisfactory answer. Was this not a serious deficiency of his theory? Numerous allied species appeared on the lowest strata in which there was evidence of any life. How could they have evolved? Here as in other cases Darwin relied on future discoveries. His confidence may be justified, for some evidence of life has been discovered in pre-Cambrian strata.

The great strength of the evolutionary hypothesis in Darwin's time was seen not only in its capacity to explain the fossils but also in the glaring incapacity of any other rival theory to explain them. The old theory that there had been a numerous series of creations and subsequent catastrophes which extinguished the earlier forms to make room for the new, more advanced forms about to be created, lost probability when it was realized how many—perhaps a million—creations and catastrophes would be required to explain the facts. The theory of successive creations, which had always had an *ad hoc* character, sinned more and more against the principle of parsimony (simplicity), which says: "Do not multiply entities beyond necessity." Its plausibility increasingly faded. Nor could it be supposed that God had embedded the fossils in geological strata to suggest to us a false theory of evolution and thereby test our faith!

Embryology, like geology, adds evidence for the evolutionary theory—the theory that present-day species derive from simpler forms of life remote in the past. The strength you assign to this evidence will depend on how plausible you find rival explanations. The basic fact to be explained is the tendency of the embryo, at different stages of its development, to resemble its ancestors, or rather, the embryos of these ancestors. The human embryo "recapitulates" in its development successive stages of phylogenetic development. Beginning as a single cell, it tends to assume a resemblance to ever more advanced forms. In particular it repeats or reflects the genealogical development of vertebrates. At one stage, for example, it shows distinctive features of fish—features, as Darwin insists, that are of no adaptive value to the embryo. Thus we cannot say that the appearance in the embryo of characters of ancestors is to be accounted for by its adaptation to its life in the womb. We must find some other explanation.

Before we mention Darwin's solution of this problem, it is important to reformulate it more accurately. It is not that the embryos of advanced forms tend to recapitulate the adult stages of their ancestors, but that they tend to recapitulate the embryonic development of their ancestors. The human embryo does not repeat stages of adult fish, reptiles, and amphibia; these may develop far beyond anything the human embryo shows. The resemblance is between the embryonic development of advanced forms and the embryonic development of successive ancestors. Thus the embryos of animals of one large class resemble one another closely, while the adult forms are widely different. It is for this reason, as Darwin remarks, that "in the eyes of most naturalists, the structure of the embryo is even more important for classification than that of the adult" (p. 224d).

As the embryo often shows us more or less plainly the structure of the less modified and ancient progenitor of the group, we can see why ancient and extinct forms so often resemble in their adult state the embryos of existing species of the same class.

. . . .

Thus, as it seems to me, the leading facts in embryology, which are second to none in importance, are explained on the principle of variations in the many descendants from some one ancient progenitor, having appeared at a not very early period of life, and having been inherited at a corresponding period. (p. 225a-b)

The embryo can therefore be looked upon "as a picture, more or less obscured, of the progenitor, either in its adult or larval state, of all the members of the same great class'" (p. 225b). But Darwin, you will note, does not make recapitulation a universal law, and in fact insists that there are broad exceptions.

The general tendency of the embryo to reflect the embryonic forms of its remote ancestors in genealogical order, and those of very different species within the same large group to which it belongs, is largely what we should expect if evolution linked these large groups together. No other scientific explanation whatever seems to be available.

V I

How does the diversification of a species help it to survive?

If a species has many varieties, some of them will be able to adapt to conditions in one area, and others to conditions in other areas. As Darwin says:

> . . . the more diversified the descendants from any one species become in structure, constitution, and habits, by so much will they be better enabled to seize on many and widely diversified places in the polity of nature, and so be enabled to increase in numbers. (p. 54a)

Thus carnivorous animals soon reach a limit to their natural rate of increase unless some varieties are able to adapt themselves to new conditions, to feed on new prey, or perhaps to vary their diet with vegetables. The same principle is known to hold for grasses and other plants. Darwin points out that in a small area where there is no barrier to immigration and the struggle for existence is very keen, a great diversity of life is always found.

But if diversification of structure, constitution, and habits within a species gives it such an advantage, how explain the survival of Australian marsupials, such as the kangaroo, which fall into groups differing little from one another? Darwin has suggested the answer above. Australia was cut off from other large land masses on which highly diversified carnivorous mammals developed. Marsupials survived because they did not have to contend with these very successful carnivores.

Is the advantage of diversification within a species like that of the division of labor in the organs of a single body? Darwin says it is, and argues that a stomach adapted to digest meat only, or vegetables only, will absorb more of the nutriment from these substances than a stomach adapted to digest both. (See p. 55a.) Such specialized digestive organs may well be more efficient, but does this imply that animals able to live on meat alone, or vegetables alone, would have an advantage over those which are able to subsist on both? Is it not reasonable to suppose that many of the most successful mammals, including man, have been greatly aided in the competitive struggle by their ability to vary their diet? What would have happened to the American Plains Indian if he had had to depend entirely on game and could not fall back on his corn or other vegetable matter?

It appears that diversity of organs in the individual body does not always have survival value. Another example is furnished by the persistence for many epochs of some of the simplest organisms.

Is the persistence of many of the lowest forms of life consistent with natural selection?

It is perfectly consistent, according to Darwin, because natural selection does not imply that all forms of life continually advance in organization and specialization: ". . . it only takes advantage of such variations as arise and are beneficial to each creature under its complex relations of life. And it may be asked what advantage . . . would it be to an infusorian animalcule—to an intestinal worm—or even to an earthworm, to be highly organised" (p. 61a). It would be no advantage to them, and geology tells us that infusoria (protozoa and minute metazoic forms), which have a "really wondrous and beautiful organisation," have persisted for immense periods of time— perhaps 500 million years—up to the present.

The longevity of lower species may be due to their "beautiful organisation," or to the lack of competition from higher forms. Fish, which came into existence some 400 million years ago (in modern reckoning), were not jeopardized by the development of mammals, for the two groups scarcely ever come into competition. In general, the newer development in evolution lives by the death of its ancestor, but there are broad areas in which, by virtue of superior organization, isolation, or lack of competition, the older forms exist concurrently with the new orders.

Must we not conclude, then, that over a great part of the organic world for immense stretches of time no evolution takes place, and natural selection is at a standstill? And in the same great areas must we not conclude that it is not higher organization—greater differentiation and specialization—which enables groups to survive, but rather low organization which is somehow "beautiful"? Is this beautiful organization merely one that works? Or is Darwin able to describe structures and functions which account for "perfect" organization? Is what Darwin says about "retrogression of organization" (see pp. 60d-61d) relevant here?

Is sexual selection different from natural selection? How does it work?

Darwin describes sexual selection as a *form of selection*. This form of selection depends not on a struggle for existence in relation to other organic beings or to external conditions but on the struggle between the individuals of one sex, generally the males, for the possession of the other sex. The result to the unsuccessful competitor is not death but few or no offspring. (See p. 43d.) Sexual selection is thus conceived as a form of natural selection in which a contest decides which animal is to mate, or mate most often, or to mate with the most fertile animals. The contest is usually between the males for the females and usually is not fatal, and the more vigorous or the better-armed of the males are those which will probably have the most offspring.

But the question arises whether the males which are successful in winning the contest for mates are also the most fertile and the best adapted in other aspects. Might not the very size and strength, the especially large horns or antlers, etc., of the successful males militate against their survival? Might not the increased size and the emphasis on offensive and defensive weapons employed in intraspecies conflict prove costly handicaps to the species? Was this not one of the reasons for the disappearance of the dinosaurs and other monstrous reptiles of the Cretaceous Period? What favors the survival of the strongest and most redoubtable individual and his progeny need not favor the survival of the species, the genus, or the family. The group itself may simply exhaust its food supply.

Sexual selection takes two forms. The male of the red deer corrals a harem of hinds and fights off other males who dare approach, and the hinds of course have no choice in the matter. In other cases Darwin believed that female choice or preference determines which male gets a mate and reproduces his kind. Thus male birds of paradise and peacocks display their finery before the females, who seem to make a choice, presumably of the male with the most gorgeous plumage. He states that

. . . if man can in a short time give beauty and an elegant carriage to his bantams, according to his standard of beauty, I can see no good reason to doubt that female birds, by selecting, during thousands of generations, the most melodious or beautiful males, according to their standard of beauty, might produce a marked effect. (p. 44b; see also pp. 95c-97a)

It is not necessary to assume that female birds make a choice according to their standards of beauty—an assumption that could not be confirmed, in any case. There are other ways of explaining the female behavior. It is now known, for example, that the colorful plumage on the male may be necessary to stimulate sexual activity in the female or to warn off rival males, and the same is true of the melodious song. The display of the male may serve as a signal which "releases" instinctive activity in the female, but only at a particular point in her development, and the peculiarities of the male to whom she succumbs need not play any part. Another effect of display or strong markings is to distinguish one species from another related one. Since a female who mates with a male of another species is not likely to have progeny, or at least not fertile ones, such discrimination of species mates is favored, in natural selection.

In some species, however, male and female are much alike. What is to prevent the male from attacking an approaching female by mistake? Sometimes pacific postures are assumed or signals given by the female, and there may even be a court-ship dance or ritual, but there is no evidence of female choice except in the sense of responding to stimulation, or to the strongest stimulation.

The effects of sexual selection are seen mostly in polygamous animals, as would be expected, and these are usually herbiv-orous; indeed the sexes in the great carnivores are much alike. The subject of sexual selection has been developed in many directions, but the framework that Darwin built remains mostly intact. Darwin attempted to explain the beauty of plants and animals, but also the exquisite perfection of com-plex organs such as the eye, the first by sexual selection, the second by natural selection.

How can the eye have arisen by accidental variations and natural selection?

Darwin admits that this puts a strain on his theory:

To suppose that the eye with all its inimitable contrivances for adjusting the focus to different distances, for admitting different amounts of light, and for the correction of spherical and chromatic aberration, could have been formed by natural selection, seems, I freely confess, absurd in the highest degree. (p 85d)

He nevertheless goes about courageously to trace the most advanced eyes, found in monkeys and men, in birds and cer-tain insects, back to the simplest photochemical cells, and to argue that, in the long run and given plenty of competition, even a very slight improvement in visual sensitivity will tend to be preserved. The earliest eye is simply an optic nerve ter-minating in cells sensitive to light, but with no lens or other means of refracting the light. We have all heard of animals which are phototropic (i.e., move toward the light) or nega-tively phototropic (i.e., move away from the light) but are incapable of forming any image. Perhaps the development of a lens which first permitted an image of the world to appear could be regarded as the greatest mystery. How could the lens gradually emerge by preservation of slight variations tending in this direction?

Could we say that light-dark sensitivity is gradually refined to the point where the animal can discriminate the form of an approaching object from its background? Would this not reduce some of the mystery to a mere quantitative increase of sensitivity? And would not even a slight improvement of this kind give the individual and its offspring a selective advantage? We still should not have a lens, but only an approach to it. The lens itself, Darwin suggests, might well arise, as in certain starfish, from a gelatinous substance at the end of the optic nerve, forming a convex surface, as in the cornea[9] of higher animals. The effect of the convexity is to concentrate the rays of light, and this, Darwin says, is "the most important step towards the formation of a true, picture-forming eye; for we have only to place the naked extremity of the optic nerve . . . at the right distance from the concentrating apparatus, and an image will be formed on it" (p. 86b).

What alternatives are there to Darwin's theory of natural selection? The creation theory is not open to scientific verification and, moreover, seems to make God responsible not only for the perfection of the eye but also for the endless cruelty and blundering waste of the struggle for existence. Another alternative is called "orthogenesis," the theory that there are certain trends of development inherent in what is inherited. Thus it has been held that there is a persistent trend toward the perfection of the eye, not only in the mammals, culminating in the primates and man, but also in completely unrelated groups, such as birds and insects. These parallel developments cannot be accounted for by natural selection but only by an inherent, underlying tendency. Unfortunately such a tendency is difficult to confirm and does not lend itself to experiment. Orthogenesis is now rapidly losing ground to Darwinism, or rather to neo-Darwinism, which is Darwinism implemented by the science of genetics.

[9] The outer covering of the eye.

The following questions are designed to help you test the thoroughness of your reading. Each question is to be answered by giving a page or pages of the reading assignment. Answers will be found on page 384 of this Reading Plan.

1 Does natural selection cause, or merely presuppose, variations within a species?

2 Do newly formed varieties in nature tend at first to remain in one locality? Does this help them to survive?

3 Is the separation of the sexes in some plants, such as the holly in North America, still in progress?

4 Is it true, according to Darwin, that *no* organic being fertilizes itself indefinitely without crossing with other individuals?

5 What interesting result followed when several varieties of cabbage, radish, and onion were allowed to seed in close proximity?

6 How does Darwin explain this result? Is it in line with one of his main contentions? If so, which?

7 Why do intermediate forms between two dominant varieties or species tend to disappear?

DARWIN

The Descent of Man

Ch. 1-4

Vol. 49, pp. 255-319

In *The Origin of Species* (1859), Darwin refrained from drawing the natural conclusion that man, like other species, has descended from simpler, less highly organized forms of life. "It would have been useless and injurious to the success of the book," he later explained in his autobiography, "to have paraded, without giving any evidence, my conviction with respect to his origin."[1] But lest he should be accused of concealing his views, he did add that by that work "light would be thrown on the origin of man and his history." As early as 1838, he had been persuaded that man was a product of evolution and had begun collecting facts bearing on the subject at that time. The appearance of the *Origin*, however, had been attended

---

[1] Francis Darwin (ed.), *The Life and Letters of Charles Darwin* (New York: D. Appleton & Company, 1898), Vol. I, p. 76.

with such heated and often rancorous controversy that he thought it wise to delay publication of this even more provocative book until the outcry had somewhat subsided and the dust settled. But when it became clear that many distinguished scientists had already accepted the mutability of species, he decided to go to press. *The Descent of Man,* first published in 1871, had taken him three years to write.

The book was enormously successful and caught the imagination of scientists and laymen alike. More scientists were on Darwin's side now that the *Origin* had broken ground, but the opposition was still very strong. In England the theologians were up in arms, whereas in Germany natural selection was connected with socialism and the book was attacked on political grounds. Even the eminent biologist R. L. C. Virchow joined in this attack. Most of the assaults, however, came from theologians.

Darwin early decided, on Lyell's advice, to take no part in controversies, for they were destructive of both time and temper. Yet he was kind to individuals who wrote to him personally, and answered their objections patiently so far as his time permitted. His gentleness and modesty were acknowledged even by his adversaries. Although few men have accomplished as much in science, Darwin gave a very moderate estimate of his abilities:

I have no great quickness of apprehension or wit which is so remarkable in some clever men, for instance, [T. H.] Huxley. . . . My power to follow a long and purely abstract train of thought is very limited; and therefore I could never have succeeded with metaphysics or mathematics. My memory is extensive, yet hazy. . . .

. . . .

I have a fair share of invention, and of common sense or judgment, such as every fairly successful lawyer or doctor must have, but not, I believe, in any higher degree.

On the favourable side of the balance, I think that I am superior to the common run of men in noticing things which easily escape attention, and in observing them carefully. My industry has been nearly as great as it could have been in the observation and collection of facts. What is far more important, my love of natural science has been steady and ardent.[2]

This was written in 1881, a year before Darwin's death, and he was looking back on a long lifetime of concentrated work, pursued with great energy in spite of much ill health and the normal cares of a large family. Of his seven children, two girls and five boys, four of the latter became prominent scientists. His books included *Variation of Animals and Plants under Domestication, The Voyage of the Beagle, Geological Observations on the Volcanic Islands and parts of South America, The Expression of the Emotions in Man and Animals, The Formation of Vegetable Mould through the Action of Worms, The Fertilisation of Orchids, The Effects of Cross and Self Fertilisation in the Vegetable Kingdom,* and a number of others, but the *Origin* and the *Descent* contain much of the material of other volumes and give the best general statements of his theories.

The American paleontologist George Gaylord Simp-

[2] *Ibid.,* pp. 82-83.

son has given the following estimate of Darwin's achievement:

Darwin was one of history's towering geniuses and ranks with the greatest heroes of man's intellectual progress. He deserves this place first of all because he finally and definitely established evolution as a fact, no longer a speculation or an alternative hypothesis for scientific investigation. His second greatest achievement was correct identification of a major element in the rise of adaptation: natural selection.[3]

[3] Simpson, *The Meaning of Evolution* (New Haven: Yale University Press, 1949, p. 268.

Eleventh Reading

I

It is important to remember that Darwin himself denied that there is any *direct proof* of the origin of species, including *Homo sapiens*. The theory of natural selection is a theory; that is, it undertakes to explain a great variety of facts—the facts of artificial selection and geographical distribution of species, of the paleontological record and embryology, etc., and to explain them better than any other theory could. So vast was the array of facts Darwin attempted to account for that the reader can easily lose himself in the intricacies and forget the over-all argument.

The theory itself may well be true, though particular explanations can be found faulty or definitely wrong. Darwin's massive argument was like a glacier which, though it could be contained at this point or that, eventually buried the opposition. Had there been enough time for the slow process of natural selection of slight variations that Darwin's theory demanded? The greatest physicist of the nineteenth century, Lord Kelvin, said no, basing his answer on mathematical calculations of the dispersal of energy by the sun and the time involved in the cooling of the earth.

Fortunately for Darwin's theory, the discovery of radioactive energy gave a far longer life span to both sun and earth, enough for evolution as Darwin conceived it. It was not until the beginning of the twentieth century, when Mendel's laws of inheritance became known, and were confirmed and extended, that Darwinism was obliged to give ground and to adjust itself to genetics in a complex theory which has been called neo-Darwinism.

The case for the descent of man leans upon the multifarious

argument for the origin of species in general, but it involves unique difficulties, for man is an animal possessing speech, high intelligence, social institutions, and a moral sense.

Darwin attaches great importance to the physical similarities of man and the vertebrate series, especially the anthropoid apes, and concludes the first chapter of the *Descent* with the following statement:

> Thus we can understand how it has come to pass that man and all other vertebrate animals have been constructed on the same general model, why they pass through the same early stages of development, and why they retain certain rudiments in common. Consequently we ought frankly to admit their community of descent; to take any other view, is to admit that our own structure, and that of all the animals around us, is a mere snare laid to entrap our judgment. This conclusion is greatly strengthened, if we look to the members of the whole animal series, and consider the evidence derived from their affinities or classification, their geographical distribution and geological succession. It is only our natural prejudice, and that arrogance which made our forefathers declare that they were descended from demigods, which leads us to demur to this conclusion. But the time will before long come, when it will be thought wonderful that naturalists, who were well acquainted with the comparative structure and development of man, and other mammals, should have believed that each was the work of a separate act of creation. (p. 265c-d)

Now why does Darwin assert that we must either admit a community of descent or confess that our similarity to other vertebrates is a "snare laid to entrap our judgment"? He is saying that it is just *as if* man were an end product of an evolutionary sequence, and if this is not so, the only other explanation would be that God created the similarities to lead us astray. Like Descartes, who allowed himself to doubt whether we really see what we think we see, Darwin entertained the idea that God may deceive us. Both men rejected the idea, but for different reasons: Descartes because God is perfect and cannot be a deceiver, and Darwin because he had another and better explanation of the facts.

Darwin, who undertook to explain more facts than anyone since Aristotle, was always willing to concede that his theory could not explain everything. He invariably took objections seriously and did his best to answer them. In fact, he often anticipated objections before others had raised them. Yet he was sustained throughout his trials of doubt by the conviction that he was moving in the right direction and that future investigations would bear out his main contentions. He was also mindful that an acceptable theory does not have to explain everything and that it can acquire great plausibility through the implausibility of rival theories.

Long before Darwin, Aristotle had noted the physical similarities between man and other vertebrates, especially the apes. By Goethe's time, the resemblance between man and the ape had become something of a scandal. A comparison of their skeletons seemed to show only minor differences. One theory was that there is a tiny bone in the jaw, the intermaxillary, which is distinct in one case but not in the other. It was a slender thread of difference and not easy to confirm by observation. The poet Goethe, who was also a man of science, maintained that the bones of the skeletons of man and ape are comparable throughout and that the difference lies only in the balance and proportion of the whole.

Darwin has a great deal to say about the remarkable similarities of man and ape not only in skeletal structure but also in muscles, blood vessels, teeth, sense organs, and even the brain. Meticulous comparisons and measurements since Darwin, and partly inspired by him, have added many points of similarity. With all the refinement of methods, it is still hard to distinguish some bones of man from comparable bones of the chimpanzee. How can these close similarities have come about if man and ape do not have a common ancestor?

There are of course many differences, too. It is a common observation that the arms of apes, and especially those of the orangutan, are much longer than those of man and the legs shorter; that the hind feet of apes are prehensile and somewhat like hands, whereas the feet of men lack this mobility. But are not these differences exactly what one should expect on the evolutionary hypothesis? If the ancestors of man were arboreal, like present-day apes and monkeys, the long arms, prehensile feet, and tail would be favorable or essential to survival. If they later took to the ground and gradually assumed an upright posture, longer and straighter legs would give speed in locomotion, and the longer arms, prehensile feet, and tail, which had served so well in the trees, would no longer be useful.

The attainment of upright posture had astounding consequences. It left the hands free to shape tools and weapons, to build fires, to construct shelters, to utilize a whole series of inventions whereby the environment was more and more brought under control. The very process by which early man achieved control over nature was also the process by which his brain developed and his intelligence grew. Each stage of progress gave him a selective advantage in the struggle for survival. On the other hand, Darwin's friend Wallace, the co-author of the theory of natural selection, was impressed by the gap between the brain of man and the brain of the ape. Although natural selection is valid in other cases, he believed it failed to explain the enormous human brain and the great advance in human intelligence. Could such great superiority over his apelike ancestors have been necessary to his survival?

"The supreme importance of these characters has been proved by the final arbitrament of the battle for life," Darwin said. ". . . He has invented and is able to use various weapons, tools, traps, &c., with which he defends himself, kills or catches prey, and otherwise obtains food. He has made rafts or canoes for fishing or crossing over to neighbouring fertile islands" p. 278a-b). The development of speech, though prefigured in the expressive communications of apes, required a great development of the brain, and gave primitive man an overwhelming advantage over all pre-human species.

The physical similarities between man and the ape support the evolutionary hypothesis; the evidence of transition between the two is even more important. Although the human hand is a precision instrument of unrivaled flexibility and endless uses, the symbol of man's dominance, it is interesting to see how far its powers have been anticipated by the dexterity of monkeys and apes. (See pp. 278-279.) For some purposes—for climbing of trees—the monkey hand is much superior to the human, but climbing trees is not nearly so important to man as is the fine shaping and manipulation of tools. He has gained far more than he has lost.

Another intermediate linkage between man and ape cited by Darwin is the locomotion of gorillas and some monkeys, which is sometimes on all fours or sometimes on two legs only, almost like a man. "Thus the gorilla," he says, "runs with a sidelong shambling gait, but more commonly progresses by resting on its bent hands. The long-armed apes occasionally use their arms like crutches. . . . We see, in short, in existing monkeys a manner of progression intermediate between that of a quadruped and a biped" p. 280b).

If the ancestors of man gradually assumed an upright carriage, with hands free, head up, and brain greatly enlarged and heavier, as the evolutionary theory supposes, many skeletal and muscular changes would be required. The exquisite balance of forces involved in human locomotion would have to be evolved from the very different quadruped equipment. For one thing, the muscles of the legs would have to be developed to sustain the greater weight, and the pelvis enlarged for the same reason. The head, backbone, and pelvis would need realignment. The interplay of muscles which served the animal on all fours would have to be transformed to achieve the much more delicate equilibrium of the biped. Here also we should expect to find intermediate forms or other evidence of the transformation. Darwin gave examples, as we have seen, but he also stimulated experts in comparative anatomy to seek for more.

Two discoveries which support Darwin's argument beautifully might be mentioned. Professor Wilfred Le Gros Clark points out that the peroneus tertius muscle of the foot, which is one of the muscles involved in maintaining erect posture, was once thought to be unique to man. It has now been established, however, that it is present in 5% of chimpanzees and in 18% of gorillas. That is, it does not occur in quadruped monkeys, but it has a certain frequency in precisely those apes which have begun to stand and walk on two feet. At the same time, it is sometimes absent in man.

Even more instructive are muscles which have one function

in quadruped monkeys and apes and quite a different one in man. Thus, in quadrupeds the gluteus maximus, in contracting, draws the thigh outward, whereas in bipeds the same muscle extends to the thigh and thus facilitates erect carriage and gait. There are numerous instances of similarity and of adaptation of old ape muscles to new uses in man, Professor Clark adds. "Data of this kind have accumulated in great quantity since Darwin's time . . . they serve to establish unequivocally his thesis of a unity of design between the two groups, and thus provide *prima facie* evidence of a genetical affinity."[4]

Another and rather amusing evidence of man's descent is furnished by the tail, which is stunted and almost invisible in apes, which are closest to man, and occurs in man only as a diminished rudimentary organ. At an early stage of the human embryo, Darwin points out, there is a real tail which clearly projects beyond the lower extremities or legs. At birth, however, the tailbone proper, or os coccyx, is short, consisting of only four vertebrae, affixed together and not movable. The dwindling of this structure in the higher apes and its further reduction in man, together with its full-fledged appearance at one stage of the human embryo, certainly points to a common ancestry of man and ape. Whether it supports the theory of natural selection is another question.

A long tail is obviously most useful in arboreal life, but how could natural selection explain its virtual disappearance in the chimpanzees and in man? Darwin points out that the length of the tail varies greatly among apes, even among those of the same species. Can we suppose that those individuals with shorter tails would possess an advantage in the struggle for survival? Darwin remarks that some of the higher apes do a great deal of sitting. Would there not be an obvious advantage to the animal in taking his rest in this position rather than reclining? Would he not remain more alert to enemies and possibilities of food while sitting, and therefore be more likely to survive?

[4] "The Study of Man's Descent" in *A Century of Darwin*, ed. S. A. Barnett (Cambridge, Mass: Harvard University Press, 1958), p. 180.

Darwin's explanation is different. He states that the upper part of the tail has been modified to support internal parts, serving as a sacral extension of the vertebral column. This modification, he says, "is directly connected with the erect or semi-erect attitude of . . . the anthropomorphous apes" (p. 283c) and the erect carriage of man. As for the tail proper, or os coccyx, Darwin is inclined to think that this must have been rubbed or chafed when the animal took a sitting posture and that this injury was transmitted over many generations by inheritance. (See p. 284a-b.)

When Darwin resorts to Lamarck's inheritance of acquired characters, it is usually because he cannot find a good explanation in terms of natural selection. In the next paragraph, however, he indicates that he is not so certain of the scope of the natural selection principle as he had been when he wrote the *Origin* twelve years before. He emphasizes that many evolutionary changes are to be explained by Lamarck's principle, and that "in the earlier editions of my *Origin of Species* I perhaps attributed too much to the action of natural selection or the survival of the fittest. I have altered the fifth edition of the *Origin* so as to confine my remarks to adaptive changes of structure . . ." (p. 284d). Only changes of structure which adapt the organism to his environment and have survival value, he says, could be explained by natural selection. To have forgotten this at times was "one of the greatest oversights as yet detected in my work" (p. 285a).

Yet natural selection, taken together with overproduction of all species and chance variations, remains Darwin's basic principle of explanation of evolutionary change. It is important to remember that the evolution of every structure need not be explained in itself. The modification of one structure may be tied up with the modification of others in accordance with the principle of correlation. (See p. 284c.) Thus the gradual assumption of semierect posture and gait in the anthropoid apes involves many correlated modifications from head to foot—new alignments and proportions of muscles and bones which are interdependent.

II

Embryology, as we saw in the *Origin of Species,* furnishes sensational evidence for evolution. The stages of the human embryo give even more striking support for the last step in evolution, the descent of man. The life process of man begins with a single large cell, the ovum, which is fertilized by the spermatozoon. The fertilized ovum then divides into two cells, which again divide successively into 4, 8, 16, 32 cells, and so on. Finally, the cells begin to arrange themselves to form a primitive gut, and a stage is reached in which the human embryo is like a jellyfish and other Coelenterata. In succeeding phases, the human embryo closely resembles ever higher animal forms, or rather, an embryonic stage of these higher animals.

At an early stage, as Darwin points out, the embryo ". . . can hardly be distinguished from that of other members of the vertebrate kingdom. At this period the arteries run in arch-like branches, as if to carry the blood to branchiae which are not present in the higher Vertebrata, though the slits on the sides of the neck still remain . . . marking their former position" (p. 257c). In fish, it will be remembered, the arteries carry blood to the gills (branchiae) to collect oxygen. In man and other higher vertebrates, on the other hand, the arteries go to the lungs. What is striking is that the human embryo should reflect this stage of vertebrate development. The human embryo will never develop gills, nor is the arterial flow in that direction of any use to it. What could the explanation be, except that the fish is a very distant, little honored ancestor of man?

How would the theory that each species was produced by a special act of creation explain this strange appearance of fish-like circulation in the embryo of man? How would it explain the close similarity of the embryos of fish, birds, and mammals, or the structural resemblance of the embryos of dog and man, as is shown by Darwin's diagram? (See p. 257a-b.) All these forms must have a genetic affinity, i.e., various kinds of kinship in the evolutionary process. What else will account for these facts?

When Darwin was a young man at Cambridge, Karl Ernst von Baer announced his principle that in the earliest stages of their development all embryos belonging to a large group of animals, such as the vertebrates, are much alike, and that the younger they are, the more closely they resemble one another. As the embryos grow older, however, they diverge more and more. Thus the human embryo about three weeks old resembles the embryo of a dog or that of a monkey at a corresponding stage of development, but it does not resemble either animal at birth, or not nearly as much, and resembles the adult animal even less.

The so-called law that "ontogeny repeats phylogeny" is something quite different. It states that the embryonic development of the individual recapitulates or repeats the structures of the *adult* form of its ancestors, first, of the most distant ancestors and then, successively, of the more recent ones. This so-called law of recapitulation stimulated much research, but it has now been discredited. It was put forward by Darwin's follower Haeckel, but not by Darwin himself. Darwin wrote: "No other explanation has ever been given of the marvellous fact that the embryos of a man, dog, seal, bat, reptile, &c., can at first hardly be distinguished from each other" (p. 265c). He did not say that the human embryo resembles the adult animal lower on the scale. He knew that the human embryo is never anything like the mature monkey, seal, or reptile. The structural similarity holds only for a certain stage of embryonic development, after which the monkey, the dog, the bat, etc., each goes its own way and develops in different directions. Is this not just what the theory of evolution would lead us to expect?

In the adult forms, to be sure, homologous structures are to be found. The hand of man or monkey, the flipper of a seal, the wing of a bat, the foot of a horse or elephant, Darwin says, have a close similarity of pattern which is quite inexplicable on any other theory than that these animals had a common progenitor. (See p. 265a-d). The occurrence of structures homologous to the human among vertebrates provides a strong argument for the descent of man. The resemblance of the human embryo at an early stage of development to embryos of lower vertebrates at certain stages of *their* development is quite a different argument which supplements the first.

III

Darwin lists a great many physical similarities between man and apes, some of which we have touched on. One of the similarities which we have not yet mentioned is that both are subject to some of the same diseases, and susceptible to the same attacks of insects and parasites. This implies, Darwin says, that man agrees in constitution with apes, especially with the higher apes, and that blood and tissues are chemically alike. Does this consideration, to your mind, give much support to the theory of the descent of man? Would the fact that nowadays higher mammals, especially monkeys and apes, are inoculated with human diseases, in order to determine the nature, symptoms, progress, and cure of these diseases, tend to strengthen Darwin's contention? Would the fact, as recently reported, that monkeys and apes are the only animals besides man which suffer from the common cold, be in line with expectations?

Schopenhauer once remarked that the monkey is one animal that will never be regarded as beautiful. This is because he is too much like man, and can therefore be seen only as a caricature of man. Darwin dwells at length on the ways in which monkey and ape anticipate the characteristic behavior of man, his shifts of feeling, emotions, and the ways they are expressed. Some monkeys even weep, and others make a laughing noise, contracting facial muscles much as men do. (See p. 333c.)

You might question whether the watering of the eyes is really weeping and whether the laughing noises express hilarity, but Darwin seems right in emphasizing the emotional kinship of man and apes. The psychologist D. O. Hebb has recently reported his discovery that one cannot make progress in the study of the learning ability and emotions of chimpanzees by observing their behavior at a given time. To understand these animals, to predict their behavior, or even to be safe in attending to them in their cages, it is necessary to interpret the personality behind the behavior. A chimpanzee who seemed to be docile and cooperative, or timid or affectionate, might turn out to be really sly and malicious, and on his good behavior only when the human attendant or his cage mates were looking, or on guard. Another animal was continually caught attacking his cage mates and sometimes the attendant himself, yet it was found that, although quick-tempered, his resentments were short-lived, that he was fundamentally good-natured and not really dangerous because you could always see the cause of his anger and prepare for it. In short, the chimpanzees were not unlike a group of boys on a playfield. To understand what was going on, you had to know something about their personality structures.

Perhaps the most famous study of the similarities of man and ape was an experiment in which Donald, a human infant, and Gua, an infant chimpanzee, were raised together in the same home and treated alike. As Darwin would have predicted, the two infants became playmates and fast friends. At first Gua surpassed Donald in learning cooperative acts and cleanliness, for her rate of growth was faster. At fifteen months, however, Donald was superior in everything, for his period of growth was longer. (W. N. and L. A. Kellogg, *The Ape and the Child,* New York: McGraw-Hill Book Company, Inc., 1933.) The human qualities of chimpanzees, their learning ability and emotional capacity, are also emphasized by Wolfgang Köhler, in his *The Mentality of Apes* (New York: Harcourt, Brace & Company, 1926) and by many other psychologists.

Yet many doubt that Darwin has been completely confirmed. His view is that there is no "fundamental" difference between the mentality of the higher apes and man; the mental powers of men differ only in degree from those of apes. Man may have evolved from apelike forms even though as yet there are no intervening forms to mark the transition.

. . . there is a much wider interval in mental power between one of the lowest fishes, as a lamprey or lancelet, and one of the higher apes, than between an ape and man; yet this interval is filled up by numberless gradations. (p. 287b)

Whatever the difference between the mental capacity of ape and man, it is not greater than that between a lamprey, one of the lowest vertebrates, and an ape. If evolution is granted in the latter case, how can it be denied in the former? Darwin here seems to be arguing with scientists who, like his friends Lyell and Wallace, accept evolution and even natural selection for prehuman species but find it hard to believe that man evolved in the same way. Man's intellect and achievements, he is insisting, are not in a class by themselves but are comparable to those of other species.

What should we say of this argument of Darwin's, taken by itself? It sounds plausible, though there are no tests of intelligence which would give us this result. If intelligence is measured by success in solving problems of various grades of difficulty, we can determine the point at which the sharpest chimpanzee breaks down and can survey the immense stretch where he is surpassed by man. But how can we compare this stretch with that between the competence of the lamprey and the ape? It is known that there is an enormous gap between the learning ability of earthworms and chimpanzees, but how could this be compared to the corresponding gap between apes and man? Are there not two things that make such comparison difficult or impossible? Man is the only animal that has developed a real language, and he is the only animal that has a legacy and tradition, who transmits knowledge from one generation to the next. Does not this put him in a class by himself?

There are, however, certain groups of savages which transmit very little from one generation to another and are in this respect more like hordes of apes. Darwin emphasizes the gap in intelligence "between a savage who uses hardly any abstract terms, and a Newton or Shakespeare. Differences of this kind between the highest men of the highest races and the lowest savages are connected by the finest gradations. Therefore it is possible that they might pass and be developed into each other" (p. 287b). Thus if genius has evolved from the savage, why should not the savage have evolved from the ape? But the difference in intelligence between the savage and the genius may not be so great as Darwin supposes. The anthropologist Franz Boas showed that the lack of certain abstract words in a primitive language does not prove that the abstractions cannot be expressed in the language or that those who speak this language have any mental deficit. English is also lacking in many abstract terms. Secondly, the low achievement of a group does not prove its low intelligence. Its members, as some of Darwin's adversaries insisted, may have a latent intelligence that would manifest itself under more opportune conditions.

Darwin sets out in his Chapter 3 to show "that there is no fundamental difference between man and the higher mammals in their mental faculties" (p. 287c). This is what he must establish if he is to prove that man evolved from apelike ancestors by slight variations. If he is to uphold natural selection as the main agency in evolution, he must show that intelligence is a decisive advantage in the struggle for existence.

How successful is he in this enterprise? Is man akin to lower animals in sharing instincts with them, instincts such as "self-preservation, sexual love, the love of the mother for her newborn offspring, the desire possessed by the latter to suck, and so forth" (p. 287d)? Against this is the fact that man has few instincts, whereas other animals have many and more complicated ones. The distinction of man is his intelligence, and intelligence, according to Cuvier, is inversely related to instinct; the animals which have more of the one have less of the other. Darwin, on the other hand, argues that the most marvelous instincts are also the most intelligent, that the most elaborate instincts are found in the more intelligent animals such as the beaver, the bee, and the ant.

What do you think? Does the beaver build its dam from a blind, rigid, mechanical instinct, or is its instinct combined with an intelligence which adapts its flexibility to the particular materials at hand and to the lay of the land and course of the stream? And does not the instinctive nest building of birds adjust itself intelligently to the circumstances, making shift with new materials when the customary materials are lacking? But could the same be said of bees and ants, which are so much lower on the evolutionary scale? In ascribing unusual intelligence to insects such as the ant, Darwin was guided by the facts as he and his contemporaries saw them. Recent investigations have shown that the ingenuity, powers of communication, and reasoning attributed to ants are due to faulty observation or can be explained by instinctive reactions. Darwin was wrong here, but was it not good that he was? His conception of evolutionary progress would not lead us to expect that ants would have much intelligence.

Many advances have been made in the knowledge of instincts since Darwin. It is well to keep this in mind in assessing his reports, especially those which he gets from others. Experimental techniques are more reliable than mere observation in distinguishing instinct from what is learned, and also in eliminating the seductive tendency to read human motives into animal behavior. Imitation is no longer regarded as an instinct, and attention is not a close bond between man and other mammals, since the latter attend to only what presents itself as an *immediate* threat or clue to food and other basic needs. Partly because of his ability to name things, man's range of attention is incomparably broad. The same is true of the human range of memory.

In discussing reasoning in animals, Darwin was at a disadvantage, for the experimental study of learning was in the future. Yet, what he has to say is, as usual, rewarding. For example, he tells how a pike had to repeat the same painful action for three months before learning to desist, where one such experience would be enough to teach a monkey better, and he then comments:

If we attribute this difference between the monkey and the pike solely to the association of ideas being so much stronger and more persistent in the one than the other, . . . can we maintain in the case of man that a similar difference implies the possession of a fundamentally different mind? (p. 293a)

The question raised is of the greatest interest and importance. Does the learning or reasoning capacity of man exceed that of the monkey in the same way that the monkey's exceeds that of the pike? Is it in both cases merely a matter of the association of ideas being stronger and more persistent? If this were so, we could not infer that the mind of man is something fundamentally new and unprecedented.

What the laws of association are will be remembered from our readings of Aristotle, Locke, and Hobbes. They state that we tend to associate things according to their (1) similarity and contrast, (2) contiguity in space and time, and (3) cause and effect. We are likely to associate *day* with light (similarity), or with night (contrast), or with the rising of the sun (contiguity in space and time, and cause and effect). If a *horse* suddenly races around the corner, we may say it was like a cyclone, or that it was surprising—very different from what usually appears at that place—or, if we have been reading Darwin, we may think of the fossil horse which he found in South America and which was in the ancestral line of the modern horse, etc. In a sense these laws work for higher animals as well as man. In the case of animals, however, nothing directly can be known of their minds, and psychologists must study their behavior.

The learning ability of animals is investigated by giving them problems to solve, problems related to the species involved. Rats in many experiments gradually find the shortest path through a complicated maze terminating in food, but it takes many trials and, like the pike, they make the same mistake time and again before it can be eliminated. A mistake is running down a pathway that does not lead to the food. Learning, on the other hand, is associating those turns and pathways that lead to the food, are consecutively contiguous in space and time with the food, and the eating of the food. By this test the more intelligent animals are those which are the first to eliminate blind alleys and learn the shortest path to the food in the shortest time.

This sort of learning is called "trial and error." Through trial and error comes success, i.e., the pathway contiguous to the goal becomes associated with the goal which, accordingly, is reached without delay. The question now is: can all learning be reduced to trial and error and the forming of contiguous associations of means and ends? Some psychologists strongly incline to this view. If they are right, man's superior intelligence would be simply his ability to learn the correct paths to more goals, and more quickly, than apes can; if they are right, Darwin is right.

Other psychologists, on the other hand, deny that trial and error is the only, or even the typical, kind of learning. For the Gestaltists, "insight," the sudden comprehension of a total pattern, as when we recognize a face, a melody, or the solution of a mathematical problem, is the essential thing in human learning. But is it also found in higher apes? This is the crucial question. The Gestalt psychologist Wolfgang Köhler conducted many experiments in which chimpanzees, especially the smartest ones, also learn by insight, and E. C. Tolman, another Gestalt psychologist, discovers both insight and reasoning even in rats. This result is also in accord with Darwin's contention that human intelligence is not something fundamentally new but is implicit in the highest apes and is prefigured in their humble performances.

Yet the astronomical gap between the capacities and achievements of man and ape, readily conceded by Darwin himself, warns us against any hasty conclusion. The beginnings of insight may appear in chimpanzees, the rudiments of reasoning perhaps even in rats, and even fish can be taught some simple things. Yet it is hard to overcome the conviction that there is a sheer qualitative difference between man and the cleverest apes, a discontinuity that the accumulation of slight variations could never overcome, even if continued for millions of years of accidental success and natural selection of the fittest. Is not reasoning, in words at least, a unique trait of man which no animal even vaguely anticipates?

The famous philosopher and philologist Max Müller argued that if animals do not have a language, they do not have general concepts either. Without words for cat and sheep there can be no concepts of *cat* and *sheep*. Against this contention Darwin quotes his contemporary, Leslie Stephen, as follows:

"A dog frames a general concept of cats or sheep, and knows the corresponding words as well as a philosopher. And the capacity to understand is as good a proof of vocal intelligence, though in an inferior degree, as the capacity to speak." (p. 300a)

If we discount the exaggeration, must we not say that Stephen and Darwin are unquestionably right? A dog is able to recognize a cat when he sees one, and normally chases every instance of the concept *cat*. Is this not as good evidence that he has a concept *cat* as is man's capacity to say "cat" on each occasion? Moreover, the dog, at least if he is a smart one, can be taught not to chase white cats—simply by punishing him when he does. Would he not thereby acquire a concept of *white cat* as well?

You may object that the dog chases raccoons as well as cats. How can we be sure that he distinguishes between them? The answer is that he can be taught not to chase raccoons, and indeed the raccoon may do the teaching. A good sheep dog has learned never to corral anything but sheep. Similarly, a mature dog almost never attacks a puppy, whatever the breed, even though the puppy may be larger than he is. Does not this chivalry toward infants reveal a concept of *infancy*? Animals have general concepts, but whether they use them in reasoning is another and more difficult question.

But is it true that animals have no language? Darwin points out that some animals, such as ants, use their antennae for intercommunication (it would be safer to say "for signals instinctively responded to"), and that man might just as well have developed a language expressed by finger movements. (See p. 300a-b.) Can you think of any advantage of the use of the vocal cords for speech, any survival value that this means of communication might have?

In paleolithic times, Cro-Magnon man hunted large, swift animals with crude weapons; coöperation was essential. As the hunters spread out in hiding, they would have to communicate; to do so by fingers would require the listener to shift his eyes from the game or other business, and would be impossible at night. Can you think now of any disadvantage that vocal language might have had for early man?

If language were to be found in the animal world, it would be among the chimpanzees or gorillas. But how could we find out, one way or the other? The same noises can be correlated with recurrent situations in the social life of the animals. Records in fact have been made to study the delicate variations and spacing of sounds. Much remains to be done, but it is pretty clear that most of the noises of apes are expressive, like cries and grunts among human beings, which may serve as signals, but cannot be regarded as even the beginning of an organized language.

But language itself has evolved perhaps from the expressive cries and grunts of our remote ancestors. According to Max Müller, whom Darwin quotes again, there is a constant struggle for existence going on "amongst the words and grammatical forms in each language," and those which survive are, and presumably have been from the beginning of language, those which are shortest and most convenient. If some ancient languages, such as Sanskrit, are highly inflected, this does not mean that they are more highly developed than languages with simpler conjugations, declensions, etc. In a marvelous simile Darwin compares highly inflected languages to one of the Crinoidea or sea lilies, which may have as many as 150,000 bits of shell arranged in a perfectly symmetrical pattern. It does not follow, he says, that this animal is more highly developed than those with fewer parts, nor that highly inflected ancient languages are more perfect. There is no case here against evolution. Darwin concludes that

. . . the extremely complex and regular construction of many barbarous languages, is no proof that they owe their origin to a special act of creation. Nor . . . does the faculty of articulate speech in itself offer any insuperable objection to the belief that man has been developed from some lower form. (p. 301b-c)

IV

Darwin has some difficulty fitting speech and reasoning into the continuity of the evolutionary process. Technology, except perhaps for the isolated case of the beaver, is also hard to find, even in a "rude and implicit" form, in animals. Apes, Darwin says, throw sticks and are reported sometimes to roll stones down a hill against enemies. We know today also that they can be taught in the laboratory to use sticks to draw in bananas placed outside their cages, etc. In nature the apes rarely, if ever, employ tools, and other animals either lack the prehensile hands or the brains, or both, to do so. Thus Benjamin Franklin could define man as "a tool-using animal." Others, in the same spirit, have distinguished man as that animal who adapts to nature by adapting nature to him. Technology is thus a special mark of man, not anticipated by other species.

And is not a sense of beauty also peculiar to man? Darwin answers:

The sweet strains poured forth by many male birds during the season of love, are certainly admired by the females. . . . If female birds had been incapable of appreciating the beautiful colours, the ornaments, and voices of their male partners, all the labour and anxiety exhibited by the latter in displaying their charms before the females would have been thrown away; and this it is impossible to admit. (p. 301d)

There are other explanations of the male display at mating season, as we have seen, which do not oblige us to believe that the female bird is smitten with love for the male with a slightly more beautiful voice or feather display. It is now known, for example, that the exquisite song of some male birds serves to warn other males away from a particular area, or to release automatically the copulating drive of the female. In other species a less-exquisite song serves as a threat, signal, or excitant, quite as well. The idea that certain species of birds and insects have not only an aesthetic sense but precisely the same aesthetic tastes as Englishmen and other Europeans is certainly preposterous.

This generous error runs through a great deal of Darwin's account of sexual selection in the *Descent of Man.* The fact is that no other animal even approaches man's love of beauty, humor, pathos, and tragedy. It is true that men go to the opera, to picture galleries, and to plays for other than purely aesthetic reasons. Sometimes it is to make social contacts, to see important people, and to be seen themselves. Yet is there any question that men do sometimes pursue music and art for their own sakes, and sacrifice practical advantages or even go hungry to create or share beautiful things?

According to Freud, men devote themselves to art and literature only because there is in men an overflow of libidinal energies which has been repressed and has found no sufficient outlet or satisfaction in a puritanical society. Were sex and other bodily drives completely satisfied, cultural life would wither. But even if this were true, man would certainly be the only animal who compensates for a physical dearth by a kind of enchanted watching and listening and by creating forms of beauty. The female nightingale listens to the male, but only at mating season, and the bumblebee goes straight for the beautiful flower, but only when there is pollen there. The ritual dance and parade that occur at the mating season in some species have a semblance of intentional art, but they are largely instinctive means to propagation. Only man has an impractical, disinterested love of form and color and the cadence of sound. Do not all the arts, then, make this first appearance in man?

Darwin was not much interested in theology, but he was honest and courageous and always tried to give a fair answer to religious objections. He could not pretend to find among animals a belief in God or anything approaching it. Was he not obliged to admit that when it came to religion men stood alone, elevated above all other species? And whence came this belief in God? Other animals might have evolved from lower forms but man evidently bore the imprint of the Creator. Such was the thought even of Darwin's collaborator, Wallace, and of his great teacher and friend, Lyell.

Following Tylor and other anthropologists of the time, Darwin denied that a belief in God is universal in the human race. What seems to be universal is "the belief in unseen or spiritual agencies," and it is not hard, he thought, to understand how it arose. Man was confronted with inexplicable events and developments. Why was game now plentiful and now lacking? Why did one man die and another live? What brought about the seasons and made plants flourish or wilt? Primitive man imagined that unseen spirits, some friendly and some hostile to him, governed the course of nature and could confer punishments or blessings, respite or suffering, according to their mood and to the conduct of the tribe. These spirits were therefore to be appeased or controlled. Magic, Tylor held, was the beginning of religion. It was an effort to control the forces of nature on which survival depended—a kind of "poor man's science."

Darwin was evidently of the same opinion. But was it likely that magic or primitive religion would actually have survival value? Conditions of life could not have been improved by the practices employed. But in this case why should they have continued to dominate primitive societies? There is an answer which goes back as far as Plato and which was much emphasized by Durkheim and other modern sociologists. Magic and religious superstitions do not make nature any friendlier or life more secure from drought and wild animals, but they do contribute to the unity and solidarity of the group, so that individuals think and work, not each for himself, but each for all. Thus even a system of belief that involved repression, cruel punishments, and human sacrifices might nevertheless aid the group itself to survive—to institute controls and to subordinate the individual to the social unit. This brings us to the next question.

Is man the only social animal and does morality arise from social instincts? Darwin's answer to the first question is *no* and to the second *yes*. We have seen that he generally emphasized the cruel, competitive side of evolution, where one animal or species survives only through the death of another, and said much less about the tremendous role of "mutual aid." Chapter 4 of *The Descent of Man*, however, is rich in illustrations of the social instincts of animals, especially those of the higher mammals and apes, for these are closest to man and most pertinent to the rise of human morality. At the outset he lays down the bold proposition that

. . . any animal whatever, endowed with well-marked social instincts, the parental and filial affections being here included, would inevitably acquire a moral sense or conscience, as soon as its intellectual powers had become as well, or nearly as well developed, as in man. (p. 304b-c)

Social instincts, for one thing, involve pleasure in congregating together and in performing mutual services. Thus many birds and mammals, Darwin says, post sentinels to warn of the approach of enemies. But if we grant the fact, is it necessary to suppose that any sympathy is involved?

We have all heard of sheep and cattle huddling together in a storm. Is fellow-feeling a factor, or would not the warmth provided by other animals be a sufficient explanation? Or consider a monkey searching for fleas in the coat of his partner. Is it because he is sympathetic, or is he not simply looking for fleas in a hairy hide much like his own which, however, happens to belong to another animal? Looking for fleas becomes a habit with monkeys and apes and might continue even in an area from which no itch proceeds.

These are points we should have to settle before agreeing that animals are evincing sympathy. A rat on delivering her young licks their wet coats dry and clean. Is this maternal instinct or mother love, or is she not automatically licking a wet coat that looks like her own, which she always licks when it is wet? Recently experiments have been carried out to determine whether the mother rat will lick her young if she has been prevented throughout life from licking herself.

Since animals do not talk, it is hard to know what they have in mind, what their sentiments and motives are. Although extended investigations have shown great personality differences in chimpanzees and dogs, i.e., a great variety of responsiveness to cage mates and also to human attendants, it is still not clear how much they anticipate human sympathy and love. Some breeds of dogs are friendly to almost anyone, but the true hound, as Konrad Lorenz has pointed out, is a one-man dog, very protective of its master but indifferent or hostile to everyone else. But how far in either case are feelings of love and respect or "self-command" involved?

Darwin also argues that the frequent conflict of instincts in animals lays the rude foundation for human regret and remorse, as when a dog, rebuked for chasing a hare, ". . . pauses, hesitates, pursues again, or returns ashamed to his master . . ." (p. 309c), or the mother bird who, torn between two powerful urges, finally migrates, leaving her young to perish in their nest. The unfulfilled instinct would leave the animal dissatisfied. If it possessed a more developed brain, images of frustration and loss would linger in the mind, amounting to something like regret. If language should be available, the now manlike animal would be able to label situations in which one instinctive urge is to be sacrificed for another, and his regard for the approbation of his fellows, which is based on the instinct of sympathy, would incline him to conduct conforming to the common good. The instinct of sympathy thus evolved would then be further strengthened by habit.

Morality, according to Darwin, is not actually present in animals, even in the highest; it occurs there only in an embryonic form. In the same way, various reflexes which appear in the human infant seem remote from the complex performances of walking, running, and dancing, which will soon supervene, yet the former are the foundation of the latter and develop into them. The dog who follows his master obediently is not really faithful in the sense that a man is faithful to his friend, for he does not compare the worth of his master to other men, nor recognize his duty, nor make a free choice. But can this be right? "Faithful as a dog" means a high degree of fidelity, whereas the expression "faithful as a man" would arouse only doubts and misgivings. The answer seems to be that the dog, on his obscure canine level, mimics a fidelity so perfect as to be rarely found in man.

Is not the "innocence of childhood" another such expression? Young children are not really so innocent. They simply have not gone far enough on the road to morality to be capable of sins and treachery. The foundation of adult morality is nevertheless to be found in the groping of the child at different stages of its development. One famous account of this evolution of morality will be found in Jean Piaget's *The Development of Morality in the Child.*

If Darwin's theory of evolution is true, we should expect to find human morality prefigured in the higher animals. If morality did not arise suddenly, fully formed, we should expect to find a lower stage of ethical development in savages. Darwin has no difficulty in supplying instances of cruel, inhuman codes and practices, including infanticide, ceremonial human sacrifices, sexual licentiousness, and gross intemperance of all sorts. It is true, he says, that murder, robbery, treachery, and the like are generally forbidden within the group, for no group that condoned such crimes could long endure. But in general, the same offenses, when committed abroad, are permitted and even approved. The more scalps a Plains Indian collected from other tribes, the greater his reputation.

There are three respects in which the morality of savages falls below the standard of civilized man, according to Darwin. Sympathy is confined to the tribe and is not extended beyond. Savages lack the reasoning powers to distinguish the evil consequences of certain practices, and are wanting in discipline and self-control. (See p. 316a.)

Could we not agree that savage morality shows these shortcomings without admitting that they are at a lower evolutionary stage? Must the difference between the savage and the civilized man be biological? Is it not rather cultural? Suppose that young children of present-day primitive people were given the same education as European or American children. Would their development under these conditions be a fair test of their native ability? As a matter of fact, young children of Australian bushmen (a people regarded by Darwin as low in the evolutionary scale), when educated in the big coastal cities, have shown no deficit of intelligence or achievement.

In the light of present-day findings about races of men, Darwin was certainly wrong in one important respect. Although the races of men vary in other qualities, there is no evidence that any race is less intelligent or more primitive than any other. In some physical features, it will be remembered, the Negro is closer to the anthropoid ape, but in other features, the white man is.

Present-day savages, or preliterates, although culturally primitive, are not more primitive in the evolutionary scale. To find anything approaching an "ape man" or "missing link," we must look to the fossil record. In Darwin's time, however, very few remains of early man had been found. The Neanderthal skull had been discovered in 1856, three years before the *Origin* appeared, but it was, although of great antiquity, "well developed and capacious," as Darwin admits (p. 281c). Its cubic contents were, in fact, almost as great as those of modern man—*Homo sapiens.*

This did not tend to support the evolutionary view, since one would expect early man to be less intelligent and hence to have a smaller brain case. Darwin, of course, did not believe that the size of the brain case was an infallible measure of intelligence of an animal, but he did hold that comparative measurements of the brains of animals at different levels of evolutionary development established a general correlation. The Neanderthal man was a disappointment—too human. So also were the Cro-Magnon skeletons which turned up in 1868, five years before Darwin's death. Cro-Magnon men were tall, with skulls even larger than those of modern man.

In 1891, however, the fossil fragments of the so-called *Pithecanthropus erectus* were discovered in Java. The find would have delighted Darwin. In many ways this early man, dating back to the Pleistocene, about a million years ago, was midway between man and the anthropoid apes. The *Australopithecus* was even more apelike. Numerous other discoveries have since filled in the record of the descent of man. There are still many gaps, but new data accumulating year by year give increasing support to Darwin's hypothesis.

V

What is the explanation of secondary sexual characters in man? Could they have had survival value?

Secondary sexual characters are those which differ between male and female but which are not necessary to reproduction. In many of the higher mammals, the male is larger and stronger than the female, and often is supplied with horns or antlers. This dominance of the male, as Darwin points out, is found in herbivorous animals rather than in the large carnivores, and indeed the female lion or tiger may well be the deadlier of the sexes. The dominance of the male is also associated with polygamy and is found among anthropoid apes. In man, too, the male is generally larger and more formidable, although in primitive societies women do most of the hard work. Men, however, almost always do the hunting and fighting, which call for reserves of strength and sudden bursts of energy.

Darwin argued that male rivalry results in the victory of the strongest and thus favors the survival of the group. When strength is carried too far, however, as among the ancient dinosaurs, the survival of the group may be jeopardized, which is something for *Homo sapiens* to think about at the present turn of history. The strongest reproduce their kind because they overcome their rivals or, as Darwin suggests, because the females select them. The idea that cows prefer the strongest, most virile bulls, or female birds the best singing mate, is implausible and unnecessary. In the human species, however, it might play a part. Strength, broad shoulders, height, etc., so far as they are represented in the germ plasm, might be perpetuated in the species by female choice. Is there any other way of explaining the physical dominance of the human male? Is male competition so keen in human societies that smaller, weaker males perish or fail to mate as often as the strong?

The secondary sexual characters of the female are even more interesting in this regard. The broad hips, narrower shoulders, typical distribution of fat, etc., have nothing to do with virility, and women lacking these characteristics reproduce and care for their young as well as the others. How then can these useless female differentiae have spread over such a large part of the globe except by male preference? In some species of birds it may be important for the female to be clearly distinguished at mating season, for then she can be identified at once, and the male, instead of fighting what looks like another male, can proceed at once with the courtship. In human societies it is more probable that male preference played the decisive role in producing the distinctively female figure and pulchritude. Darwin discusses this question, but is mainly concerned with primitive peoples where male preference, as he explains, has less scope. (See pp. 571 ff.)

What is the origin of art? What survival value could art have had for man?

We have seen that Darwin wrongly traces the love of beauty to the animal world and gives it a role in sexual selection and the survival of the "fittest." In savage societies there is no doubt that ornaments, apparel, cosmetics, and mutilations of endless variety render the individual more beautiful and therefore more desirable. But how could such preoccupation with adornment and self-enhancement, which involves so much time, care, and self-inflicted pain, give any advantage to the particular group? Would it be more apt to survive in the struggle for existence? Could it be supposed that those who spent most time ornamenting themselves were also the most energetic, virile, and capable? Darwin points out that savages also paint, ornament, or mutilate themselves to appear more terrible in battle. The flare of colors and the wild movements of the war dance can serve also to stir feelings to the battle pitch. Such activities might be advantageous to the group.

In some of the most primitive people we find arrowheads, spears, and other weapons and tools finished off smoothly and symmetrically, with a care which has little or nothing to do with efficiency. It is hard to find a society, past or present, in which some design or insignia is not introduced. It is known that the inlaid emblems or pictures often bear a magical significance, but sometimes they are evidently gratuitous. Even when they have a magical purpose, as in the beautiful cave drawings of Cro-Magnon man in Altamira and many other sites in Europe, the skill and pride of workmanship far exceed the scope and use of magic. What evolutionary advantage does the inspired portraying of game animals have to the hungry Cro-Magnon man in his darkly lit caves? Could magic be supposed to have had survival value?

It seems clear that at one point in human history humor arose, and when it did it provided a means to reduce tension and bloodshed within the group. Laughter could also be employed to ridicule and correct deviation from group standards. Music, in its various moods, could regulate the emotional life of the group, and so also dancing.

These are, at any rate, some of the questions that we must ask in the light of Darwin's theory of natural selection. Of the various men within the family of Homines, only modern man— *Homo sapiens*—has survived. Competition was severe. Is it likely that art should have developed and survived if it had not aided men to survive?

Can we learn what is good and right from evolutionary progress?

While Darwin held that ethics arises in evolution and has adaptive value—promoting cohesion and reducing conflict within the group—he did not at all contend that the survivors are always the fittest in a moral sense. On the contrary, he emphasized the frequent reversion to parasitism and other degenerate trends.

T. H. Huxley fought Darwin's battle against the enemies of evolution on many platforms and was sometimes called "Darwin's bulldog." He sharply criticized, however, the idea of an evolutionary ethics put forward by some of Darwin's admirers. Ethics does not follow the path of evolution, but must rather proceed in the opposite direction. "What we call goodness or virtue," he said,

involves a course of conduct which, in all respects, is opposed to that which leads to success in the cosmic struggle for existence. In place of ruthless self-assertion it demands self-restraint; in place of thrusting aside, or treading down, all competitors, it requires that the individual shall not merely respect, but shall help his fellows; its influence is directed, not so much to the survival of the fittest, as to the fitting of as many as possible to survive. It repudiates the gladiatorial theory of existence.[5]

The process of evolution may well explain the origin of moral sentiments,

. . . but as the immoral sentiments have no less been evolved, there is, so far, as much natural sanction for the one as the other. . . . Cosmic evolution . . . is incompetent to furnish any better reason why what we call good is preferable to what we call evil than we had before.[6]

[5] T. H. Huxley, *Evolution and Ethics, and other Essays* (New York: D. Appleton & Company, 1898), pp. 81-82.
[6] *Ibid.*, pp. 79-80.

T. H. Huxley's descendent, the contemporary biologist Julian Huxley, takes an opposing view:

But if we cannot discover a purpose in evolution, we can discern a direction—the line of evolutionary progress. And this past direction can serve as a guide in formulating our purpose for the future. Increase of control, increase of independence, increase of internal co-ordination; increase of knowledge, of means for co-ordinating knowledge, of elaborateness and intensity of feeling—those are trends of the most general order.[7]

Although these progressive trends are to be found in evolution, there are also static phases and regressions. Is not Huxley arguing that we can learn what goodness is from evolution because we can discern certain main trends in it which are certainly good? But how could we know that these trends are good unless we already knew what goodness is? Is the argument not circular? Which Huxley is right?

Can evolution explain man's uniqueness?

Genesis 1:26 reads:

And God said, Let us make man in our image, after our likeness: and let them have dominion over the fish of the sea, and over the fowl of the air, and over the cattle, and over all the earth, and over every creeping thing that creepeth upon the earth.

This account of man's origin asserts man's uniqueness unmistakably, for no other animal is said to be created in God's image nor assigned dominion over the earth.

The question is whether Darwin's theory that man arose from apelike ancestry, by an accumulation of slight variations having survival value, also accounts for man's uniqueness. How can a quantitative accumulation engender a difference of quality?

Aristotle defined man as "a rational animal." He possesses science; animals have none at all. Aristotle also defined man as "a political animal." He has instituted governments and a great array of other institutions, which no other animal even approaches. Moreover, man has created the arts and technologies,

[7] Julian Huxley, *Evolution, the Modern Synthesis* (London: George Allen & Unwin, Ltd., 1945), pp. 576-577.

foreseen results of skill and purpose, and his conduct respects moral codes and religion. In animals we find not a sign or shadow of such activities. Man thus seems to stand not at the top of an easy slope, gradually rising from the Miocene forests of the Old World monkeys, but on a high promontory, cut off from other creatures.

There is no doubt Darwin was impressed with this argument and did his best to meet it. He looked forward confidently to future research to make the task easier. But perhaps the argument could be parried by a philosophical consideration. In his *Logic,* Hegel emphasized the principle that quantity passes into quality. Quantitative increases can continue for a long time to produce only quantitative changes, but a critical point is often reached at which something qualitatively new emerges. Thus quantitative changes accumulate until there is an avalanche, an earthquake, an explosion. The water on the stove begins to boil, the overheated house catches fire, a new organic compound arises from the old which is unique in its properties. Is it not possible then that man's qualitative uniqueness is a by-product of a million years of quantitative modifications? But to show that human evolution is possible, we must remember, is not to prove that it is a fact.

The following questions are designed to help you test the thoroughness of your reading. Each question is to be answered by giving a page or pages of the reading assignment. Answers will be found on page 384 of this Reading Plan.

1 What factors cause organs to become rudimentary?

2 What function in other species did the muscles have which move the human scalp?

3 What is the significance of the fact that in the human embryo the great toe was found to be shorter than the others?

4 Why are rudimentary organs so variable?

5 What is Darwin's explanation of the hair on the human body?

6 What embryological fact supports this explanation?

7 What explanation is given for "the inferiority of Europeans, in comparison with savages, in eyesight and in other senses"?

8 Why have the canine teeth in man a deeper root than the other teeth?

9 Does Malthus hold that the reproductive rate is greater among savages than among civilized peoples?

10 Why does Darwin say that "it might have been an immense advantage to man to have sprung from some comparatively weak creature"?

WILLIAM JAMES

The Principles of Psychology

Ch. 9-10

Vol. 53, pp. 146-179, 191-194, 204-223

J ames's *The Principles of Psychology*, which it took him twelve years to write, ten years longer than his contract with the publisher had stipulated, turned out to be the most successful book on psychology ever written. It might also be called the most brilliant, humane, witty, unimpeded, and many-sided book on the subject. Fairly bursting with original ideas and rich in illustrations, combining philosophy, psychology, physiology with the rapid reflections of a master essayist, the *Principles* gave impetus to diverse developments in psychology and had far-reaching influence in philosophy and other fields. The book was not at all systematic and had no such pretension. The science of psychology was in its infancy, James held, and was only a part of a larger science of living beings which had been as yet scarcely envisaged.

James is the founder of *functionalism* in psychology. Under the influence of Darwin he looked upon the various mental processes—perception, memory, attention, emotion, volition, and thought—as different ways in which the biological organism adapts itself to its environment. The structural psychology developed by Wundt in Leipzig and by Titchener in this country was content to analyze the contents of consciousness, of which sensations and images were considered the basic elements, to describe their surface qualities accurately by means of a painstaking introspective method. James, on the other hand, wanted to discover the function which mental processes serve in the life adjustments of the organism. Whereas Wundt and Titchener talked of contents, James was interested in dynamic processes. They explained structure in terms of simple elements, he in terms of its function.

This concern with function, which marked a new movement in American psychology, was really a return to the psychology of Aristotle, which also aimed at the inner meaning, purpose, or function exhibited in vital processes. James's functionalism is most easily seen in his account of instinct, emotion, and the stream of thought. Later it bore fruit in his doctrine of pragmatism, which, with the additions made by Peirce and Dewey, became the most original and distinctive American philosophy.

Although primarily a functionalist, James was too volatile and open-minded to be only that. As an empiricist—he later called himself a "radical empiricist"

—he could not but recognize that introspection yields first-hand reliable data. He also borrowed a great deal from the British associationists, such as Bain and James and J. S. Mill. But their determinism seemed to him a fatalistic creed. Fortunately for his peace of mind, he discovered in the human ability to shift attention what looked like an open door to freedom of the will. His first act of free will, he gaily reported, was to believe in free will. James also learned much from German experimental psychology, and he made physiology of the brain a part of general psychology. He learned even more from Charcot and the clinical psychology of France. Localization of functions in the brain, multiple personalities, the mystical trance, all in turn became fascinations. Nothing indeed was foreign to him, and to every topic he imparted his own light touch and perspective.

Twelfth Reading

I

The life and genius of James are well described in R. B. Perry's two-volume work *The Thought and Character of William James*. His father, Henry James the elder, was like Socrates, convivial and picturesque. With a deeply religious nature, but too independent and original to associate himself with any established church, he finally built up his own system on the mystical speculations of Swedenborg. James's brother Henry, a year younger, spent most of his life in Europe, and their voluminous correspondence displays their intellectual intimacy and solid friendship. But Henry, who was on his way to becoming America's greatest novelist, did not always meet his brother's approval. His exquisite concern with the nuance and detail of the lives of his highly sensitive characters struck William as overdone. Henry's style ran too much to *"curliness."* What he should *"cultivate* is directness of style. Delicacy, subtlety and ingenuity will take care of themselves."[1] On the aim and goal of human striving, however, both men were in agreement. This might be described as full awareness, intensity of feeling, and understanding.

William James was a long time deciding what to make of himself. At eighteen years of age, we find him studying art in Newport, Rhode Island, under the well-known painter William M. Hunt. Although he soon shifted to scientific courses in chemistry, anatomy, and biology at Harvard University, his brief trial at art was not forgotten. In periods of discouragement he could confess to Henry how pale and empty philosophy seemed to him in comparison with the visual splendor of

---

[1] Ralph Barton Perry, *The Thought and Character of William James* (Boston: Little, Brown & Company, 1935), Vol. I, p. 329.

Italy which his brother was then enjoying, and how he envied his choice of the aesthetic life.

James went on to the Harvard Medical School and eventually acquired his M.D. degree in 1869. His studies were interrupted, however, by a trip to Brazil as an assistant to Louis Agassiz, who headed the expedition, and by a severe depression which led him to drop everything and go off to Europe for eighteen months. In Europe he studied under very distinguished men—Helmholtz, Virchow, and Bernard—and stored up many impressions of Germany and Continental society. In 1872 he became an instructor in physiology at Harvard and then Assistant Professor of Anatomy and Physiology. But in 1889 he shifted to what had been his real passion for some time, and for the next eight years held the post of Professor of Psychology at Harvard. In 1890 *The Principles of Psychology* finally appeared.

James's idea of the stream of thought, or stream of consciousness as it is now usually called, has had far-reaching influence. The mind is no longer regarded as a pattern or mosaic of sensations and images but rather as a stream in which everything is passing into something else. The present moment is full of bright colors, sounds, tactual sensations, anticipatory images, and the like, but they are not self-sufficient elements. Their role is to refer beyond. By them we mean and deal with the objects which concern us in the world. They are clues and counters used in our continual adjustment to an ever-changing environment.

Nowadays we have the so-called stream-of-consciousness novel, the inspiration being mostly Jamesean. Such masters as Proust, Joyce, and Henry James in some of his novels make a point of tracing in detail the flow of inner experience of their characters, depicting the world as it looks from the inside rather than as it appears in an objective public view. The uncompromising revelation of private worlds marks a gain in subtlety and veracity in both psychology and literature.

Psychology begins with the fact that thinking is going on. "If we could say in English 'it thinks,' as we say 'it rains' or 'it blows,' we should be stating the fact most simply and with the minimum of assumption" (p. 146b). What is most certain and undeniable in mental life is that *it thinks* or *thought is going on.* If we say "I think," on the other hand, we seem to be assuming that there is an *I* apart from the thinking, and also that this *I* is doing the thinking. But can we observe an *I* as something different from the thinking? And are we sure that this *I* is really doing the thinking? Often when we say "I think . . ." we merely repeat what the newspaper or some companion has said. Perhaps "it thinks . . ." or "one idea is that . . ." would be a more modest and accurate expression.

For James, however, thought as experienced is personal. "The universal conscious fact is not 'feelings and thoughts exist,' but 'I think' and 'I feel.' No psychology, at any rate, can question the *existence* of personal selves" (p. 147b). How can James be so sure of this? He is certain of it because the self, as he conceives it, is not something over and above the stream of its experiences (or thoughts), not transcendent of its experiences, but inseparable from them. Thus, if the experiences are admitted to exist, so also must the personal self. The self that James accepts is thus the *empirical self.* What he rejects is a *transcendent self,* one that transcends the stream of consciousness. The advantage of the empirical self is that its existence cannot be denied, and must be conceded even by those who go on to add a transcendent self.

But is it true that all consciousness is personal, either mine or yours? Kant said that the *I think* must be able to accompany all our perceptions, but he does not say that it actually does. Nor does James claim that every thought is a part of personal consciousness, but only that it "tends to be." He is thinking of cases of automatic writing and split personalities which were under investigation at the time. Certain subjects can be induced to write on a sheet of paper while they are fully engaged in conversation. They are surprised and shocked later to see what they have written; it is strange and alien to them, as if dictated by someone else. In other words, the thoughts which appear on the paper are apparently "not part of a personal consciousness." But if the subject disowns them, whose thoughts could they be?

James alludes to Pierre Janet's famous patient Lucie, whose ear could hear questions and whose right hand could write down the answers, though Lucie herself, who was otherwise engaged, knew nothing about it. Was not the listening and answering a clear case of experience which was no one's experience? No, says James, for besides Lucie—as Janet admits— there was also a subordinate person, Adrienne, who was making use of Lucie's brain and body. The thoughts were not impersonal; they belonged to either Lucie or Adrienne. In Morton Prince's case of Sally Beachamp, about whom he wrote a book,[2] there were no fewer than three of these subordinate persons whom he could summon to life by turns. Only one of them knew what the others were up to. That they were distinct persons was shown by the fact that each had different habits, beliefs, memories, ideals, and different personality traits. The splitting off of extra persons is a form of hysteria. There is not just one unitary consciousness but what James called "co-conscious" persons, persons who are able to seize control of different organizing centers of the same brain. The dissociated personalities "form no important exception to the law that all thought tends to assume the form of personal consciousness" (p. 149b).

Lucie and Sally Beachamp represented extreme pathological forms of a phenomenon that occurs in mild degrees in normal men. We say that Jones is a grouch or tyrant in the office but an altogether different person on the golf course, or that Brown is a new man when he gets home with his children. All of us have different personalities in contrasting company and circumstances. The big difference is that our home personality can remember what our office self does and thinks, and vice versa, whereas split personalities are usually unaware of each other. We shall return to this phenomenon later in discussing the consciousness of the self. Our present concern is with the traits which, according to James, distinguish the stream of consciousness.

[2] Morton Prince, *The Dissociation of a Personality* (New York: Longmans, Green & Co., Inc., 1957).

II

The second trait is incessant change. James defends the extreme thesis that nothing in consciousness remains the same. But can we not look out whenever we wish and see the very same blue in the sky and green in the grass? Yes, James says, but what remain the same are the *objects*—the sky and the grass—not the sensations. The sensations themselves change constantly in different contexts, lighting, expectation, mood, and with changes of brain states. Does this square with our experience? Does not a blue surface appear brighter when put on a dull neutral background, and duller on a bright blue, and is not orange juice sweet after lime juice but sour after honey? If you saw a man in a room in which walls, furniture, etc., were twice the normal size, would he not shrink in size, as he does when he moves away from you? When you are looking out the window do not grass and trees and water really change their hue constantly as the clouds fly over and past the sun? There are scores of well-attested phenomena which support James's contention that sensations constantly vary with the conditions of perception. Think, for example, of the Perkinje phenomenon. In ordinary illuminations the blues and the greens recede into the background, whereas the reds and yellows advance toward you. As the dusk of evening comes, however, the order is reversed. The greens and blues, of the books on your bookshelf for example, now come forward and the reds and yellows recede.

We do not ordinarily notice these changes of sensational values, James points out, for what interests us are not the sensations as such but the world which the sensations mean, i.e., advertise or point to. This is well illustrated by what is called "phenomenal constancy," a large area of research developed mostly since James's time. We tend to see the colors which usually enable us to distinguish one object from another, i.e., "object colors," not the colors which we would see if, like the artist, we were more interested in the colors than in the objects that have them. Thus we go on calling the sky blue though it is overcast and gray, and the grass green though it is really brown with frost. We also are in no doubt that a piece of coal seen in bright sunlight is still black and that a piece of chalk in deep shadow is still white, though it is easy to prove that this is not so. The reason is that we have formed habits of identifying coal and chalk in different illuminations. These habits have great adaptive value to the organism; perceiving the precise shade in a particular illumination is most useful to the artist and the color specialist.

But what must we think of James's further contentions? He writes:

We feel things differently according as we are sleepy or awake, hungry or full, fresh or tired; differently at night and in the morning, differently in summer and in winter, and above all things differently in childhood, manhood, and old age. (p. 151a)

And what about his claim that for the *same* sensation to recur in the mind the brain would have to be unmodified, which is a "physiological impossibility"? (See p. 151a-b.)

Many experiments have been carried out to determine whether, or how much, sense perception is affected by the changes to which James refers. It is known, for example, that what we experience is often modified by what we expect, and that expectations can vary from moment to moment. Let us consult our own experience. If we are listening intently for the door bell to ring we sometimes "hear" it when no one has been near the door. Similarly, runners at the mark waiting for the signal which starts the race "jump the gun." There is also a tendency not to hear or see things that are unwelcome, to perceive beauty when things have been praised and ugliness when they have been condemned. The world looks sad when we are sad, and gay when we are gay. Fatigue can cause the focus of attention to become diffused. Some studies show that it can also change the size and shape of what is perceived. Recent psychological experiments in the field of perception confirm James's general thesis undoubtedly, at many points, and perhaps beyond his expectations.

Sensory experience is also known to be controlled by brain states. We see this particularly in the study of perception in patients with brain injuries. On the other hand, it does not follow that if the brain is constantly changing, and sense perception depends on the brain, then sense perception must also be in constant flux. If James meant this (see p. 157b), it is an overstatement. Subtle changes in the brain need not be reflected in sensation.

To appreciate James's originality, we must bear in mind that the psychophysics of his time assumed, as a matter of course, that the same physical stimulation would produce a sensation of the same intensity on every occasion. Subjective states of the subject were more or less ignored. The dominant introspective psychology concentrated on the extensive properties of sensory experience and tried to avoid the meaning, reference, and purpose involved.

James did not deny the validity of psychophysical investigations, nor dismiss the findings of introspection. He was a man of vision and enthusiasm, but he usually kept his balance. Some laws of sensation could be very important, even though sensation was an unreal abstraction from the richness of experience. James makes a similar point in criticizing Locke and Herbart:

No doubt it is often *convenient* to formulate the mental facts in an atomistic sort of way, and to treat the higher states of consciousness as if they were all built out of unchanging simple ideas. It is convenient often to treat curves as if they were composed of small straight lines, and electricity and nerve-force as if they were fluids. But in the one case as in the other we must never forget that we are talking symbolically, and that there is nothing in nature to answer to our words. *A permanently existing "idea" or "Vorstellung" which makes its appearance before the footlights of consciousness at periodical intervals is as mythological an entity as the Jack of Spades.* (p. 153a-b)

According to Locke, as we have seen, the mind at the beginning has no content except simple ideas, such as yellow, hot, smooth, and sweet, which are fixed and immutable. All the complex ideas are combinations of these simple elements, plus those which arise when we reflect on the operations of our minds. Thus the idea of *justice* would be a mosaic of ideas of sensation plus ideas of the mind's activities. To understand *justice* is to see how those simple indestructible elements have been combined to form it. James rightly admits the convenience of this atomistic analysis but insists that in fact ideas are constantly changing and are not the same in two occurrences.

But would this be true of the simple idea of *blue,* or the highly complex idea of *justice?* Does he not go too far? I say the sky is blue when it is light blue and when it is dark, when it is bright blue and when it is dull, when it is cerulean and when it is baby blue; but may not the color be blue on all these occasions? Similarly, though justice is certainly an ambiguous word, does it always change its meaning with new contexts? May there not be an identity in diversity, at least for some meanings of the terms? James once debated this point with the famous British philosopher F. H. Bradley. For Bradley identity was required; for James only similarity. Justice is a class of similar meanings.

III

The third feature of the personal stream of thought is felt continuity. The stream is not a chain nor train nor anything jointed together; it flows. When novelty arises, it emerges gradually from what went before; there are no sharp breaks. But does not a sudden thunderclap make a sharp break that leaves us speechless? Where is the continuity here? James answers that this experience is really a transition from silence to thunder. We hear the thunder supervening upon the silence (which is really composed of tiny background noises) and we feel the silence fading out while the roar of the thunder comes to a peak. Then the clap reverberates, diminishing and fading out, while some new experience takes the focus of attention.

Let us illustrate the continuity of the personal stream of consciousness by other examples. All the notes in a melody may be qualitatively different, and if played staccato there are gaps between them, yet the melody is not heard as a series of notes but as a unity. This is because the reverberations of the first notes are heard while the later notes are being played, and when the last notes are sounded we hear along with them the reverberations of all the preceding ones. How else could we appreciate the whole melody?

Does not the same thing happen when we hear a sentence?

The words and phrases of "in *The Last of the Mohicans* Fenimore Cooper showed sympathy with the Indians" are all qualitatively distinct from the others, yet the sentence is grasped as a single meaning. The sentence is too long to be caught in one "perceptual present," the time required for a perception. Suppose that three perceptual presents are needed. Then when we hear the words "Fenimore Cooper showed sympathy," the phrase "in *The Last of the Mohicans*" is reverberating in the mind, and when we hear the last phrase "with Indians" the reverberations of the two preceding phrases fuse with it into a single meaning. Each phrase looms quickly into consciousness when spoken, and then fades out, to be gathered together, when the last phrase is heard, into a unitary meaning. (See James's diagram on p. 181a.)

But is not anticipation another factor aiding smooth transitions? Halfway through a familiar melody we anticipate what is to come. Simultaneously with the middle notes, we not only hear reverberations of the first notes but also anticipate the last. The same is true of the apprehension of the meaning of spoken or written sentences, for these always show familiar structures, both grammatical and semantic. Having apprehended what looks like the subject, we wait for the verb, then for the verb's modifier or object; and having heard the word "went" we anticipate a *where*. This continual anticipation or surmise of what is to come eases transitions and adds continuity to the stream of subjective life.

The greatest breach in continuity to be found in nature, James believes, is that between one self and another. But how about the yawning gap that occurs every night when we fall asleep? Descartes and his followers, James points out, settle the matter *a priori* by defining the soul as a thinking substance, for it then follows that thinking must continue all night long. We have seen that Locke rejects this view on empirical grounds, asserting that if the mind were active during sleep men would not so easily forget. James, however, thinks a pretty good case can be made for the continuity of conscious life on *emperical* grounds (see p. 131b). At least we know enough never to *"take a person's testimony, however sincere, that he has felt nothing, as proof positive that no feeling has been there"* (p. 137b).

Two questions are involved here: *Does the mind ever go completely to sleep with no trace of consciousness?* and *How much of a breach of continuity would there be if it did?* The arguments for the view that we never go *completely* to sleep, as reviewed by James, are striking, but are they not mostly indirect? The somnambulist has no memory of his activities, the dissociated subject loses track of his split-off experiences, we commonly fail to attend to sights and sounds that we nevertheless feel, and forget many waking experiences and most dreams, etc.; therefore, may we not dream all night long without sharp attention at the time or recollection afterward? The answer to this could be "Yes, that might be, but is there any positive evidence for it?" If some of our dreams are so weak and dim as to be scarcely above the threshold of consciousness, the evidence that they are would be hard to come by. But perhaps the electroencephalogram will someday resolve the question. If certain action currents were known to measure degrees of consciousness, we could then determine whether consciousness ever lapses during sleep.

In the meantime, some of the phenomena cited in support of perpetual consciousness admit of other explanations. Is it not the case, for example, that some people can decide, before going to sleep, when they are going to rise in the morning, and then wake up precisely at the appointed time? (See p. 131b.) It is not clear that being conscious all night would explain this ability, but it might help. Another possibility, however, seems more plausible. The man who possesses this ability has not been born to it but has developed the habit, when wishing to rise early, of looking at his watch at intervals during the night. Toward morning he goes into a shallow sleep and looks at his watch more often. But this is only at the beginning. With practice he learns to enjoy a deeper sleep, wake up less often, and finally, dispenses with his watch altogether. How is this possible? There are, as we well know, certain noises which are typical of different periods of the night and morning, and there may be differences of illumniation. Also bodily sensations vary progressively as the sleeper gets more and more rest. When the sleeper looks at his watch he also becomes aware of these accompanying clues. Eventually, by a process of conditioning, he makes use of these clues to guess the time without consulting his watch, and wakes up at the time he said he would.

This explanation is not complete, but it has the merit that it can be improved, and empirically confirmed or disproved, and it illustrates the empirical approach which James almost always favored.

James, of course, had no stake in perpetual consciousness. His main point is that when gaps in consciousness occur there need be no breach in felt continuity. When Peter and Paul wake up in the morning, each picks up the thread of his own existence again without jar or jolt, with no sense of interruption. Peter remembers the events of his biography and Paul his; but neither, strictly speaking, remembers the other's. Peter's feeling of waking up is plainly continuous with Peter's stream of consciousness, and Paul's coming-to is continuous with Paul's stream; but the awakening of neither is continuous with the other's stream. Peter does not have to look into the mirror, and then at Paul, to know that he is not Paul; he knows at once that he is himself.

But how is this possible? How can he immediately recognize himself after eight hours of oblivion? How can the stream vanish and then reappear at a later time? James emphasizes again and again the role of the brain in the continuity of conscious life. It is the brain of Peter which keeps intact during the night the neural patterns which provide the basis for Peter's waking habits and expectations. When the stimulations of morning light or noises, or of events in his viscera, break through the synapses[3] to reach the cerebral cortex, Peter wakes up, and these neural patterns are activated. He looks around and sees *his* hands.

How can he be sure that they are his? Merely seeing them might not be enough, for we know that if subjects are shown photographs of many hands, including their own, they usually

---

[3] Connections of the neurons or nerve cells.

cannot identify the ones that belong to them. Peter, however, is in no doubt. He cannot only see his hands but can move them at will and feel them move, and he knows that this could not be true of any other hands in the world. Thus, even if he had forgotten his name, his family and friends, and place of business, he would still know—would he not?—that this hand was his and that he was still, in some sense, himself.

The test of such hypotheses, as the physician and empiricist James was one of the first clearly to see, requires a study of pathological cases. Would a patient with paralysis and anesthesia, who could not move or feel his arms or legs, suffer alienation, a loss of identity? Similarly, would a loss of memory impair the consciousness of self? There are, of course, plenty of victims of amnesia and of fugue states to study. We shall return to this question. For the present, however, our interest is in the main features of the stream of thought.

I V

Philosophers had always recognized relations, but it was left to James to put feelings of relations on the map, to convince the world that the *transitive* phases are as important in the stream of thought as are the *substantive*. Conscious that he is breaking through with something new and challenging, James charges that both the sensationalists and the intellectualists have failed to do justice to the experience of relations. He exaggerates when he says that Hume went "so far as to deny the reality of most relations *out* of the mind as well as in it" (p. 159a), but we can see what he meant. For Hume nothing exists except sensations ("impressions") and ideas which are "faint copies" of these sensations. Now how could a relation be either a sensation or an idea of sensation? We say that the ceiling is *above* the floor, but do we see anything between the two, in the nature of a sensation or a faint copy of a sensation, which could be described as *aboveness?* We see a pattern of color between ceiling and floor, the color of the wall and of intervening objects, but we see nothing that could be called a relation—nothing, that is, which is also a sensation. The relation is seen, but it is not a sensation.

Hume's sensationalism thus did not allow for feelings of relation, for relations as primary experiences, nor did Kant's intellectualism. Kant held that relations are not given to us as their terms are, but superimposed on sensations by the transcendental faculties of Intuition and Understanding. This left them, James thought, only a shadowy existence. For him feelings of relations were the dynamism, the push and thrust, the life blood of experience, and are to be found everywhere. We all recognize that connectives such as "if" and "but" are relational, but it was James who discovered that there are corresponding feelings, feelings which can become strained and anxious, sometimes amusing, if a speaker stops on one of these words. Consider, for example, the lines of *Humpty Dumpty:*

And he was very proud and stiff: He said "I'd go and wake them, if—"
. . . .
And when I found the door was shut I tried to turn the handle, but—[4]

The role of feelings of relation is enormously important in conscious life. One has only to think how verb forms such as "betrayed," "denounced," "embraced," "married," make us yearn for their objects, and how indeed almost all parts of speech set the mind in zealous movement, in one direction or another.

Akin to feelings of relation are feelings of tendency. These are even more remote from the tidy assortment of sensations, emotions, and copies thereof which, according to Hume, are the exclusive stock of the mind. James cites as examples the feelings evoked by "Wait!", "Hark!", and "Look!". You can easily think of others. They do not say anything at all, but merely stir up expectation of different kinds. More striking are the feelings of tendency at work when we seek to recall a name we have forgotten. The blank in the mind when we try to recall the name *Spalding* is quite different from that which appears when we try to recall *Bowles,* and yet they are both blanks. The difference between the blanks has no name, and James points out that, in general, our psychological vocabulary

---

[4] Lewis Carroll, *Through the Looking-Glass* (Cleveland, Ohio: World Publishing Company, 1946).

is very limited. The difference between the blanks consists of contrasting feelings of tendency which reveal something of what is to come. But could it not be merely functional; one sets up probing in one direction, the other in a different? What do you think?

Feelings of tendency are also illustrated by the intention to say something before we say it. The curtain has just fallen at the end of *Hamlet* and your friend asks you how you think the production compares with others you have seen. Do you think before you reply? You don't have much time for thinking. Do you know what you are going to say in advance? It is extremely unlikely that you know what words you will use— that you have a visual or auditory image of them before you begin to speak. But if you do not know the words you will use, how can you foresee your reply, which the wrong words would completely distort? James's answer is that in such cases we have a fleeting premonition or divination of our meaning, which will be articulated as we proceed to speak.

The intention *to-say-so-and-so* is the only name it can receive. One may admit that a good third of our psychic life consists in these rapid premonitory perspective views of schemes of thought not yet articulate. (p. 164b)

Such vague premonitory previews of schemes of thought, according to James, guide our own speech in advance, enable us to size up the speech of others before they are half finished, and facilitate our reading aloud, with proper cadence and emphasis, prose we have never seen before.

But how, we might inquire, can vague premonitions, which for James are really vague images, give us helpful directions, guide us to the name we want (Mr. Spalding) rather than some other, or supply in advance even the general scheme of what we are about to say? We are apt to think of a feeling of tendency as a kind of arrow pointing in the right general direction, but an arrow is of no use unless we see what it is pointing toward. May it not be possible, though James rejects this interpretation, that we only *think* such vague feelings give direction, that we are really guided by a very rapid association of ideas?

The objection to this view would be that we are not aware of such associations in the instant pause before we answer our friend's inquiry. We do not have time to try out or rehearse alternative answers and then choose the best. The objection is not final, however, for physiological psychologists have recently pointed to evidence that thinking may proceed by trial and error, even though the associations do not appear in consciousness; lightning-fast trials and corrections are continually taking place in the brain.

James insists that brain processes are essential to thinking. If we were to concede also that trials and corrections take place in the brain which are far too rapid-fire to occur in consciousness, it might help to explain a number of things. We are continually struck by the celerity and sureness with which the mind covers unknown ground to reach an ingenious solution or discovery. Retracing the steps of inference and analogy we find large gaps. How could these have been navigated except by faster-than-thought shortcuts in the brain, by processes of which the thinker, of course, was unaware? And how, for that matter, could we have the quick exchange of brilliant conversations, involving careful choice of alternatives and daring shortcuts in reasoning, if a lot of the work were not done subconsciously, in the cerebrum?

That we have a premonition of what we are about to say is denied by some authorities, as James points out. (See p. 182a.) Speaking for himself, one contemporary behaviorist reports that he rarely knows what he is going to say beforehand. When asked a question he begins to talk and finds out as his words are formed what it was he "meant" to say. Sometimes he is satisfied, sometimes quite surprised. Does this sound like an overstatement? In any case we shall probably have to admit that instead of choosing words to fit his meaning, a speaker knows what he means only by words that come to mind, that bob up suddenly owing to associative processes in the brain.

James insists that behind every "psychosis," i.e., mental state, there is a "neurosis," i.e., neural activity. He objects only to the impoverishing of the stream-of-conscious experience; he insists that it is rich and "thick," suffused with *overtones* and *fringes*.

Overtones are strictly the partial tones which are fused with the fundamental when a musical note is played. They account for the difference between the voice of a flute and a violin playing the same note. In a metaphorical sense, however, James can say that all experience has its overtones. For example, a man says to me "Many people in America did not understand Hitler," a statement which is certainly true. Why, then, does it arouse uneasiness and indignation? All communications have their overtones, their tendencies, if not tendentiousness, and they are fused—come in one package—with the facts communicated. We tell our child at night, "It is late," and he replies, "Oh, no"; the unpleasant overtone is not an inference but is stuck to the fact. Similarly, I look out the window at a familiar expanse of water which is usually cheerful. Why is it somber and disquieting today? I remember that I have recently received a letter announcing the death of a friend by drowning. The countryside, houses, autos, dogs, people are thus laden with overtones, which often change according to my moods, and with the association of ideas.

All perceptions, memories, expectations, reasonings are also swept by the fringe of earlier events. As we have seen, the fringe is made up of reverberations from experiences that went before. The melody is a melody only because earlier notes are fading out while later ones are played, and the same seems to be true of trains of reasoning and of all consciousness so far as it is dramatic or developmental.

Most of our mental life seems to be alive with tendencies and expectations, as James says, but must we not be on our guard against the inference that they are *always* conscious? James writes:

> If we know English and French and begin a sentence in French, all the later words that come are French. . . . And this affinity of the French words for each other is not something merely operating mechanically as a brain-law, it is something we feel at the time. (p. 170a)

Are we continuously aware of a feeling that the French words are appropriate when we speak French, or is there merely a continuous lack of a feeling of inappropriateness? James goes on to say:

Our attention can hardly so wander that if an English word be suddenly introduced we shall not start at the change. (p. 170a)

The fact that we are shocked when an English word occurs in straight French discourse does not imply that we were consciously expecting only French words. We may start when walking along a familiar street to find that it is blocked, but it does not follow that we had been consciously expecting it to be open. Habits based on brain patterns, as James elsewhere explains in detail, often take the place of conscious processes.

The fourth feature of the stream of thought is that it is cognitive and concerned with objects independent of it. We are not ordinarily interested in our sensations as such but in the qualities of external things to which they point. Not the whiteness itself, but the cover of snow which has fallen overnight which it advertises; not the muffled roaring sound in itself, but the indication that the ocean is not far away. Thought primarily points to and knows the external world, and only secondarily and occasionally turns back to examine its own contents for their own sake.

While consciousness for James, as we have seen, has a personal quality, and is felt as *mine* (see pp. 147 ff.), we cannot say that it is always accompanied by a consciousness of self. Under anesthetics, James reports, there can be consciousness of things while the thought of self disappears. (See p. 177.) But how can consciousness be felt as *mine* when the awareness of self is lost? It will help to remember that James, in the latter case, is attacking what he took to be the Kantian view that the "I think" accompanies every perception.[5] Consciousness of this *I* or self is quite different from the Jamesean feeling that my conscious objects are *mine;* on the other hand, I am not usually, but only occasionally, self-conscious.

The stream of thought is cognitive; what does it know? It can make itself the object, but it is primarily and ordinarily directed out upon the external world. The associationists wrongly conceive the object of thought as a collection of ele-

---

[5] This was not quite fair to Kant, for Kant said only that the "I think" must *be able to* accompany every perception.

ments. A sentence is objectively a set of words, but to infer that the experience of the sentence is also a collection is to commit "the psychologist's fallacy," as James called it. This is to assume that what is true of the object must be true of the thought that knows it. (See pp. 128-129.)

The Kantians also start out with the notion that the object of thought is a collection, but realizing that a thought must have unity, that a thought is, after all, *one* thought, they assert that there is a transcendental principle that unifies "the manifold"— the mere collection of elements. James replies that there is no need for such a unifying principle. "*Whatever things are thought . . . are thought from the outset in a unity . . .*" (p. 180a-b).

To illustrate this original unity of the object of thought, James again takes our apprehension of a sentence. The problem is how the thought of the sentence, which seems to go from subject to verb to object and to be complete only when the sentence is finished, can still be a unity—a unity from first to last. But how is this possible? Does not the meaning of "The pack of cards is on the table" change as it unfolds? James's radical answer is that the sentence has no real parts—no subject, verb or predicate, but only *time-parts*. We are aware of the meaning of the sentence before we begin to pronounce it "in the form of an intention to utter that sentence" (p. 181b), and throughout the process of pronouncing it, but in different ways. When we are through we glimpse the meaning again, as fully expressed. As the stream of consciousness flows we have the following stages:

1.———→(The pack of cards is on the table)
2.　　　*The pack* "　　"　　"　"　"　　"
3.　　　The pack *of cards* "　"　"　　"
4.　　　The pack of cards *is on* "　　"
5.　　　The pack of cards is on *the table*
6.　　　(The pack of cards is on the table)←———

In 1, we intend the whole meaning, as something to be expressed, while in 6 we grasp it as something expressed. In 2 the whole meaning is present too, but the pack is emphasized as one phase of this meaning. In 3, 4, and 5, progressive phases are emphasized.

We have already pointed out that number 1 can be questioned. Number 6, however, seems undeniable, except when the sentence is too long. In this case would we not have to rely on memory which would piece together the incomplete strands of the sentence? Numbers 1, 2, 3, 4, and 5 all become doubtful when we consider the following sentence from Thomas Erskine's speech at the Trial of Warren Hastings:

> But if it be true that he was directed to make the safety and prosperity of Bengal the first object of his attention, and that, under his administration, it has been safe and prosperous; if it be true that the security and preservation of our possessions and revenues in Asia were marked out to him as the great leading principle of his government, and that those possessions and revenues, amidst unexampled dangers, have been secured and preserved; then a question may be unaccountably mixed with your consideration, much beyond the consequence of the present prosecution, involving, perhaps, the merit of the impeachment itself which gave it birth—a question which the Commons, as prosecutors of Mr. Hastings, should, in common prudence, have avoided; unless, regretting the unwieldy length of their proceedings against him, they wish to afford him the opportunity of this strange anomalous defense.[6]

To grasp the whole meaning of this sentence before and at every stage of its pronouncement would seem impossible; the speaker could only fit its incomplete parts together with the help of memory. It is logically a true sentence, however, not a series of sentences. Yet the speaker, on the verge of such a sentence, must have some presentiment or suspicion of what he is going to say. If he does not have the "entire thought" before him, as James says, he may have what James elsewhere describes as a "preview" or "premonition." No one since James seems to have made this much clearer.

V

We usually take it for granted that we have only one self. James distinguishes three selves: the material, the social, and

[6] "Thomas Erskine Points out the Inevitable Consequences of Empire" in *A Treasury of the World's Great Speeches*, ed. Houston Peterson (New York: Simon & Schuster, Inc., 1954), pp. 186-187.

the spiritual. A useful summary of the characteristics of these selves will be found on page 212. The bodily self includes not only the body and its instincts and appetites but also the adornment, shelter, and security of the body provided by wealth, and even one's immediate family. According to James, the material self is formed largely by instincts. Even the accumulation of property is for James instinctive, but we shall discuss the theory of instincts later on.

Let us now raise the question whether this material is something we *are* or something we merely *have*. In the latter case we might *be* the same person if our body were transformed, our house and possessions scattered, and our family spirited away. Could the question be resolved by observing a man whose material self has been suddenly uprooted and grossly distorted? Inmates of Nazi concentration camps, according to Bruno Bettelheim,[7] had to fight to retain their continuity with the past, their sense of personal identity, and very often failed. Would not such experiences suggest that the material self is at least part of the real self?

The same question might be asked about the social self, which is the "recognition" we get from others. The prisoners just mentioned were shattered socially as well as materially, yet contacts with fellow prisoners were maintained. What would happen to a man totally deprived of society—to a Robinson Crusoe before the coming of Friday? The Robinson Crusoe of the story did not cease to be a social being, for his habits of thought kept society alive, and he reacted to unseen friends and institutions throughout the day. Perhaps this was inevitable. Aristotle defined man as a political animal, and this implies that it would be impossible to find a man who was not social. It might be thought that the so-called wolf-children, children alleged to have grown up among animals and without human contacts, would prove an exception. Reports have it that such children never attain a human level of intelligence and ability, but in none of these cases are the facts well accredited.

[7] Bruno Bettelheim, *The Informed Heart* (The Free Press of Glencoe, 1960).

The overwhelming influence of society, of its rewards and punishments, its solace and criticism, is beyond doubt. In some Eskimo societies, for example, criticism in the form of ridicule and the threat of ostracism is enough to control behavior, no police or courts of law being necessary. In almost any community, fear of disgrace can lead men to risk or court death, and honor is inculcated in the youth as the best safeguard of institutions. Yet the social self, according to James, is not the deepest self, not the inner core of a man's identity. One reason is that there is more than one social self. A kind and devoted father may be cruel and ruthless in business, and a deceitful politician may be the soul of honor among friends. But where there is a plurality of selves there can also be rivalry and conflict. How can we decide which of our social selves shall become dominant unless there is a deeper self which can think the conflict through and resolve it? How is it that our stern business self can be suspended at the right time and our party self released?

More fundamental than the social self or selves, then, is what James calls the spiritual self. Here we reach the last wrung of the ladder, the inner core of our concrete being, "the Self of selves." What is it? It is myself as *thinker,* as ever active and striving, áttending, overcoming opposition, giving or withholding assent to what is posed and proposed, the continuing source of all our activity. The thinking which is our innermost reality is thus far from passive contemplation. It implies purposiveness, struggle, and hindrances to be overcome. As on the levels of the material and the social self, so here on the level of the spiritual self, we have much to gain and lose.

$$\text{Self esteem} = \frac{\text{Success}}{\text{Pretensions}}, \text{ James said, i.e., success di-}$$

vided by pretensions. He thereby anticipated recent studies of "the level of aspiration." Where the level of performance is close to the level of aspiration, and the latter has been pegged pretty high, the result is self-esteen; where there is a large discrepancy between the two levels, frustration results. The for-

$$\text{mula would be: Frustration} = \frac{\text{Pretensions}}{\text{Success}}, \text{ or, } \frac{\text{Aspirations}}{\text{Performance}}.$$

To avoid frustration many subjects peg their aspirations low and can thus enjoy success on a more modest plane. The ideas behind these experiments are all in James; what they add are simply measurement and confirmation. Now the specifically spiritual self-esteem is success divided by pretensions to intellectual and moral superiority. (See p. 212.)

Would you say that all men have these spiritual pretensions, or does James extend his generalization too far? And do all men in fact regard spiritual self-esteen as better than any other self-esteem, or are there in this regard different types of men? Would anyone who rated himself low intellectually and morally be satisfied with himself, even though he enjoyed health, well-being, property, a fine family, friends, sympathy, and social success? This question would be difficult to answer. How could a man who has a poor opinion of his own mind and morals enjoy friends, social success, a fine family, or even health? Such a man, you might say, would be so frustrated as to enjoy nothing. Enjoyment of all these things would presuppose a measure of esteem for one's own intelligence and intentions. Or can the esteem of others, if it is large enough, make up for a want of self-esteen?

The spiritual self, as James describes it, appears to be an undeniable fact of conscious life. But when we try to find this self it eludes us.

> . . . it is difficult for me to detect in the activity any purely spiritual element at all. Whenever my introspective glance succeeds in turning round quickly enough to catch one of these manifestations of spontaneity in the act, all it can ever feel distinctly is some bodily process, for the most part taking place within the head. (p. 193b)

When we look for the spiritual self as something different from spiritual acts and processes, we find only fluctuating feelings of strain and tension. There is no question that such sensations of strain and effort occur when we concentrate on an intellectual task or make a hard moral decision, and the only question is whether this is all that occurs. In solving a mathematical problem we may furrow our brow, tighten our scalp, and sensations may also arise from the muscles which adjust the eyes for near and far vision. In working ourselves up to a hard moral decision, viz., to be just to a man who has been unjust to us, sensations may be felt in the thorax owing to a change in the rate and depth of breathing, in the throat, in the face and neck, and tension may spread to various groups of skeletal muscles. Whether anything besides these sensations of effort and strain accompanies our spiritual activity each of us can investigate for himself. We have only to look into our own minds.

Speaking for himself James declares that the *Self of selves* consists "*mainly of the collection of these peculiar motions in the head or between the head and throat*" (p. 194b). If the dim, unanalyzable part of what he feels is like the part that is distinct, "*it would follow that our entire feeling of spiritual activity . . . is really a feeling of bodily activities whose exact nature is by most men overlooked*" (p. 194b). But is there no other reason than these feelings of effort for thinking that the spiritual self exists? Might we not argue that a spiritual self is needed for religion and the moral life, that there must be a responsible agent to reward and blame and save?

Such a consideration, in James's view, falls outside empirical psychology. Philosophers who have claimed some other access to the self than James allows have usually taken one of two positions: (1) The self as the subject which knows cannot become its own object, for then it would cease to be subject, cease to be itself. We must therefore distinguish between knowing, which involves subject and object, and feeling or enjoying, which does not. The self feels or enjoys itself immediately (not as an object), while the self is experiencing other things or objects. (2) The instant after the self has experienced an object, it can look back and glimpse itself experiencing that object. At the moment I hear a clap of thunder I cannot also experience the self that hears it, but a moment later my attention can flash back to the self having this experience. Both of these positions can be made plausible, but for the hard-boiled empirical psychologist, intent upon facts rather than theories, James's view has more appeal.

It is but a short step from our awareness of the spiritual self to our awareness of personal identity. How I know that I am the same person as I was when an infant, that the selfsame I has been operating continuously in spite of momentous changes and breaks for sleep, had long been regarded as a philosophical problem. For James, there is nothing mysterious about it. Saying I am the same as I was yesterday is not more difficult than saying that a pen is the same. (See p. 213b.) Judgments of sameness are all of the same form, but is there not an obvious difference? If we look at a man from the outside, as we do a pen, his identity would be defined by his appearance, his fingerprints, his track in space-time, and would be a matter for the police. But when it is a question of personal identity each must look into his stream of consciousness for proof that he is still the same. What, then, do we find?

Many authorities had claimed that the real self or ego is the subject which has perceptions, memories, and all other experiences, but is never itself an experience. This pure ego knows, or has for its objects, everything that is experienced, but never itself becomes an object; it stands above the stream of thought. It is what we previously called the transcendent self.

This pure ego is not only the darling of theologians and philosophers of many hues but it is also favored, as James admits, by common sense. It is indeed easy to see its plausibility. We all say: "I know the multiplication table," "I am angry," "I love the moonlight on the ocean," "I doubt it will rain," etc. We identify our self with the *I* which knows, has emotions, loves, and doubts, but not with that which is known, felt, loved, or doubted. That you love Mary and John or a young brood at home may be the most important thing about you; it is not *you*. You are not the loving, thinking, planning, triumphing, but the identical subject which does these things. It is this subject or ego which remains the same throughout your checkered career while everything else is in flux. This subject of all experience, this pure ego, is about the only thing which does remain invariant, and we know that however drastic the change in our fortunes, ideas, or feelings it would always remain the same. Even if *I* say "*I* am a changed man," the *I* that says so is the same old *I*.

What, then, can be James's objection to recognizing the pure ego as the genuine self and the key to personal identity?

Although James's answer is elaborate and brilliantly diverse, his main objection is that the closest examination of conscious life fails to reveal any trace of it. He finds the thinking, the remembering, the emotions, but not the identical subject which thinks, remembers, and feels. He therefore discards the fiction of a transcendent *I* and undertakes to explain our sense of personal identity in terms of the empirical *me*. Remembering now becomes a relation between the present stream of consciousness and past states of the same stream. The thinker becomes part of the present stream, the thought another part, and so on. But how can an experience of mine do my thinking, remembering, and hoping? To common sense this will appear absurd, James conceded, yet only on this hypothesis can a *verifiable* psychology be built.

How, then, is the statement "I am the same self that I was yesterday" to be interpreted? James's reply is that what distinguishes *my* ideas, recollections, and emotions from alien ones is a feeling of "warmth and intimacy." When I awaken in the morning I take up the thread of my personal existence without difficulty because what I remember from the day before has this warmth and familiarity. This feeling is first and foremost a bodily feeling, a kind of "animal warmth," and even the recognition of our spiritual self has no other basis.

. . . we feel the whole cubic mass of our body all the while, it gives us an unceasing sense of personal existence. Equally do we feel the inner "nucleus of the spiritual self," either in the shape of yon faint physiological adjustments, or (adopting the universal psychological belief), in that of the pure activity of our thought taking place as such. Our remoter spiritual, material, and social selves, so far as they are realized, come also with a glow and a warmth; for the thought of them infallibly brings some degree of organic emotion in the shape of quickened heartbeats, oppressed breathing, or some other alteration, even though it be a slight one, in the general bodily tone. (pp. 214b-215a)

Twenty-two years later, in his famous essay "Does Consciousness Exist?", James emphasized the role of breathing, particularly: "The 'I think' which Kant said must be able to accompany all my objects, is the 'I breathe' which actually does accompany them."[8] It will help in understanding James's

---

[8] William James, *Essays in Radical Empiricism* (New York: Longmans, Green & Company, Inc., 1943, p. 37.

radical view if we now take note of the continuous mass of vague sensations going on in the chest and throat as we breathe. This mass of sensations arising as the intercostal muscles contract and relax is in the focus now, but it is usually in the background. In the foreground are our focal fears, ideas, aspirations, but behind them is this continuing mass of sensations, giving a sense of our bodily presence and personal participation. What else, we might ask, gives us this sense?

The feeling of warmth and familiarity is not the touchstone of personal identity. This feeling itself is based on the continuing similarities and continuity which bind our experiences into one stream. Similar perceptions, ideas, emotions, etc., tend to recur in the same biography, and changes and developments are almost always gradual. If they are not, if a man should suddenly wake up in China, without transitional experiences, and notice in the mirror that his appearance had greatly changed, would he still recognize *himself?*

Even this desperate quandary might not destroy a man's sense of personal identity if only he retained his memory. But if all recollection of his past life were gone, then we know that his old self would also have vanished. Men who suffer complete amnesia and find themselves in a new environment, must, as we know, develop new selves. Even by itself memory is a powerful cement to bind the strands of the self together, for you can remember (potentially) all your own conscious past but nothing of the inner experience of others.

Our sense of personal identity thus arises from the feeling of warmth and familiarity, but behind this feeling is a sense of similarity and continuity, made possible by memory.

VI

Does not the fact that a man is always choosing what he wants give him his sense of personal identity? Is not the feeling of self the feeling of choosing?

An important feature of the stream of thought which we have not yet mentioned is its voluntary character. (See pp. 184-187.) Whether we are perceiving, remembering, reasoning, or enjoying or creating works of art, James holds, it is we ourselves who decide what we will actually come to grips with. In perceiving, I am highly selective; I welcome some items but reject almost all. A man who has climbed the few steps in front of his house a thousand times cannot tell you just how many there are, but he can turn to the exact page of a book where he once read a passage he liked.

The eliminating and choosing, whether in perception, memory, reasoning, or aesthetic activity, is largely personal and peculiar to each of us. We shift our attention to what interests us personally, and, according to James, it is only in this power to turn our beam of attention where we please that we enjoy free will. Our question then is this: Does not this power to continually choose what interests us provide a continuous sense of personal identity? In choosing, we are personally active in behalf of our personal interests. Do we not thereby affirm our difference from the whole neutral mass of alien existence?

It might be said that this factor of personal choice is included in James's account of our sense of personal identity, that the things we choose are precisely those which come to us with an aroma of warmth and familiarity. Moreover, is not the choosing itself—this display of personal power—experienced simply as sense of effort or tension? In this case, James would have included this factor of choice in his own view, though without emphasizing it.

Is the soul superfluous from a scientific point of view?

We have seen that James rejects the transcendent self—a self over and above the stream of thought. It is unobservable and has no scientific value. The soul, as a simple, immaterial substance transcending the stream, is also rejected. James admits that great authorities have been certain that they directly perceived the soul and that the soul is necessary to explain our conscious life. He, on the contrary, cannot find the soul nor see any use for it. It is the outgrowth of the "sort of philosophizing whose great maxim, according to Dr. Hodgson, is: 'Whatever you are *totally* ignorant of, assert to be the explanation of everything else' " (p. 223b).

What is the soul supposed to explain? One thing is personal identity. How would we verify the hypothesis that the soul is responsible for our sense of personal identity? We should first have to show that a stream of consciousness possesses a kind of unity constituted by similarities, continuity, associations, expectations, warm feelings of appropriation, etc. Next, we should have to attribute this unity to the soul. But why take this last step, James asks. All that has been verified are the existence of the unity and the mental processes in which the unity occurs. The personal memories and our perceptions of similarities and continuity establish our identity, not the proposition that there is a soul which has these perceptions and memories.

The friends of the soul, however, will ask: How can there be perceptions and thoughts if they belong to no one? Does not perception imply a perceiver and thought a thinker? Can experiences be the whole show? James answers that we have evidence that experiences depend on brain states. "The bald fact is that *when the brain acts, a thought occurs*" (p. 222b). To suppose that states, in turn, depend on the soul is fanciful and entirely superfluous. There may be religious reasons for accepting the soul, James admits, but no scientific justification whatever. The only verifiable thinker is "the passing Thought" (p. 223a).

Must we conclude that James is entirely right, or can we assign some use to the soul in empirical psychology? If the soul is conceived not as a separate substance independent of the body but as the functioning of the organism or as the principles according to which it functions, it can have explanatory value. Structure and function are known to be interdependent. For example, after an injury a man begins to regain the ability to walk, and thereby builds the tissues which will make possible further gains. He does this by trying to walk, or rather by trying to move as best he can toward his friends, the dinner table, the recreation hall. By exercising the function, the physiological structure is gradually restored, and restoration simultaneously furthers improvements in function. Such inter-dependence of structure and function is more understandable, perhaps, if the soul, as in Aristole, is conceived as the principle or "inner meaning" of the activity of the organism.

What self do we love in self-love?

Do we love the material self, the social self or selves, the spiritual self, or "the mere pronoun *I*," James asks. The pronoun *I* of course is a jest. But the pure ego, or transcendental self, is also a cold spectral thing at best. No one cares a rap for it. First and foremost we have a warm regard and tender concern for our own body; if we did not, it would not long survive. The strongest instincts incite us to serve its needs and to ward off injury, and this primitive selfishness is always with us. James goes further:

> *My own body and what ministers to its needs are thus the primitive object, instinctively determined, of my egoistic interests. Other objects may become interesting derivatively* through association with any of these things, either as means or as habitual concomitants; *and so in a thousand ways the primitive sphere of the egoistic emotions may enlarge* and change its boundaries. (p. 209a)

But just how is the original love for our own body extended to other things? Why do you like to be praised, for example? This is perhaps understandable on James's theory, since praise produces certain pleasant reverberations somewhere in the body—maybe in the viscera. In any case, the fact is well attested. The body is then the real recipient of praise, whether it is praise of my knowledge, my family, or my friends. Friends and family do things for me, bring me food, books, and other things that tend to minister directly or indirectly to my body's needs. They are also present when I am at dinner and resting in front of the fire, and thus are associated with the glow which is afforded by food, warmth, and ease. In this way, too, family and friends are absorbed in my love of *me*.

But how would I come to love my generous, self-sacrificing self? According to James's theory the selfish bodily self can expand to include the most benevolent and disinterested de-votions while still remaining itself. Unselfish dedication to science or humanity gratifies the viscera of some men more than other activities they might pursue. Of the objects they call *mine*, the dearest are those which are farthest removed from their own body, though they are dearest only because the body is affected.

In evaluating James's paradoxical doctrine, it might be well to think of something he may have left out of his account. Do you love people, for example, only because they minister directly or indirectly to your bodily needs, or do you love them for their beauty or wisdom whether they serve these needs or not? The *cause* of your loving a person might be the effect produced in your body, but need this be your *reason* for loving him, or that which you find lovable in him?

The following questions are designed to help you test the thoroughness of your reading. Each question is to be answered by giving a page or pages of the reading assignment. Answers will be found on page 384 of this Reading Plan.

1 In what way are *"secondary personal selves"* stupid and contracted?

2 What explanation does James give of so-called "spirit-control" of mediums and automatic writers?

3 Is there any evidence, according to James, that we ever experience the same bodily sensation twice?

4 How does brain physiology confirm James's view that "experience is remoulding us every moment"?

5 Do we feel our bodily selves, according to James, to be the seat of our thinking?

6 Why are the "transitive parts" of the stream of thought likely to be overlooked or misjudged?

7 What common error explains why "all *dumb* or anonymous psychic states have . . . been coolly suppressed"?

8 What introspective distinction between sensations, percepts, and concepts does James find?

9 What is the probable cause of "the sense of familiarity"?

10 To what is the difference between knowledge by "acquaintance" and "knowledges-*about*" reducible?

WILLIAM JAMES

The Principles of Psychology

Ch. 25-26

Vol. 53, pp. 743-757, 796-829

J ames's early biological and medical training gave its impress to every topic he discussed. Inner consciousness was of the first importance, and the subtle flow and nuance of the subjective life must be explored to the last dim cranny; yet the qualities of consciousness must have their basis in brain activity. Psychic experiences fade out gradually and overlap one another, James said, but the same is true of neural processes. "As the total neurosis changes, so does the total psychosis change" (p. 157b).

This very characteristic emphasis on *total* pattern in both cases is significant. James gave a careful account of the contemporary controversy over the localization of function in the brain, but when it comes to thought, he said, "the whole brain must act together." Consciousness " 'corresponds' to the entire activity of the brain, whatever that may be, at the moment" (p. 116a), a conclusion which anticipated the present outlook in neurophysiology.

In his treatment of the stream of thought and the consciousness of self, as we have seen, James sought to anchor experience in brain activity. He did the same in dealing with habit, attention, association, sensation, perception of space and time, memory, reasoning, instinct, emotion, and even will. Yet James rebelled against the automaton theory that consciousness is a mere reflection of neural activities, that it has no power whatever to direct its own course. In the struggle for existence among existing and possible experiences, consciousness can load the dice, making for a desired outcome. This subjective freedom, so essential to James's later "Will to Believe" and to his philosophies of pragmatism and pluralism, is elaborated in the chapter on "Will," which we shall consider below. Before doing so we shall look into James's theory of emotions, where human consciousness *is* a mere reflection of physiological processes.

Although James was always radiating ideas, the two chapters on "The Stream of Thought" and "The Consciousness of Self," which we have discussed, and the two chapters which we are about to explore, "The Emotions" and "Will," are considered the most original of all. Bertrand Russell once said that "James's mind was a battle-ground of medical materialism and the mysticism suggested by Swedenborg. His learned self was scientific and his emotional self cosmic;

neither led him to attach great value to the ego."[1] We shall see, however, that this is truer of the chapters that we have studied than it is of the chapter on "Will." In the latter, his activism, meliorism and pragmatism hold sway, and the pure ego threatens to return to the field, still unconquered. Consistency, which has been called "a virtue of small minds," was not James's forte, and we are fortunate that he preferred to give his abundant mind free play.

[1] Bertrand Russell, *Journal of Philosophy,* Nov. 23, 1922.

Thirteenth Reading

I

After the publication of *The Principles of Psychology* in 1890, James's main bent of interest turned from psychology to philosophy. He lacked the temperament and the patience for psychological experiments, and it was left to his colleague, Hugo Münsterberg, to carry on his laboratory at Harvard. Moreover, he found the results of such studies increasingly trivial and disappointing. He still gave lectures on psychology, such as the *Talks to Teachers on Psychology* (published 1899), and he condensed his *Principles* into a one-volume text, *Briefer Course,* but daemonic forces were driving him to new achievements in a broader field. In the next few years he laid the foundations of pragmatism, a philosophical development which was to become the distinctive trend of the twentieth century. To free his mind for this enterprise, lesser interests must be renounced. "I've served my time and bought my freedom," he jibed in 1898, "and must employ my ebbing sands of life for things parasitic, insolent, and inconclusive."[2]

The adjectives used to describe his own philosophical enterprise are typical of the man, whether as philosopher or psychologist. Often he gave a better exposition of an adversary's ideas than the adversary himself had done, and was reluctant to condemn any idea without repeated hearings and reviews. His colleague George Santayana said of James:

I think it would have depressed him if he had had to confess that any important question was finally settled. He would still have hoped that

[2] Ralph Barton Perry, *The Thought and Character of William James* (Briefer Version) (Cambridge, Mass: Harvard University Press, 1948), p. 200.

something might turn up on the other side, and that just as the scientific hangman was about to despatch the poor convicted prisoner, an unexpected witness would ride up in hot haste, and prove him innocent.[3]

In his famous essay "The Will to Believe," James took up the cudgels in defense of religious belief, intimidated by the growing authority of science and evolutionary theory. He argued that anyone has a right to believe what will give meaning and value to his life, so long as it is not known to be false. In his *Pragmatism,* he put human values before all else, asserting that truth is nothing but what is useful—useful to human beings—and what is useful is always true.

He denounced all philosophical absolutisms (such as that of Hegel and of his own colleague at Harvard, Josiah Royce) which seemed to justify cruelty and injustice on earth and to call for human sacrifice. In his *Pluralistic Universe* he opposed to the rigid "block universe" of the absolute idealists a pluralistic universe where human diversity is uppermost, where tolerance, uncertainty, adventure, humor, and sanity are in the saddle. Meanwhile in his *Varieties of Religious Experience,* in which he made important advances in the psychology of religious experience, he had shown the closest sympathy and understanding of psychical research and mysticism, while yet retaining all his scientific poise and respect for facts.

I I

James begins his chapter on "The Emotions" with the comment that emotions and instincts are intertwined and inseparable. The pugnacious instinct is accompanied by the emotion of rage; the instinct of flight and concealment, by fear.

Contrary to a current view that man, being endowed with reason, needs fewer instincts than other animals, James maintained that he has more, and that any of these taken by itself can be quite "blind." The distinction of man, however, is that when he has experienced these instincts *in their results,* his memory and inference can modify and adapt them to the

---

[3] George Santayana, *Character and Opinion in the United States, With Reminiscences of William James and Josiah Royce and Academic Life in America* (New York: Charles Scribner's Sons, 1920), p. 82.

situation. They are now accompanied by foresight and cease to be "blind and invariable." Moreover, most instincts are normally supplanted by habits, which are typically quite variable and adaptive, and subsequently fade away. (See page 712b).

Among the peculiarly human instincts, which James took over from his contemporary, Professor Preyer, are sucking, biting, clasping, crying, etc. These are relatively simple mechanical responses and are now called reflexes, not instincts. Locomotion and vocalization, which wait upon the maturation of the child's nervous system, are much more complicated and varied, and the latter especially depends upon a learning process of which James was only dimly aware. The role of learning is even more prominent in James's instincts of emulation, acquisitiveness, constructiveness, sociability, cleanliness, and the hunting instinct. Hunting and constructive activity are obviously learned, in great part, and learning cleanliness, we all know, goes against the grain.

With the rise of learning theory in American psychology, beginning some thirty years after the appearance of the *Principles*, the instinct theory fell into disrepute. Explaining a miser's hoarding by the strength of the acquisitive instinct seemed to be merely hanging the problem on a convenient peg, and no explanation at all. In making his instincts variable and modifiable, adaptable to the situation, James avoided some of the objections to instinct theory. Meanwhile his insistence on the physiological base and adaptive use of human motivation helped to unify man as an animal with man as a psychological and social being. His theory of instincts, like his theory of emotions, was a big step forward in a unified conception of human nature.

In his account of the emotions, James does well to start off with the "coarser emotions," since in their light his theory is more easily understood. In coarse emotions such as rage or fright, James says, we usually think that some object—a sudden insult or a car approaching us in the wrong lane, for example—first excites the conscious emotion, which is then followed by bodily changes, e.g., rapid breathing and heart rate, increased perspiration, etc. James's theory, on the contrary, is that

> . . . *the bodily changes follow directly the perception of the exciting fact, and that our feeling of the same changes as they occur* is *the emotion.* Common-sense says, we lose our fortune, are sorry and weep; we meet a bear, are frightened and run; we are insulted by a rival, are angry and strike. The hypothesis here to be defended says that this order of sequence is incorrect . . . that the more rational statement is that we feel sorry because we cry, angry because we strike, afraid because we tremble. . . . Without the bodily states following on the perception, the latter would be purely cognitive in form, pale, colorless, destitute of emotional warmth. (p. 743a-b)

If the bodily changes did not occur, the perception of a car approaching us in the wrong lane might cause us, because of habit or inference, to veer off the road or onto the shoulder, but the alarm, the agitation, the wave and rush of feeling would be lacking. In those who are habituated to hazards of the kind, cold and composed avoidance may occur, but the experience would not be called emotional. The emotion itself arises only when nervous impulses are sent from the brain, i.e., the cerebral cortex, down to the viscera and to the skeletal muscles, and afferent impulses, produced by the changes in muscles and viscera, are transmitted to the cerebral cortex where they are transformed into a pattern of sensations. This pattern of sensations *is* the emotion.

Suppose we begin crossing the street and then notice a speeding car bearing down upon us. We jump to the curb in a fraction of a second, and only then become aware that we are breathing fast, that our heart is going like a triphammer, that we are perspiring and perhaps trembling, and have a dull feeling in our stomach. This commotion may endure long after the danger has passed. Is not this what we mean by fear? And do we not jump to the curb before we have had time to experience fear?

Let us take another example. Suppose we are suddenly insulted, and immediately shout: "You are a blankety-blank liar!" Not until an instant later do we feel a wave of indignation sweep over us, often surprising, sometimes sickening. Does it not appear that our anger in such cases is simply an awareness of bodily changes, the pounding of the heart, the fast breathing, the sinking in the stomach, the clenching of the fist, the tension of extended patterns of muscles? The feeling of indignation could hardly be the cause of these bodily changes, since it does not precede them; the changes must rather be the cause of feeling.

Further evidence for James's theory is provided by cases where we do not know the cause of our emotion. We are overtaken by a feeling of sadness and depression. We know not why. What is this feeling? It does not refer to any object whatever, but seems to consist of a mass of ill-defined sensations throughout the body. Later on we may be able to trace our sadness to something we have seen or heard which is associated with sorrow or tragedy in our past experience, but at the time the feeling seems to be no more than an awareness of vague but pervasive bodily changes.

James makes a great deal of pathological cases in which *"the emotion is objectless"* (p. 749a). A manic-depressive patient is periodically elated and then depressed, without any external cause, even when the external circumstances would normally produce the opposite emotion. Since the cause of the feeling in this case is not external, must it not be internal? Can the elation and depression be anything else but the awareness of the alternating bodily changes?

One test of the theory would be the possibility of realizing the bodily changes without the corresponding feeling. Actors are said to mimic all the passions without feeling them, and the rest of us can do this to some extent. How then can emotion be an awareness of bodily changes? James points out that the actor can control facial muscles and skeletal muscles in general, but not the smooth muscles of the viscera, for these are involuntary. If he could superinduce other bodily changes, how do we know he could not experience the full emotion? The evidence points this way, he says. The panic of fear is increased by flight, grief by continued sobbing, anger by "working ourselves up" into a pugnacious state. On the other hand, "Refuse to express a passion, and it dies" (p. 751b).

But is this true? Could it not be said that expressing our emotion, far from prolonging, actually extinguishes it? Blowing our top and venting our grief restore our usual calm. James's reply to this objection is complex. The most important points are that giving way to our tears or teeth-grinding might increase our grief or rage up to a certain point, but after that the emotion subsides; it has spent itself, as we say. Flying into a passion intensifies our anger but may also remove it. Repressing the expression of fear and other strong emotions, on the other hand, can result in noisy outbreaks later' on, or in a disturbance taking pathological forms. Here James touches on a theme which, as we shall see, is of central importance in Freud. Repression of strong emotion, by refusing to express it, can have unhealthy consequences, James states. Why then do we urge our children to curb their temper fits and tears? It is because we want them to think—to find a rational solution to their quandaries. (See p. 754a-b.)

The decisive test of this epoch-making theory of emotion would be to exhibit cases in which the bodily changes, said to be the source of emotion, are disturbed or cut off from consciousness. Would a man deprived of sensations from skeletal muscles and viscera be incapable of emotion? James examined some hospitalized patients with abnormal visceral conditions, but the results were not of great value. How could he know what their emotional life was before the visceral troubles began, and if he did not know this, how could he tell how much their emotions had changed?

In 1906 Sherrington picked out a dog of a "markedly emotional tempefament," very affectionate but given to violent fits of anger, and then cut the afferent nerves conducting impulses from the viscera, skin, and muscles behind the shoulder. This meant that the cortex, the organ of consciousness, was cut off from most of its own body; the dog could feel little or nothing of those bodily changes which, according to James, are necessary to emotion. Yet, Sherrington reported, this gross elimination of sensation in the dog produced no obvious change in her emotional character. "Her anger, her joy, her disgust, and . . . her fear, remained as evident as ever."[4] When a cat with which she was unfriendly approached too closely, she flew into a rage; she was aroused when a visitor who had excited her anger before paid a call. There seemed to be good evidence that the dog's emotional life continued as before, that her emotions were not merely expressed outwardly but also felt subjectively. But can we be absolutely sure of this?

We can be more certain in the cases of persons whose spinal cord has been severed at the neck owing to an accident. Although deprived of all sensation below the neck, they still display and report emotions.[5]

In the face of such evidence, how is it possible for some psychologists still to accept James's theory—"the James-Lange theory," as it is usually called—and for all to concede his contribution to the field of emotions? It is easy at this point to become bogged down in details and complexities. James's main contribution was to recognize the role of visceral and muscular contractions in the more intense, "coarser" emotions, for James did not claim that his theory was adequate for the subtler sort. His insight led to the discovery by Walter B. Cannon[6] that the viscera are involved in ways that James had not suspected. In emergency situations, for example, sugar is released into the blood stream, and there is an additional secretion of the hormone adrenalin, which acts upon visceral organs via the blood stream. These visceral reactions release energy and prepare the organism to put forth its ultimate effort in defense, flight, or aggression. Cannon also showed that the hypothalamus in the midbrain is also involved, but more recently it has been demonstrated that this structure is concerned only with the outward *expression* of emotions. James

[4] C. S. Sherrington, *The Integrative Action of the Nervous System* (New Haven: Yale University Press, 1906), p. 261.

[5] N. L. Munn, *Psychological Development* (Boston: Houghton Mifflin Company, 1938), pp. 422-424.

[6] W. B. Cannon, *Bodily Changes in Pain, Hunger, Fear and Rage*, 2nd ed. (New York: D. Appleton & Company, 1929).

was evidently right in seeing the cerebral cortex as the source of the emotion itself.

Just where did James's theory go wrong? We can begin by testing it in our own experience. When you accidentally meet your enemy on the street, your indignation or aversion is simultaneous. Seeing him and feeling aversion are one process; you see his *hateful* face as soon as you see his face. In our previous example of jumping to the curb before a speeding car, the fear attitude may get lost in the shock and excitement, but does it not generally appear immediately? Do you have to wait a second after you see your sweetheart to feel that she is charming and wonderful, or does it not come to you at the first moment of recognition?

This is not to say that the visceral reactions and the contractions of muscles are not important, but only that they come later and are not essential to the emotion-as-attitude, i.e., the admiring, the fearing, the indignation, etc.—the immediate stand we take toward the object. The depth, force, and poignancy of emotion certainly owe everything to the waves or ripples of bodily feelings. We can agree with James—up to a certain point—when he says, speaking of subtler emotions:

. . . unless we actually laugh at the neatness of the demonstration or witticism; unless we thrill at the case of justice, or tingle at the act of magnanimity; our state of mind can hardly be called emotional at all. It is in fact a mere intellectual perception of how certain things are to be called—neat, right, witty, generous, and the like. (p. 757a)

An Oxford don who was a great expert on humor is said to have always listened calmly to a joke. After his colleagues had laughed uproariously, he would quietly remark, "Yes, there is that joke." This would be an example of a purely intellectual recognition of humor. It is very different from the cases where we appreciate a joke very well indeed but for some reason or other must pretend we do not. When the joke is on the boss we can remain silent. Laughing adds to our sense of the humor but is hardly necessary to it. And would not the same be true of the "thrill" and "tingle" that James mentions? In addition to an intellectual recognition of justice and heroism, do we not have an immediate emotional attitude of admiration? If I tell you of a boy who dove through a hole in the ice to rescue a companion, and by swimming under the ice finally succeeded in pulling him out of another hole farther downstream, do you not feel a prompt and warm approval? Or must approval wait until the slow action of the autonomic system has furnished a pattern of visceral sensations?

But we must avoid selling James's theory short. Visceral changes, such as quickened heart rate and breathing, are not essential to emotional attitudes of fear, anger, admiration, etc., but contractions of skeletal muscles of some sort may be necessary. The patient whose spinal cord has been severed can still feel contractions of muscles in the head, and awareness of these may be involved in the emotions which he reports having. The part played by muscular contractions in inducing what James calls "feelings of tendency," which are no doubt part of the emotional experience, cannot be discounted. The components of emotion need more study.

The emotional attitude that we have been discussing is not self-explanatory. It may be clear in what it refers to—the fearful, hated, or charming object—but it is not clear at all in itself. If you try to describe it, you come out with a description of its object. The more we can learn about the role of muscular contractions in attitudes and emotions, the more scientific will be our understanding of them and the more we shall be able to value James's contribution.

III

The will is one of the most fascinating, important, and perplexing topics in psychology. It is so baffling when studied by itself that most contemporary psychologists consider it only in relation to personality. Instead of dealing with the will itself, they merely distinguish different types of personality according to the kind of choices each is prone to make, and point to pathological developments, for example, in which a decision of any kind becomes all but impossible (abulia). The general subject of will is full of bogs and fog. But James never avoided a subject because it was difficult; he was enticed by it if only it was important.

The first requirement of voluntary life, according to James, is that we have carried out involuntary movements in the past and are able to remember them. (See p. 768.) Only if we have previously moved our body and limbs involuntarily can we have expected to move them voluntarily. Would this always be true? Can we not voluntarily pronounce a foreign word which we hear spoken for the first time? You could combine sounds which you have produced before into a word entirely new to you, but suppose that the word is the French *embonpoint,* and that you have never before uttered the syllables. Could you at will contract the right muscles to articulate them?

James's contention, then, is that in order to carry out an act of will we must have memory images of the act to be performed. When we performed the act previously, whether passively or intentionally, we experienced certain sensations of movement, i.e., kinesthetic sensations. The stimuli for these kinesthetic sensations were contractions of a particular set of muscles. Now, when we are about to repeat the same act voluntarily, we must have a kinesthetic image of that particular pattern of sensations, for this is simply the idea of the act to be performed.

What evidence does James give in support of this contention? He cites well-known facts about patients suffering from anesthesia of one area or another, that is, patients who do not receive sensations from skin or muscles in certain areas. Let us take an example of our own. In some diseases, such as paresis, the muscles of the legs are capable of contraction, but the patient is not conscious of their contraction, receives no sensations (or very few) from muscles, tendons, or joints. When the disease is well advanced he is unable to walk if blindfolded. When he is allowed to watch his legs, i.e., is guided by visual sensations, he has no difficulty. Normal people also need the guidance of sensations and memory images to walk, but the sensations and images in this case are kinesthetic. Since the paretic has no kinesthetic sensitivity in his legs he must substitute visual cues and cannot walk without them.

James points out that the same thing happens when a subject under hypnosis is told he has no feeling in his arm; this arm can then be placed in any position and he has not the slightest idea of its whereabouts. But if he does not know where it is, how can he carry out any definite act, such as waving goodby, cleaning his shoes, or writing a letter? The hysteric who seems to be unable to feel anything in some area, and yet has no physical defect which would account for it, is no better off. He also cannot carry out concerted acts. All such cases, James holds,

. . . show the absolute need of *guiding sensations* of some kind for the successful carrying out of a concatenated series of movements. It is, in fact, easy to see that, just as where the chain of movements is automatic . . . , each later movement of the chain has to be discharged by the impression which the next earlier one makes in being executed, so also, where the chain is voluntary, we need to know at each movement just *where we are in it,* if we are to will intelligently what the next link shall be. (p. 770a)

If you have any doubts about this, try walking blindfolded. If you do not know where your right foot is—i.e., if your kinesthetic sensations do not inform you where it is—how can you know whether to throw it forward or retract it? In swimming, similarly, we must know where our legs are at every point if we are to carry through. We must also, as in shifting from low to high gear, have kinesthetic images corresponding to sensations which previously accompanied such a chain of actions. In playing the piano, the guiding kinesthesia is naturally far more complex.

Voluntary action requires these guiding sensations and images; it requires only them. In ". . . *perfectly simple voluntary acts there is nothing else in the mind but the kinæsthetic idea, thus defined, of what the act is to be"* (p. 771b).

James now deals at length with an objection to this contention, endorsed by some of the great authorities of his time, namely, the theory that a *"feeling of innervation"* is also necessary to voluntary action. When we "wind up" and get set to throw a ball, how do we know how much to let go and how much to hold back? A nice balance of muscles is necessary. According to this theory, the motor impulses, which go out to activate the muscles, are attended by a feeling of innervation specific to each specific situation. It is this feeling which guides the throwing of the ball and other such acts, and enables us to adjust the pattern of contractions appropriately.

James rejects this theory and arrays evidence against it. There is no reason to suppose that the discharge of the motor nerves is sentient, i.e., is felt, and much reason opposed to it, nor is there need for such a supposition. Sensations excited by the contraction of our muscles are sufficient to tell us where our limbs are, and kinesthetic images are sufficient to guide our voluntary acts. James's view has been completely vindicated, and the "feeling of innervation" is now only a scientific curiosity.

The conception of "ideo-motor action" is of the greatest importance in James's theory of will. He begins with the question whether the "bare idea" of the act to be performed is sufficient to bring about its enactment. (See p. 790a.) His answer is that sometimes a movement "follows *unhesitatingly and immediately* the notion of it in the mind" (p. 790b), and when this happens we have ideo-motor action. In other cases a decision, fiat, or consent interposes between the idea and the act.

Suppose you are walking on the street and someone calls out "Look out below!" You automatically look for shelter and glance upward. If someone suddenly exclaims "Watch out," action generally follows immediately. When the alarm clock rings, the idea that it is time to get up is often sufficient to get you out of bed at once; and the request "Close the door, please" is frequently acted upon with thoughtless promptitude. The idea itself is sufficient to release action; this is ideo-motor action. In deep hypnosis all action seems to be ideo-motor; the subject is extremely suggestible, up to a point, and acts the moment a suggestion is given him. What we have, and the hypnotic subject lacks, is inhibition. Were it not for our inhibitions in the form of *conflicting* ideas, our movements too would all be ideo-motor.

If we do not at once act upon the idea of getting up, it is because we entertain other ideas—excuses—which conflict with getting up. If we do not automatically close the door when requested, or jump to attention when someone says "Watch out," it is because of some counter-idea, e.g., that one should maintain one's dignity and not be "taken in" or ordered about. But on thousands of occasions throughout the day no conflicting ideas arise. The idea of the time of day comes to mind; we look at our watch. We think of water and at once go for a drink. Ideas, in short, are magnetic, and we feel the pull even as we resist them, and when we resist them it is only because other ideas pull harder. James concludes:

> . . . *every representation of a movement awakens in some degree the actual movement which is its object; and awakens it in a maximum degree whenever it is not kept from so doing by an antagonistic representation present simultaneously to the mind.* (p. 792b)

We thus begin to act upon an idea even when it is inhibited by a conflicting idea. A child smitten with the idea of the cookie jar moves toward it and then, under the sway of a conflicting idea, moves unhappily in the opposite direction. Adults often do the same. We move toward the phone and then retreat again. Even when we do not actually move, some muscle fibers, answering to conflicting ideas, will contract, and we feel the tension. Ideas are magnetic.

When one idea alone comes to us, according to James, we act on it unfailingly. When it is inhibited by another idea there is conflict and we are in a state of indecision. So long as we waver between alternative ideas we are said to deliberate, which can end in a decision or in some distraction which engages the mind elsewhere.

IV

James's "five types of decision" disclose some of the complexities of the subject. The *reasonable type* of decision is that in which the sense of conflict is at a minimum, for the choice is left to reason, or to the stronger reason. Although we feel quite free in the process, it is the *"right conception,"* once we have found it, that really does the deciding, and we accept the verdict almost passively.

In the second and third types it is not the *right conception* that decides, and "the final fiat occurs before the evidence is all in" (p. 796b). In the second type we drift indifferently with the current of events, allowing our course to be determined *from without,* accidentally. In the third type there is what James describes as accidental determination from within. What does this mean? How could determination from within, i.e., self-determination, be accidental? We must remember that a state of indecision can become painful when prolonged, and intolerable to passionate and forceful men. When the odds are evenly balanced, it is a relief to stake one's lot with one side or the other masterfully, to take a stand rather than to vacillate. In the fourth type, deliberation is ended by an internal change of pace. A serious, strenuous mood intervenes and we become mindful of our duty, responsibility or dire consequences, which are sufficient to end our wavering.

The fifth type of decision is the most important, for it is only here that free will, as James understands it, can enter. Here, as in all other types except the first, the evidence is not sufficient of itself to turn the balance one way or the other. To effect a decision we throw our own weight on the scale pan; we put forth an effort. Whereas in other cases it is some reason or the evidence which inclines the beam, here it is the will. "The slow dead heave of the will that is felt in these instances" (p. 798a), says James, distinguishes these willful decisions from all the others, and the *"feeling of effort"* is always present.

Whether the will power that comes into play in these cases is something distinct from motives, James does not undertake to say. That is a metaphysical question and he is writing as a psychologist. But is there not a difficulty here in either case? If the will power is distinct from the subject's motives—his purposes, intentions, reasons for deciding in a given fashion— does not the subject become a pure ego, over and above the stream of consciousness, a conception that James has explicitly rejected? But if the will power is *not* distinct from the subject's motives, how is the fifth type of decision any different from the third? In the third type also a man puts his own weight in the balance, engages himself by strenuous fiat, throws down his gauntlet, espouses a cause, without sufficient reasons for doing so. Might not the feeling of effort also be present in such cases?

As a psychologist who is proud of his empiricism, James wanted to avoid the pure ego—the soul and Kant's transcendental ego alike—since no such entity could be observed or described. As a philosopher and a freewheeling meliorist, James was strongly attracted to free will. But it was free will in a pragmatic sense, which might be expressed by the affirmation "We can make our lives what we will." But what kind of will power is needed for this? Is it lodged in a traditional soul or in our motives? The soul outrages the empiricist, and the motives, which are not ourselves, but seem to act *on us*, do not appear to provide for free will. We shall return to this subject later.

The five types of decision could be regarded as characteristic of different types of men or situations. If the issue were whether to wed a particular girl, Type 1 would wait until the evidence about the girl was all in, until he was satisfied that he knew what was the right or the best thing to do, and then his decision would be made *for* him. It would not be made *by* him unless he were to identify himself with reason. Immanuel Kant makes this identification, but not James. Type 2 sees the way the wind is blowing—how relatives, friends, and the girl herself are taking the marriage for granted and making plans for the wedding. He sees little to object to and consents to the drift of things. Type 3 does not submit to external determination. There are strong forces that favor the marriage and others that oppose it, and it is for him to decide, to take a stand, to pledge his faith where he chooses. The facts of the case are not decisive, but *he* is. Type 5 would behave much the same, it would seem, except that he would explicitly feel the effort and the "slow, dead heave of the will." Type 4, on the other hand, has been dallying too long with the girl. A crisis comes, and in a sober responsible mood he faces up to the issue.

In discussing ideo-motor action we saw that conscious ideas naturally evoke action, i.e., tend to be enacted. Another way of putting this is that "*consciousness* ([and] the neural process which goes with it) *is in its very nature impulsive"* (p. 798b), but there are vast differences in impulsive power. The states of mind which have most impulsive power, James says, are passions, appetites, emotions, and instinctive drives; those which have least are remote, unusual, abstract, or impractical considerations, far removed from instinctive life.

Two things are needed for the healthy will. First, there must be a certain balance of impulsive power of motives. If the noninstinctive impulses, which are mostly responsible for civilization and culture, are to prevail, instinctive drives must be inhibited, *with effort.* In the normal or healthy will the noninstinctive impulses will be in the ascendant, though not, of course, to the exclusion of instinct. We shall see in the readings to come that healthy mindedness, according to Freud, requires a greater emphasis on instinctive freedom and less on inhibition.

The second requirement of the healthy will is that it act not too quickly nor too slowly but in view of pertinent facts. The action, as James says, *"must obey the vision's lead"* (p. 799b). Obviously some willful acts, by their very nature, can be more prompt than others. The more extraordinary the situation, the farther removed from trusted habits of action, the more time will be required to scan associated ideas and reach a decision. Bertrand Russell has suggested that the healthy mind will be slow and tortuous and reluctant to carry out its indignations and hatreds, but prompt and uninhibited in its loving impulses. But it is naturally difficult to lay down general rules about the healthy will with which all would agree.

James's analysis yields two interesting extreme or pathological types of will—*the explosive* and *the obstructive.* The explosive will is the impulsive, uninhibited type. According to James, we all start out with an explosive will. As infants we are endowed with impulses but with no inhibitions at all. We reach out to the hot stove and will walk off a cliff at the first opportunity if not forestalled, and indeed our exploratory impulses, so essential to the learning process, necessitate constant attendance by adults. Fear, except in the form of the startle response, is completely absent, and the impulsive life at the beginning has no check. It might be thought that in so far as adults are "infantile" they retain the explosive will.

But is not this phenomenon more complicated? The spontaneity and impulsiveness of the explosive will in the infant are soon curbed by dependence on parents or on people who play the parent role. The child is not long in learning to check some actions in favor of other more serviceable ones, in learning to control his parents and get what he wants from them. The same pattern is retained in infantile adults.

The drunkard, another illustration of the explosive will, shows the same dependence on a few friends whom he forces to play the part of indulgent parents, taking responsibility and granting forgiveness as required. Should we not say, therefore, that the typical drunkard is like the child of two; he is generally impulsive but inhibits some impulses the better to control useful friends and associates and to escape responsibility? And would not the same be true of drug addicts whom James mentions in this connection, and of other addict types? It is important to raise such questions, for if the drunkard and other addicts are pathologically dependent types, it may be that punitive laws and institutions are not the best way of dealing with them.

In the obstructed will—at the opposite extreme of the explosive will—there is too much inhibition or too little impulsion. As examples of insufficient impulsion James mentions states of apathy or exhaustion in which attention is diffused and concentrated thought and the power of choice are greatly impaired. In mental institutions we find frequent cases of abulia, in which, though the mind may be clear and alert, any decision making has become impossible.

James distinguishes cases of weak and sluggish will from those of overinhibited will. But do not the former often reduce to the latter? The will may be weak and sluggish simply because it is too inhibited, too cramped and constricted by conflict. We can watch schizophrenics in a mental hospital sitting silent and motionless for hours, taking no interest in their surroundings, indicating no desires, and apparently indifferent to everything. Is their will weak and sluggish? At one time it was thought that there were diseases of the will, as contrasted with diseases of the intellect, but this notion has been discarded. If we take another look at the schizophrenic we will see that he smiles or chuckles from time to time, though there is no external cause. He is completely indifferent and apathetic toward what happens in the world about him but not about the world within his mind. Here his will is actively engaged.

Is it not likely, as authorities claim, that the schizophrenic has retreated to his inner dream life because the conflicts of the outer world were too much for him? He could no longer endure his frustrated, inhibited self, cast adrift in the cruel competitiveness of society, and has found solace in an inner world where he can have things his own way. In this case his condition has resulted not from a weak, sluggish will but from conflict and inhibition of drives. The claim is made that all insanity, in so far as it is not due to brain lesions, has such a cause.

But must we not concede what James says about states of exhaustion? Volition, like other capacities, may be impaired by exhaustion, or by shock, whether there is conflict or not.

V

James delivers a deft blow to hedonism when he says:

The *impulsive quality* of mental states is an attribute behind which we cannot go. Some states of mind have more of it than others. . . . Feelings of pleasure and pain have it, and perceptions and imaginations of fact have it, but neither have it exclusively or peculiarly. It is of the essence of all consciousness (or of the neural process which underlies it) to instigate movement of some sort. (p. 809a)

We have already seen that ideas, according to James, are impulsive, and naturally evoke action unless they are inhibited by other ideas. It follows that hedonism, when it says that pleasure and pain are the only spurs to action, is definitely false.

Let us consider whether James is right about this. Will not the clamor of the alarm clock get you out of bed in the morning, or must it always be a pang of conscience? Is it the perception of your friend advancing toward you that makes you

smile and greet him, or must it be the pleasure of doing so?
Is it, the Mozart and Haydn quartets which entice you to the
concert and keep you in your seat, or is it necessarily pleasure?
Furthermore, do you ever actually prefer painful things, such
as swims in cold water, or run away from pleasures because of
fear, fastidiousness, or duty? James says you do. The hedonist
will have his answer, however. He will say: "Of course you
choose pains and renounce pleasures, but you do so only for
the sake of the greater pleasures. Among them are the pleasures of renunciation, of work accomplished, and of duty fulfilled." Do you think that James takes this rejoinder into account?

James is far from denying the great motive force of pleasure
and pain; he rejects only the exclusive role of these feelings.
If we introspect, i.e., watch our own minds in action, we find
that most of the time we act without reference to the pleasures
and pains involved. The hedonist, he says, may be misled by
a common confusion of two quite different things, namely, *"a
pleasant act* and *an act pursuing a pleasure."* Acting unhindered on a present impulse is naturally pleasant, especially
when it is successful, and unpleasant when hindered. Pleasure
normally accompanies unhindered action, as Aristotle put it,
and pain hindered action. But it is quite different to say that
we are always consciously seeking pleasures and avoiding
pains. This distinction was also made above, in the discussion
of Hobbes.

But if ideas—and not only the feelings of pleasure and pain—
carry their own impulse and evoke action unless hindered by
ideas with a stronger impulse, what part can the will play?
What is there left for the will to do? The idea of going to the
distant town through the blizzard to get medicine for a sick
child will be sufficient, if unhindered, to see us through this
painful mission. Why should an act of will be necessary as
well?

It is necessary, according to James, because an idea of this
sort generally has competitors which may put it out of business. We think of the blackness of the night, the chance of
losing our way in the storm and freezing to death in a snow-
drift. It occurs to us, moreover, that the child may not really

need the medicine, or that it might, after all our trouble, prove ineffectual. This first thought must be enshrined and the latter ones kept out of mind; this is the unique task of the will. As James says:

. . . we reach the heart of our inquiry into volition when we ask by what process it is that the thought of any given object comes to prevail stably in the mind. (p. 815a-b)

The key to the action of the will is *attention*.

The essential achievement of the will, in short, when it is most "voluntary," is to ATTEND *to a difficult object and hold it fast before the mind. The so-doing is the fiat. . . .* (p. 815b)

In perception, memory, association, and other processes of the mind, will is not involved; the coming and going of ideas is determined by automatic brain action. In volition we exert a mental effort to keep attending to the arduous idea until it is enacted. *"Effort of attention is thus the essential phenomenon of will"* (p. 816a). Attention, as James explains it in his chapter on the subject, is not a part or a quality of the stream of consciousness. We can shift our focus to any aspect of the stream at will, irrespective of its quality. It is not, as Titchener thought, a kind of "clearness" attaching to a part of the field of consciousness, but like a searchlight with which, as our boat goes downstream, we illuminate different portions of the dark shoreline.

First let us test in our own experience the claim that volition operates through an effort of attention. If you have an important examination to take next day and are already quite exhausted, how do you keep yourself at work through the early morning hours? Does your attention tend to wander and to become diffuse through drowsiness? Must you not force yourself to think of the coming examination and how important it is to do well? The party you are to attend, a scheduled tennis game, or how nice it would be to go to sleep, are all much easier to attend to. Thinking of the coming examination takes a big effort, and you find yourself tensing muscles to keep wanton ideas out; if your attention wanders your resolution crumbles.

We must remember that an effort of attention is needed only when what you will to do is difficult, painful, or the advantages of doing it are remote. Is it possible to think of cases in which we exert our will without *straining* to keep our attention on the object? How about the reasonable type of decision which James discusses on p. 796? James admits that when the "right conception" comes, or the balance of evidence clearly favors one side, there is no effort of attention. This is needed only when the impulsive force of the idea we will is less than that of other contradictory ideas that crowd the mind. The reasonable type of decision, then, would be no exception to James's rule that we flex our will, in difficult cases, only by fixing our attention. Can you think of any *genuine* exceptions to this rule?

James goes so far as to say that: *"The only resistance which our will can possibly experience is the resistance which [a difficult or frightening] idea offers to being attended to at all. To attend to it is the volitional act . . ."* (p. 819a). Can we accept this sweeping assertion? Is there no other point in our constitution or experience on which the will could act? We said a moment ago that we sometimes tense our muscles to keep to a difficult or unwanted task. Cannot a man raise his arm at will and somehow get his body into motion if he but decides to do so? Does not will give orders directly to the muscles of the body?

This is what many thinkers from Plato on seem to have assumed. James takes an opposite view and his reason will probably strike you as very sound. The will, the particular volition, does not act directly on the muscles; the muscles are innervated only by the motor nerves which proceed from the cerebral cortex. In the cerebral cortex there is a neural pattern which corresponds to the idea of plunging into the cold water to save a friend. If I will take the plunge, I must keep my attention on this idea, and the corresponding cortical pattern must be excited. It is only by keeping the idea focal that my will, throwing its weight in the scales, gets it enacted.

In terms of James's analysis, the problem of free will is as follows. Some ideas are easily held in attention and others only with effort. The question is whether the effort is something that we ourselves can put forth, or withhold, or whether things persist in our attention because they themselves are so exciting. Does the effort *I seem* to be putting forth when I study all night for a hard examination really come from me, or am I merely giving the only response I can to the tense situation in which I find myself? Do I force my attention to the painful and protracted task, or does not the task, given the sort of person I am, oblige me to make the effort? Is my will free or not?

The whole free-will controversy, James says, is *"extremely simple.* It relates solely to the amount of effort of attention or consent which we can at any time put forth" (p. 822a). Yet he goes on to say, quite frankly, that "after a certain amount of effort of attention has been given to an idea, it is manifestly impossible to tell whether either more or less of it *might* have been given or not" (p. 822b). For this reason he declares that, in his opinion, psychological evidence could never resolve the question of free will.

This negative conclusion reflects James's staunch empiricism. Do you think it is justified? Is not the psychologist justified in inferring motives and neural processes even when there is no direct empirical evidence for them? If this were granted, then the next question would be whether the hypothesis of free will would explain enough psychological facts to justify itself. Most psychologists today do not appear to be impressed by the explanatory power of this hypothesis.

James himself prefers to take free will as a moral postulate— a postulate of great importance since it implies that evil in the world is not fated but can be changed to good. It is fitting, he says, that this freedom which we hope is true should itself be freely chosen from among rival theories. "Freedom's first deed should be to affirm itself" (p. 823a).

V I

Would the occurrence of free will preclude a science of psychology?

". . . the operation of free effort, if it existed," James says, "could only be to hold some one ideal object . . . a little longer or a little more intensely before the mind. Amongst the alternatives which present themselves as *genuine possibles,* it would thus make one effective" (p. 825a).

James thus narrows down free will to those cases where we make a "free effort" to accomplish a hard decision. All the rest of mental life can be governed by strict causality, and predictions, so important to psychology as a science, would always be possible except in this one restricted area. But we could never know in advance how a hard decision would turn out; we could never predict whether, or how much, effort would be put forth; this would be determined not by past events but by free will at the moment.

These interruptions of the causal order of nature by the fiats of free will would be infinitesimal and infrequent. An idea would remain a little longer before the mind; a few atoms would unaccountably swerve in the brain. But the consequences, James says, might be *morally and historically momentous:* Caesar crosses the Rubicon, Napoleon invades Russia. Does psychology as a science thus break down in the area of hard decisions, where free effort is marshaled?

James suggests a distinction here which might be elaborated. He states in effect that psychology is concerned with general laws and types of behavior, not primarily with individual behavior. We can predict, in principle, how men in general are going to behave, though we are unable to predict individual choices. Thus the suicide rate of a given country may be known, though we are ignorant as to which individuals will make this irreversible decision. "However closely psychical changes may conform to law," James says, "it is safe to say that individual histories and biographies will never be written in advance no matter how 'evolved' psychology may become" (fn. 1, p. 825).

With a small margin of error, we can predict the number of individuals who will decide to get married next year in this country, though the decision in most cases will be a hard one, costing effort. And could we not also predict with a certain probability that given individuals will take the leap, whether there is free will or not? Can anything more be expected of psychology and of the other sciences of man?

Could the mind be a mere epiphenomenon?

If the mind is an epiphenomenon, it is a pure observer of what goes on but plays no part in it, exerts no influence, is not a causal agent. Descartes held that the minds of animals, if they have any, are epiphenomena. When a hound is following the trail of a hare, he is having visual and olfactory sensations, but it is not these sensations which keep him on the track, which cause his muscles to contract in the wonderfully precise pattern that propels him in the direction of the hare. What keeps him at it are the nervous impulses, which are transmitted from sense organs to his brain, and then out, to innervate his muscles. There is no need to suppose that the hound's sensations and ideas have any part in it. And besides, how could an idea, a sensation or thought, act upon the brain? How could an insubstantial idea bring about a physical or chemical change? The view that the mind is an epiphenomenon avoids this absurdity, and this is a big advantage. Then why not extend epiphenomenalism to the human mind and reap the same advantage on a higher level?

James will not hear of such a thing, though he admits that it is a mystery how the mind can act upon the brain. ". . . if we postulate the fact of the thinking at all," he says, ". . . we must postulate its power as well" (p. 821b). Why must we do so? James explains elsewhere that it is extremely unlikely that consciousness should have developed in the evolutionary struggle for existence if it had no function and was completely useless. It is difficult to believe that people would behave just the same if they had no minds and that they would survive very long if pleasure, instead of pain, had been associated with disease and the destruction of tissue.

What would happen if we had no inhibitions?

This question does not mean what you think. It has to do with inhibition as *an essential and unremitting element of our cerebral life* (p. 829a). Without it, we would go on repeating the same word like a broken record, or shaking hands, or throwing kisses, or what not, indefinitely. (See p. 829b.) Circular processes tend to establish themselves in the nervous system, and only inhibitions will cut the circuits. Suppose you are sawing wood—thrusting the saw out and then withdrawing it. If your saw is sharp, it is very easy to continue, and the process seems to accomplish itself. The reason is that the sensations arising from the completed thrust are automatic cues for the muscles which do the withdrawing. When the extensor muscle (EM) of your arm contracts (thrusting the saw out), nervous impulses are generated which go to the cortex of the cerebrum (C), and then back to the flexor muscle (FM) of your arm, and when this contracts, impulses are sent to the cortex and then transmitted again to the extensor muscle, and so on.

Thus we have the following circular process:

$$C \to EM \to C \to FM \to C \to EM \to C \to FM, \text{ etc.}$$

If you get tired, or someone suggests that it is time to have coffee, the chain is broken. The impulses reach C but are not dispatched to your sawing muscles; the energy is derailed into other pathways that give, for the moment, less resistance to the passage of the impulses. Pain, James points out, is a great inhibitor of these circular processes. (See p. 829). The child who repeats the same word over again and again is given a frown or a cookie, and stops.

The following questions are designed to help you test the thoroughness of your reading. Each question is to be answered by giving a page or pages of the reading assignment. Answers will be found on page 384 of this Reading Plan.

1 Franklin D. Roosevelt once said, "We have nothing to fear but fear itself." Does James discuss this kind of fear?

2 Does Edmund Burke say that imitating passions tends to bring them on?

3 What does Colonel Ingersoll's praise of a certain whiskey illustrate?

4 Which peoples tend to have "mercurial" or "dare-devil" temperaments?

5 "The moral tragedy of human life comes almost wholly from" *what?*

6 What criticism does James make of Rousseau?

7 What does James mean by the formula: I *per se* $<$ P
$$I + E \quad > P$$

8 Why is action from "fixed ideas" a terrible stumbling block for the pleasure-pain theory?

9 Can you name a few cases in which *"the pleasure of achievement may itself become a pursued pleasure"*?

10 Does volitional effort, according to James, fall entirely in the mental world?

F R E U D

*The Origin and Development of Psycho-Analysis
Selected Papers on Hysteria,* Ch. 3

A General Introduction to Psycho-Analysis,
Lectures 13-14

Vol. 54, pp. 1-20, 38-59, 526-539

The Copernican revolution, in Freud's opinion, robbed man of his special place in creation. His world was no longer the center of the universe but only one of innumerable worlds in an infinite space that had no center. Then the Darwinian revolution, he held, swept away man's pretense to be the work of divinity, for it had succeeded in tracing his ancestry back to earlier forms of animal life. Lastly came the cruelest blow of all. The psychoanalytic revolution, Freud said, demonstrated that man is not even master of his own house, that his most important drives and motives are unknown to him and therefore beyond his control. Self-determining reason could parade in the spotlight of consciousness, but this was largely stage play; the hidden forces which moved him behind the scenes were unconscious.

Freud gave repeated affronts to human pride. His contention that sex is the most powerful human motive, and the richest in consequences, shocked respectability and horrified hypocrisy. It was also opposed by psychologists of many schools, and still is, though less passionately. A surprising number have been won over. The further claim, now widely accepted, that sexual life begins not at puberty but in infancy, was also an insult to sentiment that had seen in the young child the symbol of "innocence."

While all these revolutions attacked hallowed beliefs and whittled down man's pretensions, they also ended by increasing his knowledge, and knowledge, Bacon said, is power. Copernicus, together with Galileo, laid the groundwork for mechanics and modern civilization. Darwin and his followers built new foundations for the biological sciences, with far-reaching practical consequences. It is still too early to assess the full impact of Freud's discoveries and theories, but it is already apparent that the vast area of psychotherapy, especially in this country, is dominated by Freudian ideas, and that no other influence is of comparable importance.

We can also see the tremendous influence that Freudian concepts, such as *conflict, anxiety, repression, frustration, autistic thinking, rationalization, wishfulfillment,* and *projection,* have had on the social sciences. Some of our leading anthropologists hold that the degree to which anxiety is aroused by the weaning and training of children in a society is the key to the dynamic forces and health of that society. To a great extent biographies are being rewritten, the arts and literature remodeled, with the help of Freudian concepts or insights. Freud was also productive in the opposition he aroused; his enemies usually learned a great deal from him, and the worth of their dissenting ideas owed much to the metal against which they were shaped.

Fourteenth Reading

I

The Life and Work of Sigmund Freud by Dr. Ernest Jones, the greatest of Freud's British followers, is now available.[1] The first volume which deals with "the formative years and the great discoveries" makes full use of the few facts relating to the first four years of Freud's life in Freiburg, in Moravia, now a part of Czechoslovakia. This makes fascinating reading, since Freud held the extreme view that the basic features of character are formed by the age of three and that later experiences may modify but not alter them.

We learn that Freud's father was a kindly but strict disciplinarian, whereas his mother was indulgent. The role played by his parents was thus in accord with Freud's later theory that the father, in general, represents "the reality principle," the mother "the pleasure principle." The father stands for denial, restraint, authority; the mother for solace and compliance with pleasure seeking. Young Freud's relations to his brothers and sisters and to other members of the household are also instructive in relation to Freudian theory, which may well have owed something to early childhood experiences. Jones surmises that the love and adoration of his mother sustained young Freud, the eldest child, through the ordeals of jealousy as the younger children successively appeared on the scene. It was this which imbued him with the sturdy self-confidence which he was to need in his iconoclastic career.

The family moved to Vienna in 1860 and Freud was to remain in that city until, in his eighty-second year, the Nazi absorption of Austria made life unbearable to him. He early

---

[1] Ernest Jones, *The Life and Work of Sigmund Freud*, 3 vol. (New York: Basic Books, Inc., 1953-1955).

showed his passion for books and study, and began reading Shakespeare at the age of eight. He was admitted to Sperl Gymnasium at nine, a year earlier than the custom was, and stood at the head of his class continuously. After graduating from the *Gymnasium,* Freud experienced great difficulty in choosing a profession. Chemistry attracted him and so did biology, to which Darwin had lately given new promise. He had also been drawn to philosophy but had "ruthlessly checked," he explains, the inclination to speculation. Although he never had any taste for the profession of medicine, he finally decided to become a medical student. Examining his motives in later years, Freud pointed out wittily that he could not recall any early " 'craving to help suffering humanity. My innate sadistic disposition was not a very strong one, so that I had no need to develop this one of its derivatives.' "[2] The fact was that his chief interests were always research and new ideas.

As a medical student, Freud worked hard in the physiological laboratory to understand what was known and also to break through to something new, but it was in another field that his real discoveries were to be made. Not having the funds to continue research indefinitely, Freud set up practice as a neurologist, and in the same year was married to Martha Bernays in a Jewish ceremony. The courtship had been stormy, partly due to difficulties arising from Freud's poverty, which continued to be a problem years after. When doubts of their mutual love had been overcome, Freud wrote to Martha:

"I admit we are now very wise to have no doubts about our love, but we couldn't be if all that had not gone before . . . Do not let us despise the times when only a letter from you made life worth living and when a decision from you was awaited as a decision over life and death."[3]

This was not just rhetoric. The man who scandalized Europe by his unconventional views of sex and marriage was a strict monogamist and a devoted husband and father. His marriage, which prospered fifty-three years, yielded six children. The

[2] *Ibid.,* Vol. I, p. 28.
[3] *Ibid.,* p. 133.

youngest, Anna Freud, following in her father's footsteps, is now a distinguished psychoanalyst and an authority on the problems of children.

Freud learned a great deal about nervous diseases, and especially hysteria, from Charcot, the greatest neurologist of the time, and spent several months in Paris with the master. Charcot's use of hypnosis in the cure of hysteria made a profound impression, and Freud himself employed the method for years, to unearth, through suggestion, the ideas and desires buried in the unconscious of hysterical patients. Later he came to see that this method had limitations, that the patient must not only know the conflict that was causing the symptoms but must also face up to it emotionally and overcome it through his own efforts. Yet Charcot's method was the first *psychological* method of dealing with nervous diseases, and thus marked a turning point, as it also suggested other and better procedures.

In 1891 Freud published his first book, *Aphasia*, which is considered his best neurological work, and two years later came his monograph on paralyses in children. More important for his future work was his association with the Viennese physician Josef Breuer, from whom he learned that hysterical *symptoms,* at least, could be eliminated by a method called "abreaction." The patient was induced to talk about his experiences, such as the first occurrence of the symptom, and thus to discharge her pent-up emotions. The trouble was that a patient, when relieved of one symptom, would most likely develop a new one. Freud saw that it was necessary to go deeper and grapple with the real cause of the disease. The so-called "talking cure" was later modified by the use of "free association," a technique which had been developed in Wundt's laboratory for other purposes. This in turn led to the method of dream analysis, which we shall discuss below.

The collaboration with Breuer resulted in their joint work, *Studies in Hysteria,* which appeared in 1895. But Freud eventually broke with Breuer, their main point of difference being Freud's emphasis on sex as the focal point of nervous disturbances. Others were to part company with him because of this insistence on the universal role of sex, though this was the crux of the theory. Breuer had been shocked when one of his patients declared that she was in love with him and could not leave him. Freud, on the other hand, was not dismayed by this phenomenon. The patients were not in love with him, he concluded, but were merely reacting to him as a substitute or "surrogate" for their real love. In the psychoanalytic situation, he came to see, one can expect a *transference* of love from the patient's father, or some other love object, to the analyst. The transference was indeed a necessary phase of the cure. It was up to the analyst to maintain his medical detachment, however, and eventually to free the patient from her transferred love and dependence upon him. These procedures became and remained essentials of psychoanalytic therapy.

Another great advance in theory came with Freud's *Interpretations of Dreams* in 1900. It was followed in 1904 by *The Psychopathology of Everyday Life,* in which it is shown how slips of the tongue, of the pen, of action, and of memory betray hidden motives and conflicts. Then in 1905 came the brilliant book called *Wit in Relation to the Unconscious,* in which entirely new angles of wit and humor are exposed, and once again it is shown how often our real motives elude the casual eye.

Freud's new theories were greeted for many years by more abuse than praise, and by more neglect than abuse. But gradually recognition came, and in 1908 a number of physicians, mostly Swiss, joined him in the first International Congress of Psycho-Analysis. Shortly thereafter the International Psycho-Analytic Association was established, and Freud was invited to the United States by G. Stanley Hall, one of the most eminent American psychologists, to explain the new therapy and the psychology behind it. He accordingly gave a series of five lectures at Clark University in Worcester, designed as an introduction to the whole subject. These were published in 1910 under the title *The Origin and Development of Psycho-Analysis.* We now turn to a discussion of this work.

I I

When a man is told that his malady is "only mental" or "in the mind," he no longer breathes a sigh of relief. Freud went so far as to say that paralysis and anesthesia which are hysteri-

cal (i.e., have their origin in the experiences of the patient) are
as hard to cure as those which are organic, that is, based on a
lesion in the brain. (See p. 2a.) This is an extreme statement,
but does it go too far? We know, in general, that conditions
which arise from mental causes, from deep frustrations in the
patient's life, take longer to cure than organic diseases. It is
likely also that they are as numerous.

Is not this paradoxical? The hysterical patient who cannot
walk or who cannot move his legs is organically quite sound.
There is nothing wrong with his muscles, nerves, or brain. The
same is true of other cases of the kind. The hysteric who is
blind, or insensitive in a part of his body, has sense organs and
brain intact. What can be the cause of such symptoms? Until
recently, Freud remarks, physicians showed no understanding
or sympathy for hysterical patients and were inclined to regard
them as malingerers. Their troubles were imaginary, for there
was nothing wrong with them physically, and it was better to
give the attention to "real" diseases. This was no doubt the
prevailing attitude. We have seen, however, that the existence
of hysteria, and the importance of the psychic component in
all diseases had been recognized as far back as Hippocrates.

Let us think for a moment about one of the symptoms of
Breuer's famous patient Fräulein Anna O, hydrophobia. She
had a dread of water, but the dread had no organic basis; it
was neurotic dread. In the intense heat of the summer she
suffered from thirst but was unable to drink. How had this
state of affairs come about? After long questioning about the
first appearance of the symptom, Anna told how some time
previously she had seen a dog which she detested drinking
water out of a glass. She had been disgusted at the sight but
could not express it, since she was then in conversation with
the dog's owner, an English governess, and had to keep up
appearances, though she disliked the woman. But how could
this momentary shock have induced a dread of water? Two
things must be remembered. She had not been able to *express*
her disgust, and, secondly, the glass from which the dog drank
was presumably very much like those from which she later
tried in vain to drink.

In order to make Anna's dread of water more understandable, let us look back to something that may be similar in our
own experience. We are eating an apple when suddenly we
see a worm crawl out of it; but in respect for our host, who
has been kind, we must conceal our feelings and go on holding
the apple. For some time after this apples are distasteful to us.
We tend to forget the crawling worm because the memory is
unpleasant, and we do not know why apples have become
repugnant to us. We quite often notice in ourselves inexplicable aversions and preferences. Why do we feel uneasy in
using a glass of a particular shape? Could it be that someone
once mashed a large beetle or caterpillar which had crawled
into such a glass, but that we have since then completely forgotten the incident?

Almost all of Anna's symptoms, Freud says,

originated in exactly this way, as remnants, as precipitates, if you like,
of affectively toned experiences, which for that reason we later called
psychic traumata. The nature of the symptoms became clear through
their relation to the scene which caused them. They were, to use the
technical term, *determined* . . . by the scene whose memory traces they
embodied, and so could no longer be described as arbitrary or enigmati-
cal functions of the neurosis. (p. 3a-b)

The "psychic traumata" were the shocking experiences which,
just because they were shocking, disappeared from consciousness, though they were still retained in the form of brain
traces, or neural patterns, and could still influence attitudes
and actions. It was as though the disgusting dog had its muz-
zle in every glass Anna tried to drink from. In the original
traumatic experience Anna had been nauseated by the dog-
drinking-from-a-glass. In later experiences the glass alone was
sufficient to evoke the disgust and to prevent her from quench-
ing her thirst.

The conversion of the traumatic experience into a hysterical
symptom thus begins to look very much like the conditioning
process which the great Russian psychologist Pavlov would
soon discover. It will be remembered that Pavlov's dogs were
repeatedly presented with food accompanied by the sound of
a bell; and, being hungry, they salivated. Salivating was the

expected response to the appearance of food, but after the food and bell had been presented simultaneously a number of times, the dog would also salivate when the bell alone was sounded. In the same way Anna's disgust, which had been originally called forth by the disgusting-dog-drinking-from-a-glass, was later elicited by the glass alone.

At the time of which we are speaking, 1895, Pavlov's conditioning experiments were well in the future. Freud talked instead in terms of the association of ideas, which, as we know, was discovered at least as far back as Aristotle. The association in question here was the similarity between a glass of water taken by itself and a glass of water polluted by the detestable dog. Associating the two by similarity, Anna gave the same response to the first as she had formerly given to the latter. Association of ideas is akin to conditioning, but conditioning would have the advantage, for Freud's purpose, because it occurs in the brain and not in consciousness. Dogs have no idea that they are learning to salivate when a bell is sounded; they do not know what is going on. Nor did Anna. She had no recollection of the traumatic experience, nor did she consciously associate it with her subsequent hydrophobia.

To get around this difficulty Freud assumed that the association of ideas may occur in the unconscious. A follower of Pavlov—a contemporary behaviorist—can reply: "The association, or conditioning, can take place in the brain. The hypothesis of the unconscious is not necessary, nor confirmable either." But would we not have to agree in the end that Freud's idea of the unconscious was at least a very dramatic and useful myth? This is usually conceded.

Association (or conditioning) also plays a leading role in the formation of other more serious symptoms. Anna had been sitting at the bedside of her patient for hours. Her arm, because of its position, had "gone to sleep"—had become paralyzed and insensitive—and she had at the same time a frightening hallucination of snakes. "Probably," Freud says, "she attempted to drive away the snake with her paralyzed right hand, and so the anaesthesia and paralysis of this member formed associations with the snake hallucination" (p. 3c-d).

Because of this unconscious association (by contiguity in space and time) of the affected arm with the frightening hallucination, the arm remained paralyzed and insensitive for a protracted period. Similarly, the hallucination apparently left Anna speechless at the time, and the unconscious association persisted, preventing her from speaking, at least in her native tongue.

Association is an essential element in the formation of hysterical symptoms, but it is not the whole story. All of us develop odd or bizarre fears. We shy away from apples because, though we have forgotten it, a disgusting worm once crawled out of one, or we dread to touch a harmless snake, or to go into a cave, or to walk down a particular narrow street, though we know no reason for it. Unlike the hysterical patients, however, we have distractions and do not allow our traumatic experiences in the past to weigh upon us. We *could* give way to our irrational fears, but we prefer to plan for tomorrow and get on with the business of life. In contrast, the hysteric becomes a slave to the associations of daily life with the traumatic experiences of his past. It is as if he were not much interested in the present or future, and indeed the hysteric is not usually a busy, ambitious person, wrapped up in plans and projects. Freud says:

This fixation of the mental life on the pathogenic traumata is an essential, and practically a most significant characteristic of the neurosis. (p. 4b-c)

Could it be that fixation is the main distinction between hysterical patients and us, that we too have had our traumatic experiences but are diverted by our many interests so that hysterical symptoms do not develop? Or is it possible, as some authorities have claimed, that anyone could become a hysteric if caught in the right pathogenic situation with no chance of escape? Breuer's patient Anna, it might be pointed out, had no other course than to nurse her dying father, though doing so separated her from the young man she loved and exhausted her energies. The irrepressible thought that all would be well if her father died aroused intense feelings of guilt. Constrained to be always at his bedside, she felt resentment but was never able to express it.

This brings us to another factor in the generation of the symptoms. The pathogenic situation is one which excites intense emotion which cannot be discharged in normal ways. Had Anna been able to leave her father's bedside and get away from the situation, or pour out her feelings to the young man in the case, or even face up to the problem in her own mind, things could have turned out differently. Thus the pent-up emotion during her endless vigil drained into abnormal channels and was "converted" into the symptoms Freud describes. Since her memories were "repressed" and had no normal outlet in thought or expression, they retained their strength and affective force, and the symptoms into which they were "converted" also persisted unchanged. ". . . *pathogenically formed ideas,*" Freud says, "*retain their freshness and affective force . . . because they are not subject to the normal fading through ab-reaction and through reproduction in states of uninhibited association*" (p. 28c).

"Abreaction" is the patient's release of repressed emotion, arising from the pathogenic episode or situation. It is the repression of this emotion which has prevented the patient from seeing the connection between this situation and her hysterical symptoms. It can be brought about by leading the patient back to the pathogenic situation by associations with the present situation in conversation, or by hypnosis. Drugs, such as sodium amytal, are sometimes used now. The outcome may be sudden and remarkable. When Anna's recollection of the snake episode was revived, the paralysis of her right arm was at once cured. Abreaction is the method Breuer used, and Freud also adopted it, to get around the patient's repression of the painful or shameful episode. *Repression,* it should be remembered, is not simply forgetting what we cannot bear to think of; it is a guilty covering up of our tracks. Unlike *suppression,* it is not a conscious process. If Anna had only *suppressed* her memory of the snake episode, i.e., consciously put it out of mind, it would have been much easier to revive it. Since it was *repressed,* it was recovered only by hypnosis.

In order to see further into the complicated mental mechanisms assumed by Freud, we might ask how hypnotism helps to revive the traumatic episode. There are various theories of the nature of hypnotism, but authorities agree that it has the effect of weakening inhibitions, of increasing suggestibility. The doctor can require the patient to recall painful trains of events and not to remember others; he can sometimes even suspend the patient's suffering by the strong suggestion that his pains will cease. Deep hypnosis certainly reduces what Freud called "resistance." This is the reluctance of the patient to bring to mind the traumatic episode, to see its relation to his neurotic symptoms, to remember anything which will disturb the neurotic adjustment in which his life has become entrenched.

But can we then say that the neurotic wants to remain neurotic? Does Anna like to have her arm paralyzed and insensitive? It is unpleasant, no doubt, but less unpleasant, so the theory goes, than facing up to the incident of the snakes which gave rise to this symptom, for this incident is tied up with her consuming sense of guilt. To avoid this she puts up barriers to natural associations through which we normally recall forgotten items in the past. The more the doctor probed to discover the critical incident, the more she endeavored to strengthen her line of defense, and the more acute her symptom became. But when, under deep hypnosis, she recalled the incident, her arm was suddenly normal again.

The cure so quickly effected stands out, in the midst of many details which will seem perplexing and ambiguous, with remarkable clarity. The theory had been advanced that the hysterical symptom was occasioned by a traumatic incident charged with guilt feelings and by the fact that the incident had been repressed. The repression is indicated by the resistance offered to its revival in memory, but when the incident was recovered through hypnotism the symptom at once disappeared.

We have so far had only a brief glimpse of the pathogenic situation: repression and the conversion of the traumatic experience into symptoms, the overcoming of the patient's resistance, and the disappearance of his symptoms by means of abreaction. These phenomena have deeper strata and belong in a context of other ideas which we shall have to discuss.

The reader will have noted that hypnosis, which is central in the above illustration, was not regarded by Freud as essential to psychoanalysis. It can remove symptoms in many cases, but other symptoms then appear; it does not remove the underlying cause. The patient does not have to struggle painfully to overcome his resistance; it is automatically eliminated by hypnosis. When the patient comes out of the deep hypnosis, he is not impressed by what he has revealed, any more than he would have been if the doctor had told him the starting point of his illness. Sometimes patients undergoing psychoanalysis, perhaps to spare the doctor's time and their own purse, hasten to confess resentment to their father, overlove of their mother, and other feelings which they think are to be wrung from them sooner or later. Freud insists that this is of no use whatever. Unless the patient struggles against his resistance, re-experiencing the concrete emotional conflicts of his early life, there is no abreaction. Hypnosis thus has its drawbacks. Besides, Freud found that many of his patients could not be hypnotized.

III

If the doctor forgoes the use of hypnosis, how is he going to get the patient to reveal the pathogenic scenes—the scenes which left the symptoms in their wake? He can tell him that his recovery depends upon getting to the bottom of his trouble and that it is up to him to determine how long the analysis will continue without progress. He can ask the patient to lie down on a couch and relax, and can put him at his ease by convincing him that nothing he says will be held against him. The analyst is clearly his friend, almost like a father, yet unlike the father because he is shocked by nothing. In fact he is the last word in permissiveness, understanding, and indulgence. Why then does not the patient talk? He does talk, but not about what interests the analyst, not about the pathogenic episodes. He has in fact developed amnesia—a loss of memory —for precisely those experiences. He does not talk of what the analyst wants to know because, in an important sense, he does not know it either.

In Freud's view, however, memories are never lost. Hypnosis alone shows that many lapsed memories can be revived. They are

in the possession of the patient, ready to emerge and form associations with his other mental content, but hindered from becoming conscious, and forced to remain in the unconscious by some sort of a force. The existence of this force could be assumed with certainty, for in attempting to drag up the unconscious memories into the consciousness of the patient, in opposition to this force, one got the sensation of his own personal effort striving to overcome it. (p. 7a)

We note here that Freud makes the patient's resistance "a force," and shall have occasion to mention again his tendency to dramatize the activities of the mind. The relation between the patient's repression and his resistance is illustrated by Freud in a humorous fashion. Suppose there is a disturbance in the hall at Worcester where he is lecturing. The disturber is ejected—*repressed*. Freud continues his lecture. Then those who have ejected the disturber sit at the door to see he doesn't come back—they are the *resistance*. The inside of the hall represents consciousness; the outside, the unconscious.

How skillfully this picture portrays the complicated facts. The region outside the hall is far larger than the area within, and this accords with Freud's theory perfectly. The unconscious is a vast realm, whereas the conscious is a small illuminated compartment where rules and properties must be observed and where certain thoughts are admitted but most are not. In one respect, however, Freud's model seems to be misleading. Freud is aware that the disturber is being evicted and his return prevented, whereas we are not conscious of our repression or of our resistance.

In another place, Freud gives a more elaborate image of the relation of forces in the mind. The unconscious becomes a large anteroom, and the throng of ideas or excitations are struggling to get into a small reception room, i.e., consciousness. In the doorway between is the doorkeeper who examines the ideas and feelings, "censors them, and denies them admittance to the reception-room when he disapproves of them" (p. 566d). If he is vigilant enough he catches the objectionable visitors at the door and sends them back into the unconscious, but sometimes one that has been admitted by mistake or oversight is ejected. This doorkeeper is Freud's famous "censor." The ideas and feelings admitted to the reception room, however, do not all become conscious; it depends on whether "they succeed in attracting the eye of consciousness" (p. 567a). The reception room is therefore really what Freud calls the preconscious or the preconscious system, i.e., conscious ideas and desires of which we *could* readily be conscious if we so chose.

The introduction of the preconscious was certainly an improvement on Freud's initial design of the mind. William James had already pointed out that focal consciousness is only a small area of illumination on a huge terrain of dim and merely possible thoughts. Freud's originality is seen in his sharp distinction between the preconscious and the unconscious and in the priority he gives to the latter. In order for thoughts and feelings to get into the preconscious system, he held, they must first be approved by the censor. They cannot emerge from the unconscious, the realm of things we *cannot* think of, and enter preconscious, the realm of things we *can* think of, at will, unless they pass the tests of decency, morality, or propriety imposed by the censor. The censor, in Freud's opinion, is a frightful prude—at least it was in nineteenth-century Vienna. He claims that nowhere in the world at any time have such dire restrictions been placed on natural sexual desires as in modern Europe, and the censor, i.e., conscience, is simply a reflection of current moral codes. The censor is simply an "internalized" social disapproval. The infant does not have a conscience; he acquires that of his parents, by learning.

The more extreme the moral code, the more intense the conflict between the individual's desires and the injunctions against them. In slips of the tongue, of the pen, in ambiguous gestures, in dreams, in painting and literature, in strokes of wit, in the revelations of the hypnotic, and in the frequency of neurosis, the existence of a repressed unconscious is proved unmistakably. They all furnish to consciousness evidence of motives of which the subject is *not* conscious. Only by a recognition of the unconscious and the conflicts it entails is a humane and effective treatment of neurosis possible. ". . . clinical psychiatry, which only recognizes a psychology of consciousness, can do nothing with [neurotic] symptoms except to stigmatize them as signs of a special kind of degeneration" (p. 559d).

It will help to see why Freudian psychology is called "dynamic" if we contrast his approach to such subjects as memory and association with that of his contemporaries. In the 1880's, Ebbinghaus studied the curve of forgetting, i.e., the progressive loss of learned material in the course of minutes, hours, and days. The loss is very rapid for the first few minutes, less rapid in the next few hours, and very slow in subsequent days and months. The general form of the curve held for meaningful material such as poetry, as well as for nonsense syllables, though in the former case the amount forgotten throughout was much less. The curve of forgetting thus depended on the number of repetitions of the material learned and the time lapse; the mind was assumed to be passive in the process, no distinction being made between passive memory and active recall.

For Freud, on the other hand, "the fading of a memory or of its affect depends . . . first and foremost . . . on whether an energetic reaction (discharge of feeling) supervened on the affective experience or not."[4] If we discharge the feeling by weeping, by confession, or by returning the insult, the affect or emotion tends to disappear or to be altered. "If the reaction is suppressed the affect remains attached to the memory."[5] It would be rash to say that Freud is squarely contradicting Ebbinghaus. He is talking about the memories personally crucial to the individual and about the affect or emotional coloring they bear, neither of which were Ebbinghaus' con-

[4] Ernest Jones (ed.), *Sigmund Freud, Collected Papers* (London: The Hogarth Press and The Institute of Psycho-Analysis, 1950), Vol. I, p. 30.
[5] *Ibid.*

cern. He is talking about memory as a means of individual adaptation, and is in the tradition of Darwin, not of the new laboratory psychology which took physics as its model.

The associationists had long since called attention to the ease with which the course of thought, as in reverie, can be traced by the association of ideas—association by similarity (and contrast), contiguity in space and time, and causality. Freud also emphasized these associative processes. It was the first step toward the diagnosis of the disease process. The patient is made to recline upon a couch and to talk about himself, revealing anything that comes into his head, concealing nothing, no matter how trivial or irrelevant it seems. One experience suggests another that is similar (or contrasting), or that was its effect or cause, or simultaneous with it. If the patient continues to talk, yielding passively to automatic associations, he is more likely to reveal clues to his disorder than he will if he plans in advance what he will report, or merely answers questions.

Freud found, however, that even this free association runs up against the fact that the crucial memories have been repressed. Months went by before one of his patients, Elisabeth von R, would reveal, or was able to reveal, the reverie in which she recognized her illicit love for her sick sister's husband. The original repression of this memory was very much alive in her resistance to its disclosure. Another patient concealed an intimate love affair for weeks, though he was well aware of the "sacred rule" that one must hold back nothing. This time the impasse was due to voluntary withholding or *sup*pression, not *re*pression. The patient consciously refused to cooperate.

Some patients, Freud reports, are exceedingly clever at evading the helpful associations and often produce remote and useless ones. And when they are at last brought to observe the "sacred rule," their resistance does not end but takes a new form.

It appears as intellectual opposition, employs arguments as weapons, and turns to its own use all the difficulties and improbabilities which normal but uninstructed reasoning finds in analytical doctrines. . . . What the critics outside shout at us is nothing new, therefore. It is indeed a storm in a teacup. Still, the patient can be argued with; he is very glad to get us to instruct him, teach him, defeat him . . . ; he is perfectly ready to become a supporter of psycho-analysis on the condition that analysis shall spare him personally. (p. 564b)

We can readily see that the course of thought on the psycho-analytic couch involves other factors besides the traditional laws of association; fears and strategies of escape must be dealt with. It becomes obvious too that the question with which we began this section—"If the doctor forgoes the use of hypnosis, how is he going to get the patient to reveal the pathogenic scenes—the scenes which left the symptoms in their wake?"—admits of no easy answer.

The disguise assumed by neurotic symptoms is a prevailing obstacle to diagnosis. The patient Elisabeth von R converted her "painful consciousness that she was in love with her sister's husband by creating for herself instead bodily pains" (p. 48d). But how could strong guilt feelings be converted into bodily pains? How could these buried feelings be inferred from pains in the legs? Could we say that if Freud had known that at the time the guilt feelings first occurred the patient was sitting on a rock, the pain symptom would have been more understandable? A rock is not a very comfortable seat, and the slight pain involved might have been attended to as an escape from the guilt feelings, and thus accentuated. The pain in the legs, which was simultaneous with the guilt feelings, might in this way have become a substitute for them. It is to be noted that after she rose from the seat the pain disappeared, to return later on, after taking a warm bath, presumably in a sitting posture. (See p. 48b.) However this may be, the clue could not have been much help to Freud so long as the incident of sitting on the stone was buried in the patient's unconscious.

Inferring the forgotten traumatic experience from the symptoms is also difficult when the symptoms are symbolic, for symbolism can take so many different forms. A young woman, Miss Rosalia H, had worked hard to become a professional singer but was hindered by an inexplicable tightening of the throat. How could this symptom, which defeated her fondest desire, have come about? On the death of her aunt, Rosalia had had to protect the orphaned children against the cruelty of their brutal father and to suppress any expression of her indignation.

It was then that the choking sensation in her throat originated. Whenever she was compelled to swallow an affront, whenever she had to remain silent on hearing a provoking accusation, she perceived a scratching in her throat, the tightening and failure of her voice. . . . (p. 54c)

The tightening in her throat (*symptom*), then, was symbolic of "swallowing an affront" (*traumatic experience*), and the symptom which had become a surrogate for the repressed idea was very persistent. The symbolism here involves resemblance as well, and accords with Freud's rule that these surrogates for the repressed ideas, though "disguised under the influence of resistances . . . must, however, show a certain similarity with the ideas which are the object of our search, by virtue of their nature as symptoms . . . must be related to the repressed thought as a sort of allusion, as a statement of the same thing in *indirect* terms" (p. 9d).

It is this resemblance between symptoms and repressed ideas (or traumatic experiences) which we noted in the cases of Anna O and Elisabeth von R. It is this resemblance that can guide the analyst in inferring the repressed ideas from the symptoms. The repressed idea will always involve conflict which cannot be expressed; that is why the repression occurs. Elisabeth was caught between her love for her sister's husband and her abhorrence of this love, which violated the sanctity of family relations. So painful was the conflict that she could not give it utterance nor acknowledge it. Anna was convulsed between two forces—the desire to punish her uncle for his abuse, and the fear and insecurity which obliged her to remain in her uncle's house and submit. She also could not express her anger and humiliation. Conflict in a situation in which emotional outlet is lacking and from which there is no escape is therefore something the analyst can always expect. In recent times neurosis, or something very much like neurosis, has been produced experimentally in dogs, cats, and other animals. It is found that if only the animal is put in a large room and left free to move about, the neurosis does not develop.

Pierre Janet, the great French psychiatrist and at one time a teacher of Freud, attributed the hysteric's symptoms to weakness and degeneration of the nervous system. Freud objected that in the hysteric, alongside impaired function, improved functioning, perhaps compensatory, can sometimes be found. Some of the patients, for that matter, were obviously very intelligent. The central fact in hysteria was not nervous degeneration but repressed conflict, and this was happily something that it was possible to remove.

The symptoms, however unpleasant, must be viewed as an escape from something worse, and the analyst asks himself in effect, "An escape from what?" What could the particular symptoms cover up and be a substitute for? This itself gives him something to start with. Even the patient's resistance, which conceals the repressed pathogenic ideas, can be a guide to the analyst, for the resistance increases and the disguise becomes more complete as he approaches what he is looking for, and he thereby knows he is on the right track. (See p. 9d.)

The *transfer* of tender feelings from earlier loves and devotions to the analyst was, as we have noted, a matter of embarrassment to Breuer. Freud saw that by this means the analyst becomes a catalytic agent or ferment, causing the patient to display the structure of his passional life. As the analysis advances, it is the task of the analyst to disengage himself as the temporary object of the patient's affection. When the transference has served its purpose, it must be eliminated.

I V

The greatest resource of the analyst, according to Freud, is the interpretation of dreams. To become an analyst, he says, you must study your own dreams.

Interpretation of dreams is in fact the *via regia* [royal road] to the interpretation of the unconscious, the surest ground of psycho-analysis. . . . (p. 11a)

Is this not an incredible statement? People once regarded dreams as prophetic, but after this idea was discredited they paid little attention to them. The great importance Freud assigned to them is understandable. In his remarkable original theory, all dreams express, usually in disguised form, repressed wishes of the dreamer. But how is it possible for repressed wishes to get past the censor who, as we have seen, stands guard like Cerberus at the gate of the unconscious? Freud's answer, in pictorial language, is that the vigilance of the censor is relaxed during sleep and that he can be caught off guard. Otherwise expressed, some organizing centers in the brain are not functioning, and inhibitions are lowered.

One is reminded analogously of the effect of alcohol. Plying a man with drinks is a well-known method of learning his secrets, although we must take care not to assume that a man reveals his true nature under the influence of alcohol. He may reveal only the drunk man's conception of his sober self, and we all know that exaggerations and distortions are to be expected. The dreamer, too, fails to tell the truth, the whole truth, and nothing but the truth. Dreams are full of evasions, disguises, symbolism, distortions. That is why *interpretation* is needed. "The manifest dream-content,'" which is the dream as you recall it when you wake in the morning and is usually confused and hard to put into words, is really "the disguised surrogate for the unconscious dream-thoughts" (p. 12a), or what Freud usually calls "the latent dream-thoughts." The "dream-work" is the process whereby these thoughts have been transformed into your dream.

Freud's claim, which is now generally conceded, is that this content of the dream is derived from the experiences of the dreamer in the twenty-four-hour period just preceding. You have been at the courthouse during the day, and at night you dream that your wife has been brought to trial. It is not very clear what she is charged with, but only that it is a serious matter. How are you to infer, from the confused images and hovering dread of such a dream, what its real meaning is? How can you get at the latent dream thought? Can it be that your unconscious wish is that your wife should be brought to trial? We are faced here with the same problem, Freud says, as that of finding the unconscious meaning of hysterical symptoms.

Freud, unlike James, sought genetic explanations—attempted always to explain psychological phenomena in terms of their origin and growth. If dream wishes are disguised to get them past the censor, we might expect to find that young children, since they are less inhibited, less moral, would exhibit fewer disguises in their dreams. If they are young enough—under five—Freud reports, their dreams are a simple expression of wishes without disguise or distortion, and can be understood as soon as we know what experiences the child had the day before. The shortest example Freud gives is that of a little boy not yet two who reluctantly gave a basket of cherries to another child, on the understanding that he should have some of them for himself. The dream he reported next morning was: "'Hermann eaten all the cherries'" (p. 495c). Here the fulfillment of a wish which had not been fulfilled the previous day, and had left the boy dissatisfied, is expressed directly, without disguise. Does not the childish dream then have the function of relieving the tension caused by the disappointment, thus permitting sleep to continue? Dreams protect sleep, but do so through a compromise. The gratification of the wish is really an hallucination.

Now adults, Freud claims, do not generally have dreams of this sort. Do you remember any? Do you ever dream that you won a race in which you in fact did not even place, or that you got an "A" in an examination in which you actually received a disappointing grade? "Transparent" *daydreams,* Freud says, can be straightforward wish fulfillments, but these are not strictly dreams because the "fulfillments of ambitious or erotic wishes . . . are . . . carried out in thought, . . . they never take the form of hallucinatory experiences" (p. 497a). Does this judgment square with your experience? Do you not sometimes have an image of yourself, "see" yourself, in a daydream, accomplishing your wishes—carrying off the prize? But would there not be one big difference, in any case? You are not *taken in* by what you "see" in a daydream as you are in a real dream.

Adult dreams, unlike those of young children, are not generally direct wish fulfillments. But Freud concedes that many are. When a dream is occasioned by bodily stimulation and there is imperious physical need—thirst, hunger, or sex—direct, undisguised wish fulfillment may occur. When starving or reduced to a diet of bare essentials, men dream of food; when lost on a desert, of cooling springs. Dreams of direct sexual gratification are common. Prisoners have simple dreams of gaining freedom. There are also dreams to the effect that we are already up and about our duty—at the office, for example—so that there is no need to get up and we can go on sleeping. Such dreams not only protect sleep, which is the general function of dreams, but also give us the comforting illusion that we are doing our duty.

The popular opinion that Freud reduced the point of all dreams to sex is thus quite wrong. There are dreams that express the fulfillment of "hunger, thirst, and the longing for liberty—comfort-dreams, and impatient-dreams, as well as those which are frankly avaricious and egoistical" (pp. 523d-524a). He adds, however, that psychoanalysis has shown that dreams in which there is marked distortion generally express sexual desires.

Why should dreams of sexual fulfillment be in a class by themselves? Freud's explanation is very elaborate and detailed, as we shall see when we come to his·account of sexuality in children. It is obvious without much reflection, however, that sexual taboos in our society are very strong, that they become "internalized" so that the prohibitions seem to come from within, not from society, and that the shame entailed by sexual infractions is unique. Sexual gratification, Freud says, affords the greatest pleasure that men can have, and yet it is precisely in this area that there is the greatest amount of repression. Is it surprising that the fulfillment of sexual wishes in dreams should take distorted and disguised forms, concealing shameful desires from the dreamer himself?

But what would happen if society relaxed its sexual taboos? Would Freud's theory of dreams no longer hold? Malinowsky, Margaret Mead, and other leading anthropologists have taken steps to answer this question in their studies of Melanesian groups in Pacific islands. Where a society is tolerant of premarital intercourse, there still remain other sexual taboos, including always that against incest, to engender anxieties and repression. We shall not attempt to sum up the evidence in this vast area except to say that it is not out of line with expectations. Change the pattern of the family, methods of rearing children, rules of sex; introduce permissiveness here and new restraints there—and you will change the habits of the censor. He will censor in general only what is taboo, and if taboos decline his work does also. According to Freud, however, his job could never become a sinecure; censorship will be necessary in any society.

Except for the dreams of childhood and the dreams of adults which are like them, the dream you recall in the morning is always less complete and less complex than the dream thought which gave rise to it. It is less because the censor has been at work. The censor is needed, of course, because there is a conflict, a conflict between sexual desires and taboos which have become internalized; the stronger the two forces are, the more he is needed.

There are three main ways in which dreams are distorted to get by the censor: *condensation, displacement,* and the *transformation* of thoughts into visual images. In condensation, parts of the dream thoughts are omitted, reduced to fragments, or blended together. In displacement, a part is replaced by a substitute which resembles or alludes to it, and the accent is shifted from what is important to what is incidental. The transformation of the latent dream thoughts into "plastic word representation" is most significant, and is a kind of trickery that is always present. For let us suppose that your unconscious wish is that your father, who has humiliated you and whose wealth you expect to inherit, should soon die. This is a terrible wish, of course, and you could not bear to express it even in the twilight of a dream, because you also love your father and would loathe yourself if you did not. The dream comes to you, however, in the form of images, or mental pictures, without labels, and so expresses no wish. You merely "see" a man on his deathbed. Even if he is recognizable as your father, which is not always the case, your wish that he die has not been expressed. On the contrary, the family which has been gathered show their grief and tears, in which you yourself seem to join. It is as if you were imagining something that you greatly regretted or feared.

The pictorial form of dreams seems to hide the wish of the dreamer. But is there not a difficulty here? If the pictorial form, and other distorting factors, hide his wish even from the dreamer, how can we say that *his* wish has been fulfilled, or even partially fulfilled, in the dream? *Consciously* he does not recognize his death wish and rejects the analyst's interpretation. Can we imagine that he is *unconsciously* gratified, or that his unconscious is appeased by the graphic delineation of death? And is it this gratification which permits the man to absorb the disturbing thought and go back to sleep? The thought, however, is not disturbing to the unconscious—far from it—but only to consciousness. Consciousness, however, knows nothing of the wish, and hence could not, penetrating its disguise, know anything of its fulfillment.

It is easy to discover other perplexities in Freud's theory. They result in part from the mythological form in which he expresses it, a form more suitable to popular exposition and preliminary understanding than to exact formulation. We have seen no evidence, of course, that there is a censor who disapproves or an unconscious which could be gratified, unless the subject is what James called a split personality, with coconscious units. Freud, however, has written copiously on every phase of dreams, and most of the objections to his theory of dreams are carefully considered, especially in *The Interpretation of Dreams* and *Revision of the Theory of Dreams*.

One common objection is that people are not so base and wicked as to wish the death of those whom they love most. All dreams therefore cannot express wish fulfillment. Freud contends that death wishes derive mostly from "the unbounded egoism of the dreamer."

Whenever anyone gets in our way in life—and how often must this happen when our relations to one another are so complicated!—a dream is immediately prepared to make away with that person, even if it be father, mother, brother or sister, husband or wife. (p. 528c)

We will understand this better, Freud claims, if we look back to childhood and to the childhood of the race. It is quite true that a child often says to his mother or playmates, "I hate you; I wish you were dead," but does he mean it literally and does he understand death? We ourselves sometimes say, "I wish I were dead," without really meaning it. On the other hand, attitudes toward death, especially in children, are difficult to construe. We must remember, above all, that a death wish does not exclude contrary wishes a moment later, or even at the same time. The unconscious, Freud says, knows nothing of logic. In this light death wishes are not so evil as they first appeared. One of Freud's best insights was that all love relations are "ambivalent," i.e., mixed with resentment and hate. "The course of true love never runs smooth," and other popular dicta, attest to this ambivalence of love. Is it not better to face the fact, as more people are now doing? If we see that none of us are gods, will we not be more tolerant of others and, more important from Freud's standpoint, of ourselves?

A more serious objection to Freud's theory of dreams is that even if all dreams have a meaning and this meaning can be discovered by analysis, the particular interpretation given often appears arbitrary. Freud was convinced that all dreams have a meaning on two grounds. First, he was a determinist—everything is both a cause and an effect. This is not a good reason as it stands, for dreams could be both cause and effect without having *meaning*. Perhaps what he meant was that dreams, like other activities, must have adaptive significance, but this need not be the case either. Secondly, analyses of hundreds of dreams of patients undergoing treatment showed that dreams held the secret of the disease and its cure. That hidden meanings could be discovered also in slips of the tongue and pen, salutations, witticisms, and art forms, supported his conviction.

But how can we be certain that the particular meaning that is assigned to a dream is the one true meaning? Why must the dream in which you stand beside your father's deathbed be the expression of wish fulfillment? Why could it not mean fear or anxiety about the event? Freud's answer is that the dream itself could suggest a great number of different meanings, but this is irrelevant.

Interpretation of dreams is finding the latent dream thoughts —the unconscious wishes that the dream expresses. (See p. 537a-b.) To discover the meaning of a dream we must not try to construe it in some plausible, conventional fashion; we must penetrate through the disguises of the surface dream to the unconscious thoughts of the dreamer. But how can we do this if we are not experts in Freudian psychology and diagnosis?

Freud claims that the interpretation of dreams gives great support to his psychological theories, his theories of the unconscious, repression, resistance, infantile sexuality, the predominance of sexual motivation in adults, etc.; but does not the interpretation of dreams presuppose the truth of these theories? Is this circularity in proof objectionable? Does it mean that to understand Freudian doctrine, you must already be a convinced Freudian?

Our perplexity about Freud's theory comes to a head when we think of common dreams in which we are frightened to death or punished. Freud's explanations are ingenious, but are they convincing? He says that anxiety dreams usually wake us up; "we usually break off our sleep before the repressed wish behind the dream overcomes the censorship and reaches complete fulfilment" (p. 534d). If the censor feels himself powerless to block the repressed wish, it always has a last resource: it "destroys sleep by bringing about an access of anxiety" (p. 535a). Is this not a puzzling business? If the repressed wish in the anxiety dream does not get by the censor and is not expressed, how can the anxiety dream be, like all dreams, the fulfillment of a wish?

On the same page, however, Freud offers two other quite different explanations. First, he suggests that wish fulfillment really includes anxiety fulfillment and punishment fulfillment, while denying that this involves a revision of his theory. ". . . anxiety," he argues, "is the direct opposite of a wish and . . . opposites lie very near to one another in association and . . . actually coincide in the unconscious." But in the next sentence he puts forward what is really a new explanation: ". . . punishment itself is the fulfilment of a wish, namely, the wish of the other, censoring person" (p. 535d). Here the wish that is fulfilled is not the repressed, evil wish of the unconscious but the moral wish of the censor. Does not this involve a revision of Freud's theory? Moreover, if the wish fulfilled may be a moral one, is it not possible that the dream of your father dying manifests a fear of the event or a guilty conscience?

The difficulty of confirming dream interpretations has been often noted. Would even the recovery of the patient (or the disappearance of his symptom) after he gives a certain meaning to his dream prove that this was *the* meaning of the dream, or that it had anything to do with his recovery? Such questions should be asked in testing the theory. Since Freud is so abundant and resourceful, the reader may well find the answer if he reads far enough. He will have to agree, in any case, that if dreams mean something, Freud has given the most thorough, intelligible, and consequential account of them.

In spite of the unsolved problem of confirming the interpretations of dreams scientifically, this method has become increasingly important in psychotherapy. Unexpected support has come from what are called "projective techniques." In the Rorschach test the patient gives away secrets of his unconscious while giving his free associations to the ink blots. In the Thematic Apperception Test he makes similar unwitting revelations while giving his interpretation of what is happening in a picture of ambiguous meaning. In tests of this kind, the patient projects, as it were, his unconscious thoughts upon a screen. He does it unintentionally by following his free associations. In so far as he is able to do this, there is added reason to think that the patient can do the same when he dreams and interprets his dreams.

V

When psychoanalysis is brought to a happy ending, what happens to the repressed wish?

Repression has led to painful and undesirable consequences. The psychoanalytic process succeeds, against a great deal of resistance, in bringing the repressed material into consciousness, and the subject thereby acquires an *insight* into the cause of his distress. There are several appropriate ways of dealing with the pathogenic wish, according to Freud. The patient may conclude that it is best for him not to reject his pathogenic wish but to accept it, at least in part. (See p. 9a.) The pathogenic wish, in the case of one of Freud's patients mentioned above, was to love and be loved by the husband of her sister. The solution for her would be to give way to this love, at least to some extent. Why would it have been difficult for this patient? (See pp. 38-43.)

A second solution is to direct the energy of the repressed wish "to a higher goal which is free from objection, by what is called sublimation" (p. 9a). But what is meant by "a higher goal"? The patient just referred to, rather than yield to her embarrassing love, might turn her attention instead to some intellectual pursuit. She was evidently wealthy, well-educated, and proud of her intellect. But would such activities have drained off the powerful sexual drive which was concentrated upon her brother-in-law? We have seen that, according to Freud, such redirection of energy is quite possible. Indeed, he held that all disinterested activity in the arts and sciences, and all the amenities and embellishments of life, are a sublimation of repressed drives, mostly sexual.

Finally, the patient may decide that his rejection of the repressed wish was wise, and he may succeed "in mastering his wishes by conscious thought" (p. 9a). The patient we have just mentioned may draw on the resources of religion and morality to support her rejection of her guilty love. This way of dealing with the pathogenic is not emphasized or elaborated by Freud. Would it not have the effect of re-establishing the neurotic condition? Would it not be simply endorsing the censor, whose severity had caused all the trouble? Or would a Socratic dialectic of morals serve to overcome evil wishes, once they were conscious?

If sexuality in infants and children is as obvious as Freud claims, why is it overlooked or so vehemently denied?

In the first place, adults forget the pleasures of being fondled and nursed, their curiosity about their parents' relations, their clinging possessive love of the mother and hatred of the father (especially in the case of the male child), and scores of other things. The forgetting, or rather *repression*, has been caused by the shame, disgust, anxiety, and moral disgrace attached to such feelings and to the memory of them. By the time of puberty, education has so obliterated the record of early erotic enjoyments and wishes that the high tide of sexual desire at that time is felt as something entirely new.

Would you say that Freud is using the term "sex" in a much wider sense than is customary, when he includes under it sensations arising from erogenous zones of the skin, from sucking and defecation? How far is he able to show a continuity between infant sexuality and adult sexuality? In attempting to answer this question, should we be on our guard against our repressions? Of would you doubt that there has been much repression? One possible way to find out what babies feel and want is to persuade adults under deep hypnosis that they are back in their tenth year, their fifth year, and finally their first year. Questioning such subjects has yielded some remarkable results, but not enough to satisfy curiosity or to silence doubts.

The following questions are designed to help you test the thoroughness of your reading. Each question is to be answered by giving a page or pages of the reading assignment. Answers will be found on page 384 of this Reading Plan.

1 What helpful result did Freud learn at Bernheim's clinic at Nancy?

2 What was the force which prevented hysterical patients from recalling critical experiences in their past?

3 What underlying purpose is served by the appearance in consciousness of a surrogate of the repressed idea?

4 Give an example of a joke which illustrates the relation of wit to the unconscious.

5 Do anxiety dreams relieve the ego of repressed wishes?

6 Why does a thorough explanation and cure of neurosis require the analyst to go back to the early childhood of the patient?

7 On what point of Freud's theory was the psychiatrist Bleuler first skeptical, then persuaded?

8 What, according to Freud, is the origin of "curiosity for knowledge"?

9 How does Freud justify his preoccupation with the sexual life of children?

10 In what two respects is the dream like a night watchman?

11 What does the fairy tale of the three wishes illustrate?

12 How does Freud answer the objection that dreams can have apparently more than one meaning?

Fifteenth Reading

A General Introduction to Psycho-Analysis,
Lectures 20-21

*New Introductory Lectures
on Psycho-Analysis,*
Lectures 30-31

Vol. 54, pp. 569-585, 818-840

T he twentieth century has sometimes been called
"the age of psychology," for never before has psychology been so important. It is not surprising, therefore, that it is sometimes also described as "the age of
Freud," for certainly no other psychologist has done
so much to transform our picture of the human mind.
But Freudian influence on various fields of psychology, Gardner Murphy contends,[1] is uneven. It has
been greatest in clinical psychology and personality,
and not much less in the area of imagination, includ-

---

[1] Gardner Murphy, "The Current Impact of Freud on American
Psychology," in *Freud and the Twentieth Century,* ed. Benjamin Nelson
(New York: Meridian Books, Inc., 1957), pp. 102 ff.

349

ing dream psychology. Freud's starting point and fulcrum is the individual, and his influence on social psychology is said to be only moderate, though in this field and in sociology more and more authors are giving emphasis to Freudian concepts of conflict, repression, substitution, compensation, etc. Oddly enough, child psychology has not been affected as much as one might expect, and many authors in this area are showing what Freud called "resistance" to his account of sexual development in the child.

Some of the opposition may come from an alert and prudish censor, but much of it stems from a scientific conscience that demands more evidence. It is hard to prove, after all, that character is formed by the age of three. Yet large borrowings from Freud's child psychology are seen in the works of anthropologists who study the coming of age in primitive communities; and the equating of taboo with neurosis opened up a broad vista of research. In the theory of emotions and feelings, Freud seems to have had little effect. He made important analyses of certain emotions, such as anxiety and sexual love, but did not contribute much new to general theory. Nor did he make important additions to classical fields of psychology, such as learning, perception, and physiological psychology. By delimiting the area in which he can claim to have made contributions, we are in a better position to understand his genius.

Even when we restrict the principal fields of his discoveries and inventions to clinical psychology, personality, and imagination, we are amazed at the breadth of his influence and at the repercussions in other areas. Anthropology, art, and literature have been mentioned. Philosophy and religion might be added, for Freudism is not only a psychological theory and therapy but also a philosophy of life. In the tradition of the Enlightenment, it sought to free men's minds from delusions which barred the way to freedom and happiness.

The outcome to many readers seemed to be a pessimism as black as that of Schopenhauer. Repression of our dearest desires results in individual deprivation and suffering, but repression is necessary for civilization and therefore unavoidable. Freudians answer that this is not pessimism but realism. They sometimes point out that repression, according to Freud, can also release other "higher" cultural desires which would not otherwise come into play. But Freud himself doubted that a civilization which sacrifices natural desires can produce happiness, for happiness, as he once said, refers not to "eliminating pain and discomfort," but to "the experience of intense pleasures" (p. 772a).

Freud vigorously opposed religion, which he regarded as a delusion, as a futile attempt to perpetuate the protection and the solace the child enjoys in the family, and he never tired of citing the evils that follow from religious repression. Christian writers naturally oppose Freudism, but usually not *in toto*. Some insights and some aspects of the therapy are valuable. There is on foot, indeed, a movement to replace

Freud's determinism by free will in a Christian revision of psychoanalysis. At the same time, some psychoanalysts, such as Gregory Zilboorg, believe that
Freudism is only superficially in conflict with religion.

The effect of Freud on philosophers is very diverse,
ranging from indifference and hostility to complete
acceptance. In the latter case, a philosopher's views
are regarded as simply ways he has taken to disguise
and overcome his fears. Freud's ideas impinge on
ethics, the theory of knowledge, and metaphysics, but
the outcome is far from clear. Yet here, as in other
areas, the shadow of the Viennese physician seems to
be growing longer.

Fifteenth Reading

I

By 1910 the main structure of psychoanalytic theory had been laid out. *The Interpretation of Dreams* had appeared in 1900, the *Three Essays on the Theory of Sexuality* in 1905. Then came the first survey of the whole field of psychoanalysis, *The Origin and Development of Psycho-Analysis* in 1910 and *Totem and Taboo* in 1913. Between 1915 and 1917 Freud gave another general survey of psychoanalysis at the University of Vienna, which was published under the title *A General Introduction to Psycho-Analysis.* Many other volumes were to follow, the last being *Moses and Monotheism,* published in London in 1939, the year of his death.

Freud's revolutionary theory progressed in new ideas, corrections, and extensions. By 1910 it had become a platform and a program international in scope, requiring devoted disciples to propagate the new doctrine and preserve it from corruption. The task was far too great for one man, even one of Freud's energy and ability. Not long after the International Psycho-Analytic Association was formed, deviation and dissension appeared in the circle of Freud's closest associates. Brilliant, creative minds do not readily follow a master, especially when he is the last word in bold invention and can offer no direct or experimental proof of his teachings.

The first to break away at this period was Alfred Adler. Freud responded with sympathy and admiration to Adler's efforts to explain character in terms of organ inferiority. When he went so far as to maintain that the real explanation of neurosis is not unconscious repression of the Oedipus complex and infantile sexuality but rather "masculine protest," a compensation for feelings of inferiority, Freud realized that their cooperation had come to an end. He admitted that Adler's views were consistent and significant but held that they were also one-sided and dangerous. But had not Adler developed an aspect of ego adaptation that Freud himself had slighted— the lifelong struggle of the ego to free itself from a sense of inferiority and failure in the face of social pressures? Many analysts were to revise Freud along this line, emphasizing social conflict, and Freud himself gave greater attention in later writings to ego adaptation to the external world. Neurotics, he once said, are children who have failed in the struggle for existence. (See p. 592b.)

The defection of C. G. Jung, while still president of the International Psycho-Analytic Association and editor of its yearbook, had numerous causes. Like Adler, Jung depreciated the role of sex in the genesis of neurosis and considered the dread of incest merely symbolic of other things, but he was far from belittling the unconscious. Indeed, his interpretations of mythology and magic in terms of unconscious meanings and symbols went to unprecedented extremes. The broadening of the libido, or sex drive, to a general tension, or to something as indiscriminate as Bergson's *élan vital,* marked the direction that dissent often took, but this was to Freud's mind a complete repudiation. He made great efforts, however, to keep Jung within his circle.

Another interesting trend of deviation, which was to become very popular, was the program of short analysis. However humanitarian it might appear, this idea was heresy to Freud. Only an extended analysis could penetrate, against the patient's resistance, to the pathogenic factors of infancy, the incestuous and parricidal thoughts, or the "primal scene" of sexual violence. A short analysis could not reach the cause of neurosis and therefore could not cure it. However, in the middle twenties Sandor Ferenczi and Otto Rank, long-term associates of Freud, were both moving toward a reduced analysis, though in somewhat different ways.

Freud could be jealous and dictatorial on occasion, but he was fundamentally fair and detached, and if offered the whole world on a platter which he considered unscientific he would not have accepted it. When Freud criticized Ferenczi for emphasizing the value of *living through* experiences rather than recalling them, Ferenczi replied indignantly that he had never dreamed of departing an iota from the master's teachings. Freud answered that he valued such a sentiment as an expression of friendship but regarded it as unrealistic.

"If you were to wait so long each time there would be an end of your productivity. So that won't do at all. That you or Rank should in your independent flights ever leave the ground of psychoanalysis seems to me out of the question. Why shouldn't you therefore have the right to try if things won't work in another way from that I had thought? If you go astray in so doing you will find that out yourself some time or other, or I will take the liberty of pointing it out to you as soon as I am myself sure about it."[2]

II

We have already seen that Freud was vehemently criticized for extending the term "sexual" beyond its usual meaning. It is usually restricted to the act of reproduction and the caresses which precede it. It can also be restricted to experiences of any kind which terminate in an orgasm, and this is the sense of "sexual" which was employed in the Kinsey reports. Freud thought them both too narrow.

His reasons for extending the meaning of the term came from a study of three sets of facts: (1) perversions, (2) neuroses, and (3) infant sexuality. People balk at calling these things sexual, but Freud argues vigorously and voluminously that they are. They are not entirely separable from one another; a perversion may be a neurotic symptom and also have its roots in infant sexuality. Kissing is a preliminary to sexual intercourse, but it may also be a substitute for it, and even a perversion. "The kiss," Freud says,

has some claim to be called a perverse act, for it consists of the union of the two erotogenic mouth zones instead of the two genital organs. But no one condemns it as perverse; on the contrary, in the theatre it is permitted as a refined indication of the sexual act. (p. 577d)

[2] Ernest Jones, *The Life and Work of Sigmund Freud* (New York: Basic Books, Inc., 1953-1955), Vol. III, pp. 57-58.

It becomes a perversion when it is employed to arouse feelings so intense that orgasm or sexual fruition results. It may also be a symptom in obsessional neurosis and mark a regression to an early stage of sexual development in which the mouth is the chief organ of pleasure.

Other activities that are normally preliminary to coitus also become perversions when they are desired for themselves and are taken to be the sexual goal. The knight of courtly love would die for a kiss, or a caress, or to see his lady love disrobed, and would seek nothing more. Sometimes it is a part of a woman, such as her foot, her hand, or her breast, which is the sole object of desire; and the fetishist, Freud remarks, finds all his pleasure in the clothes, perfume, or some quite arbitrary symbol of the woman. There are also, of course, endless perversions of sexual intercourse itself, which are described in the classical seven-volume work of Havelock Ellis, *Studies in the Psychology of Sex*. Very common and most important are those cases where the individual cannot perform or obtain pleasure from the sexual act except when he inflicts pain or humiliation on the other person, or he himself is made to suffer. In the first case we have *sadism*, and in the second *masochism*, two phenomena which, according to Freud, are in some degree invariable accompaniments of sexual life.

Freud is often charged with exaggeration. Does not everyone know that sexual perversions are rare and too repulsive to attract decent people? Yet the Kinsey reports tell us that they are very common in the United States and are often practiced by people regarded as quite average and respectable. Freud rejects the judgment of Ivan Bloch—an outstanding authority on sex—that all perversions are "signs of degeneration." He rejects it because "such aberrations from the sexual aim, such erratic relationships to the sexual object, have been manifested since the beginning of time . . . in every race from the most primitive to the most highly civilized" (p. 571c).

If the term "sexual" is restricted to the act of reproduction, many phenomena become obscured. Perversions such as homosexuality and masturbation seem obviously sexual. Freud argues that homosexuals do not form a class apart—a third sex;

they have the same sexual drive as other people do, but it has been diverted to members of their own sex, evidently by fears and frustrations encountered in the quest of normal satisfaction. Could there be, we might ask, any other explanation? Are not some men *naturally* "feminine," and some women *naturally* "masculine"? We do know that in the testes of the male there are some cells which produce female sex hormones, and that in the ovaries of the female, likewise, some cells occur which discharge male hormones into the blood stream. Might there not be more of such cells of the opposite sex functioning in some individuals than in others? And might there not be other constitutional factors which could explain, in part at least, why some individuals become homosexuals? Freud did not deny the existence of such constitutional or congenital differences, but he believed that they have little to do with the occurrence of homosexuality, which, his experience showed, was largely an acquired trait. It was acquired in lieu of normal sex relations and was itself obviously sexual.

Overt and conscious homosexuals are rare, but latent homosexuality, which is unconscious and shows itself only in a disguised form, is extremely widespread. Even when a man chooses a love-object of the opposite sex, his attitude and behavior may disclose, at least to the analyst, that his role is feminine and dependent. The line here between the abnormal and the normal is always hard to draw. All men and women, Freud implied, are in some measure latent homosexuals. Is it not true that when men are isolated from women for long periods, as in prison, a great many become active homosexuals? Does this not prove, Freud asks, that they had a prior inclination to it? But would this strictly follow? Could not a shipwrecked man learn to like raw fish without having a latent appetite for it?

Masturbation is claimed to be practically universal in children, and many adults, Freud says, never abandon it. When men are marooned or imprisoned for long periods, masturbation, like homosexuality, becomes a substitute for normal sexual gratification. Because the practice is condemned by society, it is attended by guilt feelings which may become intense, giving rise to neurotic symptoms. Freud contends that "an unsuspectedly large proportion of obsessive actions [in obsessional neurosis] are found to be disguised repetitions and modifications of masturbation, admittedly the only uniform act which accompanies all the varied flights of sexual phantasy" (p. 572c). The patient repeats some meaningless act. What can be the explanation? It may symbolize at once the forbidden gratification and the rejection of it, Freud says, or it may also be a defense against the guilty wish. Compulsive hand-washing is a common symptom which symbolizes or distracts from anxieties.

Let us take an analogy that everyone will understand. A man who is trying to give up smoking may well carry out actions suggestive both of taking and lighting a cigarette and also of rejecting it. He may also walk up and down, keep his hands busy in some meaningless routine, or invent self-punishments to put smoking out of mind. The analogy is not exact, of course, since the guilt aroused by smoking would be much less than that occasioned by masturbation, and repression is lacking.

Young boys, Freud reports, are regularly warned that the most frightful consequences, including castration, will result from a continuation of their self-abuse. As a result they are caught up in a conflict between dread and strong desire, a conflict that cannot be relieved by talking about it and protesting but must be repressed. Banished from consciousness, however, guilty desires can fester in the unconscious for many years. The ensuing conflict can produce neurotic symptoms which disable the adult. It is thus important to recognize, Freud held, that what comes into existence at puberty is not sexuality but the reproductive function, and that sexual activity begins in the first year of life. If you make the mistake of "confounding sexuality and reproduction with each other," Freud says, "you obstruct your own way to the comprehension of sexuality, the perversions, and the neuroses" (p. 573b).

Some of Freud's findings are questioned. How often do fathers threaten their young sons with castration, especially in enlightened circles in America today, and would the castration complex develop even in the absence of such threats? Would not Freud's psychopathology have to be greatly modified in the light of recent observations of primitive societies where masturbation is not punished or reproved and sex play on the part of children is permitted? The castration complex (or fear of degenitalization) is even less plausible in the case of girls, and Freud's contention that girls always long for male attributes and envy boys their possession of a male organ ("penis envy") is often regarded as a rash generalization.

We think of hunger and eating as quite separate and distinct from sex and its gratifications, and yet we are not entirely consistent about it. We accept the idea that a man's abnormal craving for food, for example, may be compensatory for the lack of sexual satisfaction. Freud concluded that hunger and sex are very closely related. The greatest pleasure of the infant is experienced at his mother's breast, where two imperious needs are satisfied simultaneously. He sucks for nourishment, but also for the pleasure of sucking, which is shown by the fact that he will continue to suck the nipple, his thumb, or some other object after his hunger is appeased. This conclusion has been corroborated. It is found that breast-fed infants tend to do less sucking of other objects than do infants who are bottle fed, presumably because it takes longer to obtain milk from the breast. Similarly, when puppies are bottle fed, those which are given nipples with large holes in them do more compensatory sucking of other objects than those which are given nipples with small holes.[3] When breast feeding in infants is not prohibited at a certain point, it has been found to continue for many years, though the individual is being nourished also by solid food.[4]

Whether the need and the pleasure of sucking in the infant is sexual in character is another question. In Freud's opinion psychoanalysis shows

how much of the mental significance of this act is retained throughout life. Sucking for nourishment becomes the point of departure from which

[3] D. M. Levy, "Experiments in the Sucking Reflex and Social Behavior of Dogs," in *American Journal of Orthopsychiatry*, 1934, 4, p. 203.

[4] F. Nansen, *Eskimo Life* (London: Longmans, Green & Company, 1893).

the whole sexual life develops, the unattainable prototype of every later sexual satisfaction, to which in times of need phantasy often enough reverts. (p. 574c)

The normal tendency of the kiss to arouse sexual desire, and the fixation on the oral phase of sexual development, when kissing becomes the perverse goal of sexual desire, are illustrations of the sexual significance Freud assigned to sucking in infancy and in adult life. The sucking of cigarettes, cigars, and pipes, or even sticks, in adults may also have a role similar to that of pacifiers in infants. We can also find in long case histories of Freud's patients indications that the bliss of breast feeding, though far in the past, is not entirely forgotten. The reversion in times of trouble to the idyllic state of infancy, of which Freud speaks, is a kind of longing for a time when we were omnipotent and free from all care, when nourishment could be had for the sucking, and the sucking itself was a pleasure.

How much such phantasies are due to the suggestions of the analyst is not clear. Under hypnosis the patient is very suggestible, but even when following his associations freely on the couch he is suggestible enough. Freud was aware of the danger of unwittingly implanting in the patient the very ideas he wanted to confirm. He was on his guard, but many critics believe that additional safeguards are needed.

The oral stage of sexual development is the first. When the child is weaned the oral receptivity, i.e., the readiness to incorporate objects, is supplemented by an aggressive, sadistic tendency. The urge to swallow and dominate things easily passes over into aggression; the nipple and other objects may be bitten and teeth gnashed in rage. The second stage is the anal erotic, in which the infant's sexual drive or "libido" as Freud calls it, is absorbed by his interest in his own excreta (*coprophilia*). Every parent knows, although there is a tendency to forget, that an infant is deeply concerned and curious about his bowel movements and at first feels no disgust at all. On the contrary, the mother's efforts to train him to use the toilet commonly misfire. The infant learns to treasure his production and hold it back, at least until he is rewarded. The whole process of toilet training, which to the parent appears only "natural," is extremely unnatural and harsh for the infant. He, whose every wish had been granted, is now thwarted, scolded, and pushed around by his own parents. The result in Freudian theory is "anal aggressiveness," which is directed against the parents and perhaps against society. The child plays in the dirt, mischievously soils his clothes and the house, and breaks and destroys things. An anal erotic vestige may remain in adults who show a desire to soil or desecrate things held in esteem, or, inversely, spend their time washing their hands, avoiding germs, and worrying about infections—common symptoms of obsessive-compulsive neurosis.

The facts here are not in dispute; we can only question whether harsh weaning and toilet training are the causes of them. Here again anthropology offers an opportunity for testing Freudian theory. Primitive people usually subject infants and young children to far fewer restraints than we do, and allow them plenty of time to grow up. If a study of various primitive societies indicates that aggression is less when child training is lenient and leisurely, and this seems to be the trend of the evidence, we should have added reasons to believe that anal aggressiveness results from too much haste in civilizing the child.

III

The Oedipus complex develops in children of both sexes around the age of four or five. The boy experiences sexual love for his mother and wants to take his father's place. He is like the king of Sophocles' *Oedipus Rex* who unwittingly kills his father and marries his mother. The experience of the girl is not so understandable. She, too, is said to love her mother physically at this time and to transfer her fixation to the father heterosexually at a later period. Freud says that mothers are often quite aware of the boy child's seductive aspirations and are amused by his puerile pretensions; and that fathers may learn of them but are not amused. Why should either parent be disturbed by the futile erotic strivings of a four-year-old boy, his curiosity about female anatomy, and the concentration of his interest in the only woman who is in sight—the mother, or perhaps the older sister? Have not they themselves encouraged such an interest? The mother is partial to the boy and delights in fondling him, whereas the father is aloof and critical and gives his daughter his approval and tender concern. The father is often needlessly severe in insisting that the boy grow up punctually and learn to obey. Is it surprising that he is drawn to his more indulgent mother and comes to hate his father?

The Oedipus complex, however, does not depend upon the attitudes of the parents; Freud says it arises spontaneously and would be found in any society, no matter what its organization and customs might be. Although the mother may laugh at the seductive intentions of her little son, she does so only because he is small and absurdly incompetent. After a few years he is summarily ejected from his mother's bed. In all societies, according to Freud, there is a horror of incest, which is regarded as the most abominable crime, and the most severe prohibitions and punishments are instituted against it. Some authorities, such as William McDougall, had argued that brothers and sisters are not attracted to one another sexually, because there is a natural distaste for intercourse among those who have been reared together from their earliest years, and the sex impulse is thus diverted to members of other groups. But in this case, why, Freud asks, should the most stringent prohibitions, segregations, and punishments have been established to prevent incestuous relations?

We shall have to admit that Freud's reply is quite devastating. But what then is his own explanation of the horror evoked by incest all over the world, in all societies—except where it is permitted to kings and gods? Is a "diffusionist" explanation possible? Can we suppose that the horror and proscription of incest had an accidental origin in one society and were from this point diffused throughout the world by traders or invaders? This is completely implausible. Diffusion would not be worldwide, and in any case would not explain why such drastic restrictions should be universally adopted and perpetuated. Evidently such a widespread phenomenon must have an indigenous origin, must arise out of conditions present in the society itself.

Freud argues that the "first choice of object in mankind is regularly an incestuous one, directed to the mother and sister of men" (p. 583c-d). Why, then, should this first choice be everywhere ruthlessly suppressed? He points out that incest and parricide are the two great crimes outlawed by totemism, which, he says, is "the first social-religious institution of mankind." It is now known that totemism is not by any means universal nor prior to other social-religious systems. But Freud was right about the main point: exogamy—the requirement that individuals marry outside a certain kinship group, narrowly or broadly conceived—is ancient and universal.

The Oedipus complex in the child seems to throw light on exogamy and the horror of incest in the race. The boy child desires his mother but fears swift retribution from his father for his unholy love and for his parricidal wish to do away with his rival. What he fears most is castration; but the desire to get rid of his father is perhaps almost as bad, since he also loves and looks up to his father. Hence the Oedipus complex is always conflictful and *ambivalent,* and may extend in some degree to the rest of the family, especially when other children appear on the scene. Then there is a many-sided rivalry for affection, with love and hatred—both sexual—intertwined. One indication of the deep sense of guilt which weighs upon the child is that at about his sixth year he enters upon what Freud called his latent period, which lasts until the onset of puberty. In this period he loses all memory of his Oedipus involvements. They are repressed—mercifully buried—in the unconscious, and his sexual urge is diverted to activities outside the family. Can these early experiences of the child give a clue to the origin of exogamy?

In his *Totem and Taboo,* Freud sifted the anthropological literature of his time in search of an answer. He started off with Darwin's theory that human society had its beginning in the primal horde, which was dominated by a violent and jealous father who was strong enough to drive away his young sons and to keep the females for himself. He then brought this conception into relation with the very paradoxical "celebration of the totem," which takes place in Australia and other areas where totemism is found. This is the celebration of the sacrificial killing and eating of the sacred totem animal, which it is forbidden to kill at other times. The paradox is that the animal is both killed and mourned. How could this be explained? "Psychoanalysis has revealed to us," Freud answers, "that the totem animal is really a substitute for the father," i.e., the father of the primal horde.[5] He elaborates his hypothesis in the famous passage:

"One day the expelled brothers joined forces, slew and ate the father, and thus put an end to the father horde. Together they dared and accomplished what would have remained impossible for them singly. . . . Of course these cannibalistic savages ate their victim. This violent primal father had surely been the envied and feared model for each of the brothers. Now they accomplished their identification with him by devouring him and each acquired a part of his strength. The totem feast . . would be the repetition and commemoration of this memorable, criminal act with which so many things began, social organization, moral restrictions and religion."[6]

With beautiful precision Freud describes the events which may have brought an end to the primal tyranny and the beginnings of organized society with its taboos, laws, moral codes, and civic ideals. The hypothesis, however fanciful it may appear, explained many things. To disguise and repudiate their guilt, the rebel brothers substituted the totem animal for the father and ruled that parricide was an unpardonable crime. To further disengage themselves from guilt they renounced the women—their sisters—and henceforth took mates from outside the group, proscribing incest as an unspeakable offense. Their *ambivalence* of attitude as they turned against their father was like that of the young boy toward *his* father, and like the boy they managed to disguise and repress all memory of their offense.

Sigmund Freud, *Totem and Taboo* in *The Basic Writings of Sigmund Freud,* ed. A. A. Brill (New York: The Modern Library, Random House, Inc., 1938), p 915.
[6] *Ibid.,* pp. 915, 916.

One may see improbabilities in this hypothesis, for which there is no direct proof at all. We have already noted that Freud was wrong in thinking that totemism was the earliest system of social controls to be instituted; and without totemism, of course, there would be no totem feast. Moreover, exogamy and social controls might have arisen without the assumed parricide. Freud himself points out that if, after the death of the father, the brothers had attempted to divide the women among themselves, jealousy and dissension would have divided them, and the horde might have been reestablished with a new tyrant reserving the females to himself. Thus if the father had died a natural death, they would still have had a strong motive for the rule of exogamy. But one should not reject the theory because of its unpleasant picture of cannibalism, polygamy, and parricide. These are common enough in our human past.

Freud would never have reached this insight into the origins of morality and religion if he had not had clues from the study of neurotic patients. Every one of these, he claims, was found to be an Oedipus or, which comes to the same thing, a Hamlet, except that the hatred of the father and the death wishes are more accentuated in the neurotic than they were in the child. The neurotic thus represents a regression to childhood, as shown by his "retrogressive phantasy-making," but the complex has become articulated and exasperated. Although later events in the patient's life have added complications to the neurosis, its kernel remains the Oedipus complex. The neurotic, in short, has failed to free himself from his parents. His dependence, his guilt, his fixation remain. He is not properly weaned from his emotional dependence on his mother, or is still dominated by his father, and is thus unable to divert his libido to a new sexual object. The neurotic woman may show the same symptoms, though the role of the parents is now reversed. "In this sense the Oedipus complex is justifiably regarded as the kernel of the neuroses" (p. 584c).

We have pointed out that some of Freud's conclusions about infant sexuality and the Oedipus complex, and about their effect on adult psychology, may result from incomplete observations. His data came mostly from neurotic individuals of central Europe at the turn of the century. There are conflicting observations. Margaret Mead found that the oral stimulation to which Arapesh children are subject up to ages three to five, when they are weaned, is far greater than in our own culture. Yet sex is apparently not involved, and the sexual life of the Arapesh adults is genital and normal. Malinowski found no evidence of Freud's latent period among the Trobriands, where sexual activity between boys and girls is unhampered and continuous from the earliest years. The Oedipus complex naturally takes a very different form, if it occurs at all, in societies where authority over the children is exercised by the wife's brother, while the father is their playmate. Such findings, which suggest that Freud's theories are culturally relative, have to be taken into account in their evaluation.[7] It is surprising to what an extent they have survived anthropological and psychological tests.

I V

You may have been wondering why Freud spends so much time talking about the "psychological underworld," and has nothing to say about "nobler thoughts and higher feelings." Freud does not deny their existence but argues that neither in the ordinary life of the ego nor in the genesis of neurosis do they cut much ice. In "The Anatomy of the Mental Personality," Lecture 31 of *New Introductory Lectures on Psycho-Analysis,* he attempts to justify this verdict by an exposition of the psychology of the ego—yours and mine. He makes light of the old philosophical problem of how the ego, which is always subject, can also be object—can also be studied. Does it not cease to be subject when it becomes object? No, Freud says, one part can study other parts, and the ego can be reassembled later.

Freud likewise defends his preoccupation with pathological egos. In them, he says, ordinary traits, which we might other-

[7] For discussion and references, see Robert R. Sears, *Survey of Objective Studies of Psychoanalytic Concepts* (New York: Social Science Research Council, pap. 1.25, 1943).

wise overlook, are exaggerated, and can be seen in clear profile. He gives a striking example. Psychotics who turn away from reality and live in their own private world complain bitterly that they are continually being watched by hostile persons who seem to be waiting for them to do something wrong. Is this not absurd? Is it not also an exaggeration of what we all feel to some extent, Freud asks? Is not this observing part of our ego what we call "conscience"? Doesn't it watch us continually, warning and reproaching us when we yield to pleasure?

The *superego* is the name which Freud gives to this critical observer of the ego's doings. But why make it a separate entity, almost a separate person? Why not simply say that in pursuing pleasure and power the ego is sometimes inhibited? Freud's answer is that this censorious observer acts independently of the ego, possesses apparently its own supply of energy, and often tortures and mercilessly persecutes the poor ego, holding it up to impossible moral standards. This reaches its peak in the sufferings of melancholia. The ego, then, does not simply inhibit its pleasure seeking; it is humiliated and tortured by an apparently independent agency, split off from the ego. This is the *superego*.

The superego is strong and independent because it usually claims the backing of a divine wisdom. Freud thinks it queer that if conscience (the superego) comes from God it should function periodically—being now benign, now reproachful and cruel. This pendular swing reaches great extremes in the alternate phases of manic-depression. We often think of religion and conscience as representing the good side of any issue that faces us; for Freud they are often on the side of disintegration and neurosis. We are reminded of Lucretius' eloquent portrayal of the crimes to which men have been driven by religious beliefs (See *Great Books*, Vol. 12, p. 2a-b), except that the crimes especially emphasized by Freud are those of man against himself, against his own health and happiness.

Conscience, Freud maintains, is a function of early training:

The influence of the parents dominates the child by granting proofs of affection and by threats of punishment, which, to the child, mean loss of love, and which must also be feared on their own account. This objective anxiety is the forerunner of the later moral anxiety. . . . (p. 832b)

When the restrictions to pleasure are only external, when the child merely fears punishment or loss of love, we have *objective* anxiety. When the parents' injunctions and warnings are *introjected*, i.e., absorbed into the child's conscience, the anxiety becomes moral. The parents do not have to punish the child; it punishes itself.

The child's conscience or superego thus takes over the parents' job and assumes all their harshness and severity but not their kindness and protectiveness. And the child's superego "may reflect the same relentless harshness even when the upbringing has been gentle and kind" (p. 832c). But how is this possible? If the child's superego can become harsh even when its parents were gentle, how does it come about that some people have an *easy* conscience? They need not be psychopaths nor morons; they may simply enjoy sunny dispositions.

When the boy *introjects* (or makes his own) the moral judgment of his father, he does it by *identifying* himself with his father. This is like the old theory that we learn virtue not from abstract precepts but by imitating virtuous men; but Freud's doctrine has irony and a new depth. Freud begins by distinguishing between identification and object-choice. When a boy identifies himself with his father, which is his first identification (see p. 705a), he wants to be like him. He also wants to take over his father's role, to displace him, which means that his attitude toward his father is ambivalent. If he makes his father his *object-choice*, on the other hand, he wants "to *have* him, to possess him" (p. 832d), and to have him he need not be like him. The boy may want both things.

Identification has many complications. The boy's first object-choice is his mother, while his identification is with his father. But what happens when "the object-cathexis of the mother," i.e., the emotional involvement with the mother, is given up, as it should be, at the age of four or five? Depending on whether his main constitutional tendency is to the masculine or the feminine, the boy (or girl) at this time will identify with the father or the mother, i.e., will try to be like the one or the other. Unfortunately, things are not as simple as this. Since each individual is bisexual, the boy does not simply identify with his father and love his mother; he "at the same time . . . also behaves like a girl and displays an affectionate feminine attitude to his father and a corresponding hostility and jealousy towards his mother" (p. 705d). The bisexuality of the little girl will be displayed in a similar way. There is still another factor that determines identification. This is rivalry. Suppose a little girl gains the father's attention by flirting and by feminine wiles. Will not her brother, who feels neglected, be inclined to himself assume a feminine role?

These complexities do not make the identification theory any easier to understand, but do they not bring it closer to the rich ambiguities of life? An important consequence of early identifications is that when they are only partly overcome they leave a form or template in the mind which reproduces similar identifications in the future. A man who has not broken up his father dependence may go through life subjecting himself to various father figures—father surrogates—reliving in relation to them his childish dependence, respect, fear, hatred, and revolt. Similarly, in quite normal people we see a tendency to identify with a lost love. A woman whose life is impoverished by the death of her husband may make him a part of herself—love what he loved, think and behave as he did. More typically, of course, men identify with their love-objects while they are still living, loving them as manifestations of their own personality, with the result that they love only themselves. This is what Freud calls narcissism.

Early object-choices (i.e., love-objects) also tend to reproduce themselves when the individual has not emancipated himself from them. Thus a man may be attracted only to women who resemble his mother; or, since guilt attaches to his infantile fixation, he is attracted only to women who do *not* resemble his mother. This looks as if this Freudian theory would be confirmed whatever a man does, for if he is not attracted to *any* woman, this too could be explained. It could mean that for him the horror of incest had contaminated the whole sex. Is this Freudian theory, then, incapable of being disproved? If so, is it not also incapable of being proved? The situation is not as bad as it looks. We have forgotten, for the moment, that a man's choice of women, like or unlike his mother, is only one fragment of the evidence. By itself it would prove nothing. Psychoanalysis takes many factors into account, takes a long time and plenty of money.

Freud's concept of identification has carried over to popular usage, not always exact. We sometimes say that a woman identifies with her husband who is hard pressed by enemies, when it would be better to say she sympathizes with him. In sympathy she feels *for* him; in identification she feels, thinks, judges, as he does. To sympathize she need not be like him nor want to be like him. English associationists regularly confused sympathy with identification, yet either can clearly occur without the other. People identify with historical characters or heroes and heroines on the stage where sympathy—as implying readiness to relieve distress—is out of the question.

The first identification in life is of crucial importance in Freud's psychology. The child identifies, as we have suggested, not with its parents but with the superegos of its parents, which is quite different. The father may be a libertine, but his superego is likely to be a moralist. The child's ego thus acquires its own superego. The superego becomes strong and firmly lodged precisely because the ego at this time is weak, undeveloped, and defenseless, and because the Oedipus conflict cannot be expressed and thus acknowledged but must be repressed and thereby preserved. The neurotic ego is not able to break its early family attachments and remains dominated by them, ready in any trial or crisis to regress to childlike dependence. Freud admits, however, that external circumstances can keep neurosis at bay. Two of the surest means of avoiding it are physical disease and an unhappy marriage, for they satisfy the need for self-punishment and suffering and drain off an excess of guilt. Sublimation of the sexual drive or libido in scientific, artistic, and religious activities is another way of holding the fort against neurosis, that is, if we do not go too far and starve the garrison.

We are now ready to discuss the three agencies of the mind by which it deals with its conflicts: the id, the ego, and the superego. Plato made a threefold division of the soul which is roughly analogous. The three parts of the soul, it will be remembered, are appetite or desire, will or spiritedness, and reason. Plato's appetite might seem similar to Freud's id, but the differences between the two schemes are more striking. The id, unlike the appetite, is unconscious. Reason has the role of suppressing desire, just as the superego has the function of seeing that desires are suppressed, or repressed. But how different are reason and the superego! Both are highly moral, but whereas reason is the key to truth and sanity, the superego is a factor in the internal struggle for existence which, as often as not, steers the soul to shipwreck and ruin.

A thorough comparison of these two divisions of the soul could easily fill a volume. Our purposes may be noted by emphasizing one significant agreement. In both cases the key to the human plight is seen in the continual struggle between the moral agency and desire. In this sense Freud is a Platonist. Since he often takes the side of desire against morality, he is sometimes regarded as an amoralist. This is hardly true. His is the physician's morality, which seeks to make the soul whole and healthy.

In the famous metaphor of Plato's *Phaedrus,* reason is a charioteer who drives two horses, one noble and obedient, representing the will, and the other passionate, headlong, and uncontrolled, representing desire. When the latter has his way the chariot is wrecked and the soul destroyed. Freud's revision of Plato's metaphor is very instructive:

One might compare the relation of the ego to the id with that between a rider and his horse. The horse provides the locomotive energy, and the rider has the prerogative of determining the goal and of guiding the movements of his powerful mount towards it. But all too often in the relations between the ego and the id we find a picture of the less ideal situation in which the rider is obliged to guide his horse in the direction in which it itself wants to go. (p. 838d)

Why has the superego been left out of the picture? We recall now that the superego is only a part of the ego that has been split off by infantile conflict and repression, a part which brings pressure on the ego and curbs its pleasure seeking but does not act in person. It is the ego that holds the reins; it is the ego that corresponds to the charioteer, or reason. The ego is the only actor on the stage, for the superego is only a back-seat driver, and the id in the adult is always bridled.

Yet we also learn that the ego derives its energy from the id, and is "only a part of the id, a part purposively modified by its proximity to the dangers of reality" (p. 838c). From this it appears that the ego is far removed from the sovereign reason of Plato, for the latter faculty is able, once it is in the clear, to undo passions and to conquer the strongest desire. The contrast, however, is not really so sharp as this. In some of his most mature formulations Plato is closer to Freud; desire can have its rights, and in fact Eros is said to rule the world.

Let us explore further the nature and relations of the id, ego, and superego. We have seen that the id is the source of the ego's energy and that it comes in contact with the external world only through the ego, which directs it toward the objects it craves, or misleads and deceives it, as the case may be. It knows nothing of contradiction, or of time, or of morality. Contradictory impulses demand fulfillment in the id, but its cravings and involvements are timeless and unaltered by the experiences of the ego. This is why the adult ego can regress to the Oedipal situation decades after it has been repressed in the id; the situation lies there always, unchanged. Thus when the patient succeeds in bringing to consciousness scenes and desires repressed in his id, they are found to be undated, and the task of the analyst is to determine where they belong in the time sequence.

But these characteristics of the id are mostly negative. What is the id in itself? We can ". . . call it a chaos," Freud says, "a cauldron of seething excitement" (p. 837b). Or we could call it a bundle of blind instincts, or better, a swarm of drives,[8] the

---

[8] "Drive" is better than "instinct" as a translation of the German *Trieb*, for "drive" does not imply inherited goal-seeking behavior, and "instinct" usually does.

most important being the sexual drive. It is also prior to the ego, both ontogenetically and phylogenetically. At one time we had no ego, let alone a superego, but were just plain id. Only gradually does the ego develop from the id—as its contact with the external world, its perceiver, thinker, public relations man. It is like a servant who tells his blind master what objects will fill his desires and leads him to them, or at least to some of them; the id cannot fill all his *desires* because they conflict and some are self-destructive. Like other servants the ego must deceive and cajole his greedy, stupid master for the master's sake and his own.

By this time you can have no doubt that Freud is extraordinarily original. Yet he is not alien to the European tradition. Freud's account of the interplay of id and ego, though rich and oriental in its imaginative power, is largely anticipated by Schopenhauer's description of the blind will and its servant, the intellect, through which alone it comes to see and understand.[9] Schopenhauer's omnipotent and ruthless Will was a will to life and a will to reproduction. Freud's id comprises two sets of instincts: Eros, or the sexual instincts, and the self-preservative instincts or drives. The two are not independent of each other but linked in conflict, for the aims of Eros could destroy life and must be checked, deflected, sublimated by the life instincts. A similar conflict is to be found in Schopenhauer's scheme. In his *Beyond the Pleasure Principle* (1920) Freud introduced another instinct—the death instinct—opposed to both the life and sex drives. This instinct had no parallel in Schopenhauer and was a superfluity, it can be argued, in Freud's system.

The instinct of self-preservation, Freud says, is "assigned to the ego." This seems reasonable, for it is the ego which must modify and deflect the blind surge of desire arising from the id, and needs some dynamic force of its own. But you will remember that Freud also tells us that the ego derives its energy from the id. How can the ego have its own dynamic

[9] Arthur Schopenhauer, *The World as Will and Idea* (New York: Charles Scribner's Sons, 1950), Vol. I, Books I and II.

energy if it derives it from the id, and how can it successfully oppose the demands of the id with energy it gets from the id? Perhaps the paradox will disappear if we drop the personification. Why not simply say that at the beginning the instincts provide the energy, but that the individual soon learns that some pathways to instinctive satisfaction are blocked or attended with pain? These pathways are then inhibited and others pursued. The energy, instead of following its original route in the brain C_1, forks off on another route C_2, which results in satisfaction. But when the energy pursues route C_2, it cannot also simultaneously pursue C_1, and the oftener it pursues C_2 the less likely it is to pursue C_1. Eventually this route leading to nonsatisfaction or pain, or both, is effectively blocked, or, as Freud would say, the ego bars the id from this outlet. The pain which brings about the inhibition of the child's sexual activity could well be the father's warnings and threats.

In the last two decades learning-theory specialists have made some progress in testing Freud's ideas. Something like human neuroses have been produced experimentally in dogs, cats, rats, sheep, goats, as also in some human subjects, usually by subjecting them to conflicting signals. Pavlov's dogs were given food when a circle was presented, but no food when an ellipse was shown. They showed that they distinguished between the two figures by salivating to the circle but not to the ellipse. When the ellipse was increasingly made thicker—more like a circle—the dogs could still distinguish it, but only up to a certain point. When a certain degree of resemblance had been reached, the animals, Pavlov reports, showed signs of acute neurosis. To them, an ellipse looked like a circle and an ellipse too; it meant food and no food.

Sometimes the procedure in this country has been somewhat different. Masserman trained cats to go through a certain routine to get food. When the learning was established he subjected them to a harmless but frightening blast of air. The cats became neurotic, i.e., the quiet ones became very active, the active ones rigid and motionless, and all of them refused food and rest. Such neuroses are often very protracted, but

Masserman, who is a psychiatrist and a Freudian, believes that the methods he found effective in curing neuroses in his cats are roughly analogous to those employed in psychoanalysis.[10]

For many psychoanalysts, however, the analogy is too rough to be illuminating. Cats and dogs, after all, do not talk and do only a minimum of thinking. Their fathers do not threaten them with castration, nor do they repress their guilt, and neurosis in animals has only a superficial resemblance to neurosis in human beings. One general answer of Masserman and those who agree with him is that knowledge in pathology has been greatly advanced by the experimental study of animals in spite of the broad difference of species. Experiments always simplify conditions found in nature or society.

You will probably agree that it would be desirable to find some way of objectively testing the factors said by Freud to produce neurosis and to effect its cure. We have only very indirect evidence for such statements as the following:

It is the ego, therefore, that is responsible for the sense of guilt remaining unconscious. We know that, as a rule, the ego carries out repressions in the service and at the behest of its super-ego; but [in hysteria] it has turned the same weapon against its harsh taskmaster. . . . here the ego contents itself with keeping at a distance the material to which the sense of guilt refers. (p. 714a)

As a general rule the superego gets the ego to repress ideas or wishes that it considers disgraceful, but in hysteria the ego represses the charges laid at its door by the superego and thereby escapes from them. What objective criteria could we have to determine whether the ego is repressing on its own or at behest of the superego? Freud's admission that ego, id, and superego are not sharply divided, that they actually overlap or shade into one another, and that the separations vary from person to person and may be altered by mental disease, though fair-minded and ingratiating, makes it even more difficult to separate their functions.

The part played by the unconscious in Freud's system has

[10] Jules H. Masserman, *Behavior and Neurosis* (Chicago: The University of Chicago Press, 1943).

been severely criticized. Consciousness is difficult enough, but how can unconscious goings-on be confirmed? Take an example of a slip of the tongue. You say to your guest as he leaves, "I hope you will come again when you can't stay so long," thereby revealing your unconscious wish. But what does it mean to say that you unconsciously wish your guest to go home earlier? Would not the corresponding neural event in the brain be sufficient to cause the slip? This is the kind of question that James once asked. I can now bring to mind hundreds of thoughts without much effort. Is it necessary to infer, as Freud does, that they must have preexisted in the *preconscious?* Are not brain processes which are usually conceded to be *necessary* also *sufficient* to produce these thoughts each time we think them? And is it not the same with the immoral wishes the patient recalls only with the greatest difficulty? Must we conclude that they preexist in a huge container or aviary—the unconscious, ready to fly out when the patient's resistance is lowered sufficiently?

Ever since Edwin B. Holt's book *The Freudian Wish,*[11] psychologists sympathetic with what Freud says have been trying to say it in behavioral terms, often with the help of physiological concepts. A recent volume by Dollard and Miller, *Personality and Psychotherapy,*[12] is an illustration. The authors attempt to demonstrate that neurosis and psychotherapy obey "the laws of learning," i.e., the laws of learning as understood by Clark Hull and the Yale School. They explain how repression, regression, and neurotic symptoms of all kinds are *learned.* Symptoms are learned when they are reinforced, when they have the effect of reducing basic needs, and symptoms are eliminated in analysis by learning new habits. Many of the resources of learning theory are brought into play to account for Freud's results, but the outcome must be regarded as only a beginning.

Let us conclude, however, with one example which suggests

[11] Edwin B. Holt, *The Freudian Wish and Its Place in Ethics* (New York: Henry Holt & Company; 1915).

[12] John Dollard and N. E. Miller, *Personality and Psychotherapy* (New York: McGraw-Hill Book Company, Inc., 1960).

the promise that lies in a behavioral formulation. When Freud analyzed a patient he inferred from certain clues in his patient's language and behavior that certain of his thoughts were repressed in the unconscious. If, however, we were able to define repressed thoughts as behavior that cannot be completely verbalized except when special efforts are made, then the existence of repressed thoughts could be verified. Would this be a gain or a false simplification?

V

What is the distinction between the pleasure principle and the reality principle?

At the beginning of life, before the ego has had a chance to develop, the infant is governed by the pleasure principle. It seeks pleasure and release from discomfort *directly*, and is, so to speak, pure id. As life becomes more complicated, the child gradually learns that it cannot always have what it wants, and that it must sacrifice some pleasures, or even put up with pain, to get others. As his ego develops he comes to terms with the hard necessity imposed by external reality, and is said to be governed by the reality principle.

Suppose two children, age six, are playing a competitive game, and they ask a three-year-old to join them. A problem at once develops. The younger child wants to win every time, and storms or weeps when he doesn't. The explanation in Freudian terms is easy. The older children have learned to forgo the pleasure of winning a particular round of the game in the expectation of winning in the future. They have learned the pleasure of winning against opposition, but the young one is under the sway of the pleasure principle and wants his pleasures served up to him on a platter, as it were, and without delay.

Under what circumstances do adults sometimes retrogress to the pleasure principle? Does the superego, according to Freud, always conflict with the pleasure principle? Neurotics are said to regress to the Oedipus situation. But is not their mentality governed, at the same time, by *both* the reality principle and the pleasure principle?

Does Freud reject the inferiority complex?

He does not reject it or claim that Adler was entirely wrong, but he does put inferiority feelings in a subordinate place:

> The sense of inferiority has a strong erotic basis. The child feels itself inferior when it perceives that it is not loved, and so does the adult as well. . . . But the major part of the sense of inferiority springs from the relationship of the ego to its super-ego, and, like the sense of guilt, it is an expression of the tension between them. (p. 833d)

Do you think Freud is right? If a man fails at school and in business, must his sense of inferiority have an erotic basis? We should have some reason for saying so, if, when he feels himself loved (while other things remain the same), he ceases to have such feelings. But would love alone—or sexual satisfaction—entirely compensate for failures in other areas? Perhaps Freud is right, on the other hand, when he says that the superego is always involved. In some noncompetitive societies superegos of individuals do not demand achievement, and the inferiority complex is said to be absent.

It has not been shown, however, that there is "a strong erotic basis" for the sense of inferiority. The contrary is at least partly true. What seems to be an erotic interest is often an attempt to prove one's power. Freud himself has called attention to the frequency with which the military terms occur in the language of courtship and seduction. Thus the fortress is "assaulted" or "besieged" and finally "capitulates," "victory" is won and a "conquest" is made, etc.

Freud does not deny the role of the sense of inferiority, but insists that Adler has exaggerated its importance. It was as if a clown should pretend to be capable of all the remarkable feats performed in the circus.

Does sublimation explain our devotion to art and science?

Freud holds that, owing to frustration of the sexual instinct, energy accumulates which may be drained off in nonsexual activities. He never describes the nature of this sublimation process in detail. We are left to suppose that our passion for

Mozart and our delight in painting pictures are substitutes for sexual satisfaction. Does this not imply that if the sexual instinct were completely satisfied, art, science, and civilization itself would decay and disappear? The answer is apparently Yes. We should remember, however, that Freud, though fearful that it might be carried too far, was not at all opposed to sublimation in principle. It might be pointed out also that some followers of Freud have distinguished repressive and nonrepressive sublimation. The latter does not deflect the libido from its larger aim of enhancing erotic feeling and sensitivity. In fact, Freud himself claimed that the purpose of Eros is "to form living substance into ever greater unities, so that life may be prolonged and brought to higher development."[13]

[13] Ernest Jones (ed.), *Sigmund Freud, Collected Papers* (London: The Hogarth Press and The Institute of Psycho-Analysis, 1950), Vol. V, p. 135.

See also Herbert Marcuse, *Eros and Civilization* (Boston: The Beacon Press, 1955), especially Ch. 10, "The Transformation of Sexuality into Eros."

The following questions are designed to help you test the thoroughness of your reading. Each question is to be answered by giving a page or pages of the reading assignment. Answers will be found on page 384 of this Reading Plan.

1 What reply did Freud make to the physician's comment that there is nothing sexual in childbirth?

2 What point is illustrated by Freud's reference to Breughel's "Temptations of St. Anthony"?

3 Do masochists long to suffer humiliations, especially at the hands of those they love?

4 How does Freud qualify his statement that "neurotic symptoms are substitutes for sexual satisfactions"?

5 What is society's economic motive in restraining the sexual activity of children?

6 What are some of the early childish misconceptions of the sexual act and the origin of children?

7 What point is illustrated by Freud's reference to the Egyptian god Horus?

8 What is the meaning, according to Theodor Reik, of the savage rites of puberty?

9 Did Freud hold that the superego is influenced only by its first identifications with its parents, not by later identifications?

10 What different meanings of "unconscious" does Freud distinguish?

11 Why does Freud decide to substitute the term "id" for what he had formerly called "the system of the unconscious"?

12 What is the aim of the therapeutic efforts of psychoanalysis?

ANSWERS
to self-testing questions

First Reading
1. 5b
2. 5d-6a
3. 5c
4. 155c-d
5. 154a-b
6. 154d-155b
7. 155d-156a
8. 154a

Second Reading
1. 178a-b
2. 180-182
3. 182
4. 182-183
5. 183c
6. 185-186
7. 187b
8. 186b
9. 188c-d
10. 187d

Third Reading
1. 654a
2. 654b
3. 665b
4. 649d-650a
5. 649c
6. 648c
7. 651d
8. 648b
9. 648d
10. 648d

Fourth Reading
1. 169c-d
2. 166d
3. 167a-b
4. 167d-168a
5. 168a
6. 162b-c
7. 164a-b
8. 164c
9. 165

Fifth Reading
1. 169d
2. 168d
3. 168c
4. 173c
5. 178a-b
6. 179
7. 181a-b

Sixth Reading
1. 1d
2. 2a-b
3. 2c-d
4. 3b-c
5. 6b
6. 6c
7. 12c
8. 15a-d
9. 16b
10. 20d
11. 23d
12. 24d-25a

Seventh Reading
1. 50c-d
2. 50d
3. 51c
4. 51d
5. 53d
6. 54d
7. 56d-57a
8. 62c-d

Eighth Reading
1. 129a
2. 129b-c
3. 135a-c
4. 138d
5. 142a-c
6. 146b-c
7. 147a-b
8. 132a-d
9. 145d-146a
10. 137d-138a

Ninth Reading

1. 274b
2. 269b-c
3. 274d
4. 277b-c
5. 278b-c
6. 279b
7. 279a-b
8. 279a-b
9. 269c

Tenth Reading

1. 40c
2. 45d
3. 46d
4. 47d-48a
5. 48d
6. 48d-49a
7. 52c-53a

Eleventh Reading

1. 258c-d
2. 259a-b
3. 258a-b
4. 258c
5. 262b
6. 262c-d
7. 270a
8. 273c
9. 276a-b
10. 286a-d

Twelfth Reading

1. 148a
2. 148b
3. 150b
4. 152a-b
5. 157a
6. 158-159
7. 159b
8. 160a

9. 163b
10. 167b

Thirteenth Reading

1. 748b-749a
2. 752b
3. 755b-756b (fn.)
4. 800a-b
5. 806b
6. 807a
7. 808a
8. 811b
9. 813a
10. 817b

Fourteenth Reading

1. 6d
2. 7a-c
3. 8d
4. 10a-b
5. 12d
6. 14d-15a
7. 15c-d
8. 16b
9. 18a
10. 534d
11. 535c-d
12. 536d-537b

Fifteenth Reading

1. 569d
2. 570c
3. 571a
4. 571d
5. 573c
6. 576b-d
7. 580c
8. 583d
9. 833b-c
10. 835d-836d
11. 836c-d
12. 840a

ADDITIONAL READINGS

I. Works included in *Great Books of the Western World*

Sexual Enlightenment of Children; The Future Prospects of Psycho-Analytic Therapy; Observations on "Wild" Psycho-Analysis; The Interpretation of Dreams; On Narcissism; Instincts and Their Vicissitudes; Repression; The Unconscious; A General Introduction to Psycho-Analysis (complete); Beyond the Pleasure Principle; Group Psychology and the Analysis of the Ego; The Ego and the Id; Inhibitions, Symptoms, and Anxiety; Thoughts for the Times on War and Death; Civilization and Its Discontents; New Introductory Lectures on Psycho-Analysis

II. Other Works

A. Histories of Biology, Psychology, and Medicine

BORING, E. G., A History of Experimental Psychology. New York: Century Company, 1929

BRETT, GEORGE SIDNEY, History of Psychology, 3 vols. New York: The Macmillan Company, 1912-21

CASTIGLIONI, ARTURO, History of Medicine, 2nd ed. rev. New York: Alfred A. Knopf, 1958

DAWES, BENJAMIN, A Hundred Years of Biology. New York: The Macmillan Company, 1952

DE KRUIF, PAUL, Men Against Death. New York: Harcourt, Brace & Company, Inc., 1932

GARRISON, FIELDING H., An Introduction to the History of Medicine 4th ed. Philadelphia: W. B. Saunders Company, 1929

HEIDBREDER, EDNA, Seven Psychologies. New York: D. Appleton-Century Company, Inc., 1933

MURPHY, GARDNER, Historical Introduction to Modern Psychology. New York: Harcourt, Brace & Company, Inc., 1949

NORDENSKIÖLD, ERIK, The History of Biology: A Survey. New York: Alfred A. Knopf, 1928

SIGERIST, HENRY E., Great Doctors. New York: Doubleday Anchor Books, 1958; Primitive and Archaic Medicine, in Vol. I, History of Medicine. New York: Oxford University Press, 1951

SINGER, CHARLES, *Greek Biology and Greek Medicine.* New York: Oxford University Press, 1922; *A Short History of Medicine, Introducing Medical Principles to Students and Non-Medical Readers.* New York: Oxford University Press, 1928

WOLF, A., *A History of Science, Technology and Philosophy in the Eighteenth Century.* New York: The Macmillan Company, 1939

WOODWORTH, ROBERT S., *Contemporary Schools of Psychology.* New York: Ronald Press Company, 1931

ZILBOORG, GREGORY, *The Medical Man and the Witch During the Renaissance.* Baltimore: Johns Hopkins Press, 1935; *Mind, Medicine, and Man.* New York: Harcourt, Brace & Company, Inc., 1943

B. Basic Books in Biology and Medicine

ABRAHAM, KARL, *Selected Papers on Psychoanalysis,* trans. by Douglas Bryan and Alix Strachey. New York: Basic Books, Inc., 1953

ADLER, ALFRED, *The Neurotic Constitution,* trans. by Bernard Glueck and John E. Lind. New York: Dodd, Mead & Company, Inc., 1917

ALEXANDER, FRANZ, *The Medical Value of Psychoanalysis,* rev. ed. New York: W. W. Norton & Company, Inc., 1936

ALVERDES, FRIEDRICH, *Social Life in the Animal World.* New York: Harcourt, Brace & Company, 1927

BELL, SIR CHARLES, *New Idea of the Anatomy of the Brain.* 1811

BENIVIENI, ANTONIO, *The Hidden Causes of Disease,* trans. by Charles Singer. Springfield, Ill.: Charles C Thomas, 1954

BERNARD, CLAUDE, *An Introduction to the Study of Experimental Medicine,* trans. by H. C. Greene. New York: The Macmillan Company, 1927

BEST, CHARLES HERBERT and N. B. TAYLOR, eds., *The Physiological Basis of Medical Practice,* 7th ed. Baltimore: The Williams & Wilkins Company, 1961

BUFFON, GEORGES LOUIS LECLERC, *Natural History, General*

and Particular, trans. by William Smellie, 8 vols. London: W. Strahan and T. C. Cadell, 1781

CANNON, WALTER B., *The Wisdom of the Body.* New York: W. W. Norton & Company, Inc., 1932

CLARK, A. J., *Comparative Physiology of the Heart.* New York: The Macmillan Company, 1927

DARWIN, CHARLES and A. R. WALLACE, *Evolution by Natural Selection.* London: Cambridge University Press, 1958

DOBZHANSKY, THEODOSIUS, *Genetics and the Origin of Species.* New York: Columbia University Press, 1937

DUNN, L. C., ed., *Genetics in the Twentieth Century: Essays on the Progress of Genetics During Its First Fifty Years.* New York: The Macmillan Company, 1951; *Heredity and Evolution in Human Populations.* Cambridge, Mass.: Harvard University Press, 1959

FERENCZI, SÁNDOR, *Further Contributions to the Theory and Technique of Psycho-analysis,* trans. by J. A. Suttie and others. New York: Boni & Liveright, 1928

GALEN, *On Anatomical Procedures,* trans. by Charles Singer. New York: Oxford University Press, 1956

GALTON, F., *Natural Inheritance.* London, 1889

GANTT, W. A. H., ed., *Physiological Bases of Psychiatry.* Springfield, Ill.: Charles C Thomas, 1958

GOLDSTEIN, K., *The Organism.* New York: American Book Company, 1939

GREGORY, WILLIAM KING, *Evolution Emerging: A Survey of Changing Patterns from Primeval Life to Man,* 2 vols. New York: The Macmillan Company, 1951

HALDANE, J. B. S., *The Causes of Evolution.* New York: Harper & Brothers, 1932

HEIDEL, W. A., *Hippocratic Medicine.* New York: Columbia University Press, 1941

HERRICK, C. JUDSON, *The Brains of Rats and Men: A Survey of the Original and Biological Significance of the Cerebral Cortex.* Chicago: University of Chicago Press, 1926

HOBHOUSE, L. T., *Development and Purpose.* New York: The Macmillan Company, 1913

HUXLEY, JULIAN, *Evolution, the Modern Synthesis.* New York:

Harper & Brothers, 1942; *Problems of Relative Growth*. New York: Dial Press, 1932

HUXLEY, THOMAS H., *Darwinism: Essays*. New York: D. Appleton & Company, 1898; *Discourses, Biological and Geological*. New York: D. Appleton & Company, 1898; *Evidence as to Man's Place in Nature*. London, 1863

JAMESON, SIR WILLIAM and G. S. PARKINSON, *Synopsis of Hygiene*, 9th ed. London, J. & A. Churchill, Ltd., 1947

LAMARCK, J. B., *Zoological Philosophy* (1809). New York: The Macmillan Company, 1914

LASHLEY, K. S., *Brain Mechanisms and Intelligence*. Chicago: University of Chicago Press, 1929

LIEF, ALFRED, ed., *The Commonsense Psychiatry of Adolf Meyer*. New York: McGraw-Hill Book Company, Inc., 1948

LOEB, JACQUES, *Comparative Physiology of the Brain and Comparative Psychology*. New York: G. P. Putnam's Sons, 1900; *Forced Movements, Tropisms, and Animal Conduct*. Philadelphia: J. B. Lippincott Company, 1918

LYELL, CHARLES, *The Geological Evidences of the Antiquity of Man*. London, 1863

McDOUGALL, WILLIAM, *Modern Materialism and Emergent Evolution*. New York: D. Van Nostrand Company, Inc., 1929

MEDAWAR, PETER B., *Future of Man*. New York: Basic Books, Inc., 1960

MENDEL, GREGOR JOHANN, *Experiments in Plant-Hybridisation*. Cambridge, Mass.: Harvard University Press, 1925

MORGAN, C. LLOYD, *Emergent Evolution*. New York: Henry Holt & Company, Inc., 1923

MORGAN, T. H., *The Physical Basis of Heredity*. Philadelphia: J. B. Lippincott Company, 1919; *The Scientific Basis of Evolution*. New York: W. W. Norton & Company, Inc., 1932

OWEN, RICHARD, *Lectures on Comparative Anatomy*. London, 1843

PARACELSUS, *Four Treatises*, ed. by Henry E. Sigerist and others. Baltimore: Johns Hopkins Press, 1941

RANK, OTTO, *Will Therapy and Truth and Reality*, trans. by Jessie Taft. New York: Alfred A. Knopf, 1945

RASHEVSKY, N., *Mathematical Biophysics,* rev. ed. Chicago: University of Chicago Press, 1948

ROSENAU, M. J., *Preventive Medicine and Hygiene,* 6th ed. New York: D. Appleton-Century Company, Inc., 1935

RUCH, THEODORE C. and JOHN F. FULTON, eds., *Medical Physiology and Biophysics,* 18th ed. of Howell's *Textbook of Physiology.* Philadelphia: W. B. Saunders Company, 1960

SCHNECK, JEROME M., *ed., Hypnosis in Modern Medicine.* Springfield, Ill.: Charles C Thomas, 1953

SHERRINGTON, C. S., *The Integrative Action of the Nervous System.* New Haven: Yale University Press, 1906

SIMMONS, J. S., ed., *Public Health in the World Today.* Cambridge, Mass.: Harvard University Press, 1949

SIMPSON, GEORGE GAYLORD, *The Meaning of Evolution.* New Haven: Yale University Press, 1949

STAFFORD-CLARK, DAVID, *Psychiatry Today.* Baltimore: Penguin Books Inc., 1952

THOMPSON, SIR D'ARCY WENTWORTH, *On Growth and Form,* 2nd ed., 2 vols. London: Cambridge University Press, 1952

THOMSON, J. ARTHUR, *The System of Animate Nature.* New York: Henry Holt & Company, Inc., 1920

UEXKÜLL, J. VON, *Theoretical Biology.* New York: Harcourt, Brace & Company, Inc., 1926

VESALIUS, ANDREAS, *On the Human Brain,* ed. by Charles Singer. New York: Oxford University Press, 1952

VIRCHOW, RUDOLF, *Disease, Life, and Man: Selected Essays,* trans. by Lelland J. Rather. Stanford: Stanford University Press, 1958

WADDINGTON, C. H., *Strategy of the Genes.* New York: The Macmillan Company, 1957

WALLACE, A. R., *Contributions to the Theory of Natural Selection.* London, 1870; *The Theory of Natural Selection.* London: The Macmillan Company, 1871

WEISMANN, AUGUST, *The Evolution Theory,* trans. by Arthur Thomson and M. R. Thomson, 2 vols. London: Edward Arnold & Co., 1904

WILLIS, R. A., *The Principles of Pathology; Including Bacteriology,* 2nd ed. Washington: Butterworth, Inc., 1961

YERKES, R. M. and A. W., *The Great Apes*. New Haven: Yale University Press, 1929

ZUCKERMANN, S., *The Social Life of Monkeys and Apes*. New York: Harcourt, Brace & Company, Inc., 1932

C. Basic Books in Psychology

ALLPORT, FLOYD H., *Theories of Perception and the Concept of Structure*. New York: John Wiley & Sons, Inc., 1955

ALLPORT, G. W., *Personality: A Psychological Interpretation*. New York: Henry Holt & Company, Inc., 1937

ASCH, SOLOMON E., *Social Psychology*. New York: Prentice-Hall, Inc., 1952

BOAS, FRANZ, *The Mind of Primitive Man*. New York: The Macmillan Company, 1911

CANNON, W. B., *Bodily Changes in Pain, Hunger, Fear and Rage*, 2nd ed. New York: D. Appleton & Company, 1929

CATTELL, R. B., *Personality, A Systemic Theoretical and Factual Study*. New York: McGraw-Hill Book Company, Inc., 1950

DOLLARD, JOHN and N. E. MILLER, *Personality and Psychotherapy*. New York: McGraw-Hill Book Company, Inc., 1950

ESTES, WILLIAM K. and others, *Modern Learning Theory*. New York: Appleton-Century-Crofts, Inc., 1954

EYSENCK, H. J., *Uses and Abuses of Psychology*. Baltimore: Penguin Books Inc., 1953

FREUD, ANNA, *The Ego and the Mechanisms of Defense*. New York: International Universities Press, Inc., 1957

FREUD, SIGMUND, *Totem and Taboo*, in *The Basic Writings of Sigmund Freud*, ed. by A. A. Brill. New York: The Modern Library, 1938

FROMM, ERICH, *Escape from Freedom*. New York: Farrar & Reinhart, Inc., 1941

GARRETT, HENRY E., *Great Experiments in Psychology*. New York: Century Company, 1930

GIBSON, J. J., *The Perception of the Visual World*. Boston: Houghton Mifflin Company, 1950

GUTHRIE, E. R., *The Psychology of Human Conflict*. New York: Harper & Brothers, 1938

HEBB, D. O., *The Organization of Behavior*. New York: John Wiley & Sons, Inc., 1949

HELSON, HARRY, ed., *Theoretical Foundations of Psychology*. New York: D. Van Nostrand Company, Inc., 1951

HILGARD, ERNEST R., *Theories of Learning*. New York: Appleton-Century-Crofts, Inc., 1948

HORNEY, KAREN, *New Ways in Psychoanalysis*. New York: W. W. Norton & Company, Inc., 1939

HULL, C. L., *Principles of Behavior*. New York: Appleton-Century-Crofts, Inc., 1943

HUMPHREY, GEORGE, *Thinking: An Introduction to Its Experimental Psychology*. New York: John Wiley & Sons, Inc., 1951

JAENCH, E. R., *Psychological Types*. New York: Harcourt, Brace & Company, Inc., 1930

JAMES, WILLIAM, *The Varieties of Religious Experience*. New York: New American Library (Mentor)

JUNG, C. G., *Psychological Types: or, The Psychology of Individuation*. New York: Pantheon Books, Inc., 1959

KATZ, D., *The World of Colour*. London: George Routledge & Sons, Ltd., 1935

KOCH, SIGMUND, ed., *Psychology: A Study of a Science*, Vols. I-IV. New York: McGraw-Hill Book Company, Inc., 1959-62

KOFFKA, K., *The Growth of the Mind*. Paterson, N.J.: Littlefield, Adams & Co., 1959

KÖHLER, WOLFGANG, *Gestalt Psychology*. New York: New American Library (Mentor), 1959; *The Mentality of Apes*. New York: Harcourt, Brace & Company, Inc., 1926

LASHLEY, K. S., *Brain Mechanisms and Intelligence*. Chicago: University of Chicago Press, 1929

LURIA, A. R., *The Nature of Human Conflicts*. New York: Liveright Publishing Corporation, 1932

MAIER, N. R. F., *Frustration: The Study of Behavior Without a Goal*. New York: McGraw-Hill Book Company, Inc., 1949

MALINOWSKI, BRONISLAW, *Sex and Repression in Savage Society*. New York: Harcourt, Brace & Company, Inc., 1927

MASSERMAN, JULES H., *Behavior and Neurosis*. Chicago: University of Chicago Press, 1943

MURPHY, GARDNER, *Human Potentialities*. New York: Basic Books Publishing Company, Inc., 1958; ———, LOIS BARCLAY MURPHY and THEODORE M. NEWCOMB, *Experimental Social Psychology*. New York: Harper & Brothers, 1937

PAVLOV, I. P., *Lectures on Conditioned Reflexes*, 2 vol. New York: International Publishers Co., Inc., 1928-41

PIAGET, JEAN, *The Child's Conception of the World*. New York: Harcourt, Brace & Company, Inc., 1929

RIVERS, W. H. R., *Conflict and Dream*. New York: Harcourt, Brace & Company, Inc., 1923

SCHILDER, PAUL, *Mind: Perception and Thought in Their Constructive Aspects*. New York: Columbia University Press, 1942

SKINNER, B. F., *The Behavior of Organisms*. New York: Appleton-Century-Crofts, Inc., 1938

STODDARD, GEORGE D., *The Meaning of Intelligence*. New York: The Macmillan Company, 1943

STOUT, G. F., *Analytic Psychology*, 2 vols. London: Macmillan and Company, Ltd., 1896

THORNDIKE, E. L., *Human Learning*. New York: Century Company, 1931

THURSTONE, L. L., *The Nature of Intelligence*. New York: Harcourt, Brace & Company, Inc., 1924

TITCHENER, E. B., *Lectures on the Experimental Psychology of the Thought Processes*. New York: The Macmillan Company, 1909

TOLMAN, E. C., *Purposive Behavior in Animals and Men*. New York: Century Company, 1932

WERTHEIMER, MAX, *Productive Thinking*, ed. by S. E. Asch and others. New York: Harper & Brothers, 1945

WITKIN, H. A. and others, *Personality Through Perception*. New York: Harper & Brothers, 1954

WOODWORTH, R. S., *Dynamic Psychology*. New York: Columbia University Press, 1918; *Experimental Psychology*. New York: Henry Holt & Company, Inc., 1938

YOUNG, P. T., *Emotion in Man and Animal.* New York: John Wiley & Sons, Inc., 1943

D. Books on Scientific Method

BECKNER, MORTON, *Biological Way of Thought.* New York: Columbia University Press, 1959

BENJAMIN, A. C., *An Introduction to the Philosophy of Science.* New York: The Macmillan Company, 1937

BOUTROUX, ÉMILE, *Natural Law in Science and Philosophy* (Ch. 8-12), trans. by Fred Rothwell. New York: The Macmillan Company, 1914

BRONOWSKI, J., *The Common Sense of Science.* Cambridge, Mass.: Harvard University Press, 1953

COHEN, MORRIS R. and ERNEST NAGEL, *An Introduction to Logic and Scientific Method*, Book II. New York: Harcourt, Brace & Company, Inc., 1934

FEIGL, HERBERT and MICHAEL SCRIVEN, eds., *The Foundations of Science and the Concepts of Psychology and Psychoanalysis.* Minneapolis: University of Minnesota Press, 1956; FEIGL, HERBERT and MAY BRODBECK, eds., *Readings in the Philosophy of Science* (Section VI, "Philosophical Problems of Biology and Psychology"). New York: Appleton-Century-Crofts, Inc., 1953

GOLDSTON, IAGO, ed., *Social Medicine: Its Derivations and Objectives.* Cambridge, Mass.: Harvard University Press, 1949

HOOK, SYDNEY, ed., *Psychoanalysis: Scientific Method and Philosophy; A Symposium.* New York: Grove Press, Inc., 1960

JEVONS, W. STANLEY, *Principles of Science.* London: Macmillan and Company, Ltd., 1924

JONES, W. H. S., *Philosophy and Medicine in Ancient Greece.* Baltimore: Johns Hopkins Press, 1946

LASLETT, J., ed., *The Physical Basis of Mind: A Symposium.* New York: The Macmillan Company, 1950

MADDEN, EDWARD H., *The Structure of Scientific Thought.* Boston: Houghton Mifflin Company, 1960

MILL, JOHN STUART, *A System of Logic: Ratiocinative and*

Inductive, Book III, 8th ed. London: Longmans, Green and Company, 1906

MOULYN, ADRIAN C., *Structure, Function and Purpose.* New York: Liberal Arts Press, Inc., 1957

PEARSON, KARL, *The Grammar of Science.* New York: E. P. Dutton & Co., Inc., 1937

PRATT, C. C., *The Logic of Modern Psychology.* New York: The Macmillan Company, 1939

PUMPIAN-MINDLIN, E., ed., *Psychoanalysis as Science.* Stanford: Stanford University Press, 1952

QUASTLER, HENRY, ed., *Information Theory in Biology.* Urbana, Ill.: University of Illinois Press, 1953

SELLARS, ROY WOOD and others, eds., *Philosophy for the Future* (pp. 202-317). New York: The Macmillan Company, 1949

SHERRINGTON, SIR CHARLES SCOTT, *Man on His Nature.* London: Cambridge University Press, 1951

SINGER, E., *Mind as Behavior, and Studies in Empirical Idealism.* Columbus, Ohio: R. G. Adams & Co., 1924

WIENER, NORBERT, *Cybernetics, or Control and Communication in the Animal and the Machine.* New York: John Wiley & Sons, Inc., 1948

WIENER, PHILIP P., ed., *Readings in Philosophy of Science* (especially Section B, "Basic Biological and Psychological Concepts"). New York: Charles Scribner's Sons, 1953

WOODGER, J. H., *The Axiomatic Method in Biology.* New York: The Macmillan Company, 1937; *Biology and Language.* London: Cambridge University Press, 1952